Also by William R. Horsfall

MOSQUITOES

Their Bionomics and Relation to Disease

MEDICAL ENTOMOLOGY

Arthropods and Human Disease

WILLIAM R. HORSFALL
UNIVERSITY OF ILLINOIS, URBANA

THE RONALD PRESS COMPANY • NEW YORK

Library of Congress Catalog Card Number: 62–11645

PRINTED IN THE UNITED STATES OF AMERICA

This book is dedicated to students of medical entomology, both academic and professional. They include in a very special way the men and women who have worked in Harker Hall through the years 1947–1961. It was for all students that this book was written; it is by them that it will be judged; it is from them that knowledge for further advances will be gained.

Preface

This is a book about what arthropods may do to man directly and to degrade his health when acting in concert with microbes, worms, or even with other insects. While more than a layman's knowledge of arthropods and the associated parasites is presupposed, the student and thoughtful reader should find it comprehensible. The latter can explore any topic of special interest to him through the treatment here, supplemented by the suggested readings and the bibliography.

Medical entomology traditionally has made its contributions to human welfare in two ways: It has developed ways and means for the recognition of arthropods encountered in epidemiological practice, and it has provided information on the structure and habits of these insects. Parasitological texts are concerned primarily with pathogens particularly in their associations with vertebrates. There is now a considerable literature on the arthropod group as components of the environments of both men and pathogenic agents. Much of this literature is not readily available to students, medical men, and agencies concerned with the health of the public. This book, then, fills an intermediate need—a thorough exposition of the extrinsic ecology of arthropod and arthropod-borne vertebrate pathogens.

Material in this book is arranged to relate arthropods to human discomfort and disease in three ways: First, the habits, morphology, and relationships of the medically important categories are discussed; second, they are considered as causes of human distress; and last, pathogens depending wholly or in part on them for transport, sustenance, or both are discussed in their ecological frameworks. In order to show that transmission chains and annoyance from insects and their relatives may be prevented or alleviated, the final chapter deals with the general aspects of control.

Chapters 2 through 5 deal with arthropods of medical importance according to the higher categories. Some morphological material is given together with information on distribution and habits as a basis for further inquiry through the literature cited. Students in the related disciplines of protozoology and helminthology should find the information and the point of view useful. The medical student and the practitioner can find enough to enable them to answer many of their own questions as well as those of patients. The sanitarian should get direct help from both the text and bibliography. Keys for identification are not included because recognition of species is of such a local nature that no combination of keys would be adequate. It is assumed that laboratory exercises at the option of the teacher will usually supplement the text in class use.

Chapter 6 will be useful to the medical practitioner who is confronted with identification of ailments induced by arthropods. There are few compendiums of this sort available to him. This text, together with cited literature, should offer ample information for complete understanding. Study of this chapter alone should make the clinician more aware of arthropodan causes of human discomfort and disease.

Chapters 7 through 13 are discussions of the ecology of numerous arthropod-borne pathogens. Separation into chapters is according to the larger taxonomic categories of parasites. Arrangement within chapters is often arbitrary. Most of the pathogens are directly related to human health, but some of veterinary significance are included for their historical value or because they illustrate specific transmission chains that differ from those of strictly medical significance. While every effort has been made to have the information up to date, parts of the field are changing so rapidly that even annual reviews are unable to keep abreast of developments. Chapter 8 lists names of viruses as if they were binomial with the word "virus" in the position of a genus name. This does not mean that the word virus has the status of genus; rather, it is done for uniformity in naming the parasites.

The last chapter presents a generalized discussion of principles of abatement and suppression of arthropods and the diseases caused by, or related to, them. It is in no sense a manual for control practices. Specific regulatory measures are seldom given because every condition dictates its own practice. Any effort to give specific recommendations would demand much more space than is justified. An over-all comprehension of strategy in operations should be useful as a guide to the practitioner.

Many persons have contributed of their time and knowledge to make this volume possible. They aided in its conception and helped clear errors from its expression. For their efforts I am most grateful, but responsibility for the final form is solely my own. Dr. Norman Levine, a protozoologist, and Dr. Walter V. Balduf, an entomologist, both read the entire manuscript and offered many helpful suggestions. Dr. Francis Kruidenier, an helminthologist, examined Chapter 8 and made constructive suggestions; Mr. Lyle Bamber, our biology librarian, gave valuable assistance in finding innumerable elusive references. The ecological diagrams were prepared by Mr. C. H. Beiger through funds provided by a grant from the Graduate College, University of Illinois. For assistance in reading proof and for typing the manuscript, I am grateful to Mrs. William R. Horsfall and Mrs. Jerry Szumski.

WILLIAM R. HORSFALL

Urbana, Illinois
March, 1962

Contents

MEDICAL
ENTOMOLOGY

CHAPTER I

Introduction

EARLY MAN AND ARTHROPODS

Man has encountered many stumbling blocks during his evolution toward a social creature. Certainly a major deterrent toward this progress has been the numerous pestilences resulting from his constant association with arthropods. For possibly a hundred centuries an escape from intimate contact with arthropodan pests was no more successful for humans than it is today for other large mammals. People, like other mammals, either accepted the annoyances, sought local situations where a tolerance level was attained, or moved to a more salubrious place. The latter became the accepted pattern for the vigorous of the species and nomadism became the rule.

A fragment of the human population drifted into southwestern Asia during the post-glacial period and found a climate there that was both dry and seasonably changeable. This became an eddy in the current of drifting humans because the salubrious features of this environment persisted. In this region man experienced a minimum of annoyance from arthropods. Food, shelter, and the necessities for existence were abundantly provided, and in time the settlements became permanent and finally gave rise to urban patterns of life. New problems that arose from the concentration of the human population were created in the new cities. During this formative period of community living the new kinds of plagues and pests were sometimes controlled to a degree by a return to the nomadic pattern. At times the sites of the cities were entirely abandoned in the quest for comfort and more abundant health.

Some time later the people pushed westward along the shores of the Mediterranean Sea, and new cities developed at those sites which provided a happy confluence of dry climate, arable soil, and a dependable supply of potable water. As groups settled in the places better suited to their agricultural practices, again they were subjected to devastating diseases, particularly those associated with arthropods. While a variable climate could be relied on to minimize hazards from a composite of diseases, the extremes imposed often meant repetitive droughts and attendant famine. Those areas dry enough to minimize disease hazards, and yet dependable enough to supply food for support of the settlements, were so rare that the population was held in constant check so that appreciable expansion was impossible. Thus urbanized man was ever caught between the forces of starvation and privation on the one hand and disease on the other. The best possibility for survival seemed to depend on the repeated abandonment of one habitation site and building on a new one, even as nomadic man moved his personal possessions at much shorter intervals.

At a very early date the people came to a degree of realization that insects in some mysterious way were thwarting their efforts toward a stable society. Wherever man went, pests always followed to plague him, while other pests new to him invariably made their appearance. At times he turned to insects in reverence in the vague hope that through his worship of them his burdens might be lifted. The Babylonians worshiped a god of pestilence which was represented as a two-winged fly. The Canaanites placated Baal-zebub, a vengeful god, also represented as a fly, while the early Egyptians considered as holy, the scarabs, a group of coprophagous beetles.

By the time of the sixth century B.C. two diseases of entomological import came to bear on the mushrooming population bordering the Mediterranean Sea. Both diseases became urban problems because cities became commercially interdependent. Malaria came because cities had to be located near mouths of rivers or on the coast. The high water table at such sites put the essential ecological complex, man and mosquitoes, in overlapping environments. Plague came because ships bore to all ports rats and fleas in their holds along with grain and other foodstuffs. Grain was the common bond that brought the essential biota for plague, rats and fleas, into concentrations of human suscepts. In the case of malaria man went to mosquitoes; for plague he brought rats and their attendant fleas to his quarters.

Here were two maladies that flourished wherever cities were established. For two millennia the populace reeled from these diseases and advancement was possible only when man could push northward into colder climates. Through the ages the only escape from these dread diseases was based on individual retreat. Medieval advice for those who could afford to move from a stricken city was to leave the city, stay away for a long time and return only after the outbreak had run its course. This practice was followed to avoid yellow fever until early in the twentieth century.

MODERN MAN AND ARTHROPODS

Late in the nineteenth century people began to reason systematically about arthropod-borne diseases. Pasteur and other workers gathered irrefutable evidence in support of the organismal causes of disease. Their immediate followers found a host of causative agents ranging from worms to protozoa and bacteria. Much later the existence of suboptical agents, the viruses, was demonstrated.

The bells which welcomed the twentieth century also sounded the knell for many arthropod-borne diseases. Ross, and coincidentally Grassi and his associates, had shown that malaria, the most devastating of all blood diseases, was carried by certain mosquitoes. Shortly afterwards, the Americans proved the validity of Finlay's culicine theory of transmission for the cause of yellow fever. At last these demon-diseases of the tropics could be controlled and the key for opening the tropical regions of the world to urbanization was finally possessed. Man ceased running from diseases of arthropodan origin as he became the master of his physical environment and was able to utilize the tropical regions of the world for human needs. The last half of this century should see both Africa and tropical South America achieve enormous progress as arthropod-borne diseases become little more than a memory over most of these regions.

The facts of the salient discoveries which lead to our present knowledge of arthropod-borne diseases should be recounted as an aid to our future efforts. Prior to the organismal theory of disease, humans were able to escape some of the ravages or to control them to the degree that only a few were catastrophic. Tribal or group lore often dictated the behavior of our prehistoric forebears just as today it determines some behavioral patterns in primitive cultures (Nuttall, 1900).[1] Urban man needed more reliable control of dis-

---

[1] References in this form in the text and in Additional Readings are to the Bibliography.

ease, and he was forced to modify his dwellings, change his sleeping
habits, regularly cleanse his body, and finally develop artificial quarantines. He learned that the swamp was miasmatic and that rats in
quantity meant epidemics of the black death. There was a slow and
indeed hazy realization that animals both large and small were the
sources of some of the most devastating maladies and annoying
problems. Modern man has resolved the complex interrelations
between the diseases of animals and humans, and today the people
of a modern society may live virtually free of those diseases which
actively depend on arthropods for their propagation.

Many specific examples of historical evidence of the theoretical
relations between arthropods and human diseases are known. Early
ideas were speculative and probably added little to our knowledge,
while some of the later theories were basic to present concepts. By
the middle of the eighteenth century some recognizable syndromes
(agents of which are now known to be transmitted by arthropods)
were thought to be arthropod-disease-related. At that time causes
were not understood as evidence was indeed tenuous. Mercurialis
(1530–1607) suggested that hordes of flies transmitted the cause of
"black death" (a confused complex of cholera, typhoid, and bubonic
plague). In 1769 Edward Bancroft wrote that yaws was related to
flies. Early in the eighteenth century Lancisi and others published
their beliefs that malaria was basically extrinsic and that it came to
man as a poison which they related to geographical locality more
than to any other factor. King (1883) observed that malaria was
basically associated with seasons of high temperatures as well as
specific localities, and furthermore disturbed topsoil seemed to have
some responsibility. Finally he stated that the rate of malaria was
definitely reduced if mosquito nets, gauze veils, or similar protective
screens were consistently used by the potential victims. Nott, a
physician living in Mobile, Alabama, wrote knowingly of yellow
fever in the mid-nineteenth century and related the disease to
hematophagous insects, but his commentary was only one among a
welter of explanations, and it could not be adequately supported
since it was made in advance of the development of the basic theory
of causes of disease. Later Maull (1880) noted the effect from the
use of screens during an epidemic of malaria that affected all families
save two in the urban area under his observation. The two families
which escaped attack slept in houses which had screened windows
and doors, while all victims of the disease used no screens. Prior to

the knowledge of the transmission chain for the virus of yellow fever, H. R. Carter repeatedly noted that the time lag between the appearance of a primary case of yellow fever and the appearance of a secondary one was much longer than any lag between subsequent cases. He suggested that this was because the agent had an extrinsic existence.

Pasteur's elaboration of the organismal theory of causes of disease turned all eyes to the microscope as the reliable device for demonstrating this relationship. Within the next four decades all kinds of agents (except the viruses) were seen, and many of them were accurately associated with the proper syndromes. The extrinsic relations were less attended, though just prior to 1880 Manson had shown that a filariid parasite in the human blood lived part of its life in the body of a mosquito. A decade later, Smith and Kilborne demonstrated that a protozoan parasite in the blood of bovines lived in a common tick and furthermore depended on that tick for transport of the agent to another host. Ross and Manson collaborated to explode the first major shell in the final battle against ignorance of arthropods in epidemiology. They proved that plasmodia, the causative agents of malaria, did in truth depend on mosquitoes during part of their development. The need for entomologists to work in a specialized area of arthropod-borne diseases was immediately apparent as the clue to suppression shifted more from the parasite-human factor to the arthropodan link. The necessity for understanding the whole ecological complex was urgent. Public health agencies were established in time and knowledge basic to an integrated attack on diseases has been systematically brought to bear on control.

Bristowe (1946) gave excellent reasons for studying insects and their relation to human health when he stated that (1) historically more premature deaths have been brought about by direct and indirect attacks from arthropods than from any other cause; (2) the bites, stings, and general allergies inflicted by many arthropods still cause widespread discomfort; and (3) vast sums of money are spent in attempts to alleviate these distresses of man. Others have commented in similar vein. Plague, typhus, and malaria are said to have killed far more people than have been destroyed in all the armed conflicts since time began (see Frontispiece). As devastators of man the proboscises of the flea and the mosquito have proved to be sharper and surer than the sword. Disraeli, a prime minister of Britain during Queen Victoria's time, called attention to the truth that the health of the public is the foundation on which rests the happiness and strength of a nation. If the people of any nation suffer for long from ill health or loss of vigor, the afflicted nation will surely perish. Those infectious diseases whose agents are borne by arthropods continue to be among the more devastating over much of the world, and their control will hasten the advancement of primitive cultures. Insects are a major cause of deficient health of many people; hence these potential enemies still require our most careful attention.

To the late W. B. Herms of California must go the credit for joining medicine and entomology in 1909 and for naming the union *Medical Entomology*. Since that time he and many others have helped those interested in this double-branched field to keep abreast of developments through the publication of books and numerous technical papers and bulletins. Historically, the practitioner of medical entomology has provided information on identification, made surveys, and studied the bionomics of vector-hosts of pathogens. More and more, the entomologist has provided basic information on transmission chains as well as extrinsic environments of the pathogens.

At one time ecological relationships between a parasite and its hosts were regarded as simple and in the manner of the observation credited to Maull above. Such relationships may be relatively uncomplicated in any one locality, but the variations in chains of transmission and the differences in basic environments of pathogens are almost endless. One object of this volume is to relate traditional entomological knowledge to the specific ecological situations which give reasons for (1) the absence of transmission or (2) propagation of arthropod-borne agents of diseases.

In our concern over their significance as hosts and vectors of vertebrate pathogens, we must never forget that arthropods still directly cause human discomfort, disease, and even death. Many of these animals sting, bite, irritate, and annoy people, while some provide allergens in hairs, scales, or body products which are responsible for discomfort or illness to sensitive persons. Some arthropods actually invade the human skin, subcutaneous tissue, sinuses, alimentary and urinary tracts, and even lymph nodes. Human reactions to these attacks are detailed in this book.

ADDITIONAL READINGS

HIRST (1953) provides us with an account of the evolution of the epidemiology of plague. In doing so he has traced the history of pandemics in the western culture.

KING (1883): "The animalcular, or insect, origin of disease is not a new idea. . . . Viewed in the light of our modern 'germ theory' of disease, the punctures of proboscidian insects, like those of Pasteur's needles, deserve consideration as probable means by which bacteria and other germs may be inoculated into human bodies so as to infect the blood and give rise to specific fevers. . . ."

NUTTALL (1900a) reviews some primitive reasoning about relationships between malaria and insects. Residents of Mindanao in the Philippines recognized as early as 1700 that mosquitoes were related to the disease. Africans in the Usambara Mountains of eastern Africa were aware that malaria was contracted in lowlands, and the word *mbu* means both malaria and mosquito in one tribal dialect.

RUSSELL (1955) has given an extensive account of the history of our knowledge of malaria and provides an example of how man moved from lore to reason in solving one of his greatest hazards.

CHAPTER 2

Arthropoda: Classes

GENERAL MORPHOLOGY

The phylum Arthropoda because of diversity of form is a morphologist's utopia. Its wealth of species and endless subspecific variants permit comparisons and relationships galore. The body structures have a direct bearing on the medical significance of the group. The appendages are modified in every conceivable way to permit insects to feed on a surface, below the surface, or even in tubular tracts of man and other animals. Mechanics of voiding their wastes and secretions provides the means for transferring pathogens to all animal hosts. The ease with which insects become hosts for agents of disease is intimately related to their morphology. It is the purpose of this book to draw attention to these morphological values, and the student is referred to any of the numerous compilations on morphology for further details.

Through a long evolutionary history, arthropods have come to be complex organisms. Their small size in relation to that of vertebrates may tend to belie the facts. For all of their smallness, they have evolved a complicated set of organ systems coordinated by an intricate nervous system. The size in turn enables arthropods to occupy microhabitats when survival is pressed. When conditions are favorable, they may expand their horizons because of high reproductive rates. In addition they are favored by having evolved jointed appendages, which enhance their capabilities for dispersal. The body covering of the terrestrial forms is capable of resisting desiccation. Thus we have small animals of high reproductive potential that may live in all sorts of limited environments and yet move easily and for great distances to new habitats.

These small, complex, mobile animals are usually short-lived, but they maintain their populations at high levels, first, because their developmental periods are short, and second, because the number of offspring produced by each female is high. Life cycles are completed within a few days to a few weeks for the vast majority of species. Some arthropods require a year for development, and a very few need two or more years. Only a few of the smaller mammals can repeat generations at so fast a rate, but this rate is indeed slow for most arthropods. No mammals have a reproductive potential even approaching that of the bulk of arthropods. Add to these the advantages of a short life and great adaptability, and we have a large group with an evolutionary advantage having no equal.

Structurally, arthropods have the following characteristics: (1) bodies with bilateral symmetry, (2) bodies composed of a linear series of somites, (3) post-oral somites which either have or have had in their evolution a pair of jointed appendages attached ventrally, (4) skeletons largely as external shells made of secreted, noncellular layers, (5) central nervous systems composed of a ventral chain of segmental ganglia joined by two parallel neural trunks, (6) circulatory systems composed basically of the coelom and a pulsatile tube located dorsally along the mid-line, and (7) embryos enclosed part or all of their lives in envelopes of maternal origin. The series of somites comprising the bodies are variously grouped into regions and are visible externally in only one or two of the regions. Cephalization and rigid sclerotization of the anterior somites results in a box-like head in the Hexapoda, Diplopoda, and Chilopoda. The linear arrangement of segments is usually visible externally on the body behind the head, and it is particularly apparent in the caudal region in most classes of the phylum. A few groups such as the spiders and mites show little outward evidence of segmentation. The jointed appendages arise laterad of the mid-ventral line and serve to propel the insect on surfaces, in liquid, or in denser media. Only one class of arthropods, the insects, may have paired, subdorsal wings hinged to the body. The sclerous exoskeleton serves for muscular insertions as well as a shield against changes in water balance. Components of the central nervous system are (1) ventrally placed, segmental ganglia showing varying degrees of cephalization and (2) paired connectives between ganglia. The anterior ganglia exercise differing amounts of control over the more segmentally oriented, posterior ones. The circulatory system is composed of the coelom proper plus a dorsal vessel and accessory, pulsatile organs. Blood or hemolymph in the coelom enters the dorsal vessel by way of valves along the tube in the abdomen, and it is propelled by peristaltic movement anteriorly along the tube and into the head, where it is released. Positive pressure created anteriorly in the coelom causes the mass of blood to move backward toward the region of lower pressure. As the blood moves along the way, it bathes all the cells. Appendages and other parts often have accessory, pulsatile organs that create differentials in pressure and prevent stasis of the hemolymph. Movements of appendages and organs contribute to the circulation of blood.

The encasement of the body by the relatively unyielding envelope presents a problem for a growing arthropod that is met in a distinctive manner. Some of the young animals simply divest themselves of the entire outer layer. Before they do so, a new skeleton is secreted directly beneath the old one, then the exterior layer is split and sloughed. The insect enlarges rapidly before the new covering becomes sclerous. In the interval that follows the developing arthropod feeds and produces new cells but changes little in size because of the confinement. Usually three or more instars comprise the entire growing period.

As arthropods mature they may change form as well as size. Some undergo such radical changes that the adult in no way resembles the developmental stages. The organs and those parts that appear as organs later in life are present all through postembryonic development as masses of undifferentiated cells known as *imaginal discs*. At the proper time in the growth process, imaginal discs change from latent to active states, and form the definitive structures.

THE CLASSES

The phylum Arthropoda is composed of about nine classes of extant forms and several that have become extinct. Differentiation of this highly plastic group early in geological history has given ample time for extensive evolution at all levels. The student of medical entomology is interested in representatives of five classes: Hexapoda, Diplopoda, Chilopoda, Crustacea, and Arachnida. Only these five will be characterized herein, while more general textbooks provide information on the other classes. Table 1 gives a summary of diagnostic characters for those classes with which the medical entomologist is concerned.

Table 1. Diagnostic Morphological Characteristics for Medically Important Classes of Arthropoda (in Adult Stage).

Characteristic		Hexapoda	Diplopoda	Chilopoda	Crustacea	Arachnida
General	Specific					
Body divisions	Cephalothorax	−	−	−	± [1]	±
	Head	+	+	+	−	−
	Thorax	+	−	−	± [2]	−
	Abdomen	+	−	−	+	−
	Many-segmented trunk	−	+	+	−	−
	Gnathosoma	−	−	−	−	+
	Podosoma	−	−	−	−	+
	Opisthosoma	−	−	−	−	+
Pre-oral appendages	Antennae: 1 pair	+	+	+	+	−
Post-oral appendages	Chelicerae	−	−	−	−	+
	Mandibles: 1 pair	+	+	+	+	−
	Maxillae: 1 pair	+	+	+	−	−
	2 pairs	−	−	−	± [1]	−
	Labium	+	+	+	−	−
	Pedipalps: 1 pair	−	−	−	−	+
Legs	3 pairs	+	−	−	−	−
	4 pairs	−	−	−	−	+
	Many, similar	−	+	−	−	−
	Many, front pair chelate	−	−	+	−	−
	Many, biramous	−	−	−	+	−
Abdominal appendages	Cerci	±	−	−	−	±
	Swimmerettes	−	−	−	± [3]	−
	Spinnerets	−	−	−	−	± [4]
	Genital appendages	±	−	−	−	−
Genital opening	Position: caudad	+	−	+	−	−

(+ = present; − = absent; ± = variable.)
[1] Minus in Podocopa.
[2] Minus in Podocopa and Amphipoda.
[3] Minus in Podocopa, Eucopopoda, Branchiura.
[4] Minus in all but Araneae.

HEXAPODA

Hexapoda is the class to which all insects belong. It is (1) the class containing the most known species (about ¾ million), (2) the one having the greatest number of pest species, and (3) the class of greatest medical and veterinary significance. Details of the class characteristics are given in Chapters 4 and 5.

DIPLOPODA

Diplopoda or the millipedes (Fig. 1) comprise a class which contains only a few representatives of a significance to medical entomology. These animals exhibit a somewhat primitive structure which is an elongated capsule beginning with a compact sclerous head and ending in a multisegmented trunk. The head bears a pair of short filiform antennae and hypognathous, chewing mouth parts.

The blunt mandibles are covered by setae and have no offensive capability. Most of the segments of the trunk are dual and bear two pairs of short, jointed legs. The legs extend ventrally, so the body is above the mass of legs when walking. The reproductive tract opens as a pair of apertures behind the second pair of legs. The tracheate respiratory system opens through spiracles placed laterally on the dual segments.

Representatives of the class belong to the subclasses Pselapognatha and Chilognatha. The former group is medically innocuous and is not considered. The latter subclass contains most of the species including all the noxious ones. The sclerous exoskeleton of the Chilognatha is often hardened further by calcareous deposits. Many are provided with a system of glands that secrete liquids repugnant to man which may either ooze or be jetted from openings of the ducts. The groups commonly seen are the glomerids (pill

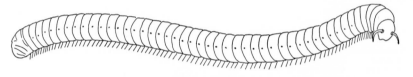

Fig. 1. Juliform millipede. (After Attems, 1926–1930.)

millipedes), the polydesmids (flat-backed millipedes), and the Juliformia ("wireworms") (Attems, 1926–1930). The medically important forms belong only to the order Juliformia. Since the order is the one usually represented in textbooks, it has come to mean millipedes to many people. They have long trunks with 40 or more dual segments each of which usually bears two pairs of legs. Some tropical forms of the order may attain a length of 30 or more centimeters. When not moving, or in response to being touched, a millipede may form a flat, tight coil in the manner of a watch spring with the head in the center of the coil. Millipedes feed on the complex medium of mixed plant materials in advanced stages of decay.

Numerous observers and notably Verhoeff (1928) have described and figured the secretory glands of the Juliformia. From about the fifth or sixth segment backward, each dual segment bears an opening to a repugnatorial gland. Each gland is bulbous and multicellular with a duct opening through the cuticula by way of a spiracle-shaped foramen. Liquid secreted by the glands is extruded as the millipede contracts its body when in the coiled position. Some liquids volatilize so quickly that they seem to be emitted as gases. Secretions from the glands are odorous and may be either clear or colored. These odors have been variously described as similar to those of garlic, chlorine, bitter almonds, and urine. Color gradations are from yellow into brown or red. These secretions are oily and only slightly soluble in water. They stain the skin yellow or brownish as does iodine, and the stains are persistent.

Millipede migrations of plague proportions have been reported in a number of places (Cloudsley-Thompson, 1949). Representatives of *Fontaria, Parajulus, Spirostreptus,* and *Spirobolus* are known to move as hordes. One such migration which extended over 75 acres of pasture was seen many years ago in the Appalachian Mountains of eastern United States. Cattle in the area refused to graze, and workmen became nauseated and dizzy from the odor emanating from the crushed bodies. Open wells were fouled by the numbers of millipedes which drowned in them. In some places the masses were noted to be a foot or more deep. A much smaller horde was seen in 1944 on Biak, an island of the Schouten Group, where tents and surrounding areas were overrun by the pests.

CHILOPODA

Chilopoda (or centipedes) (Fig. 2) is a class that contains few species of importance to medical entomology. Animals of this group superficially resemble millipedes and are actually grouped with them by some authors. However, they are only distantly related phylo-

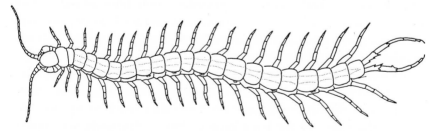

Fig. 2. Characteristic form of noxious centipedes. (After Attems, 1926–1930a.)

genetically according to Attems (1926–1930a). The morphology of the group has been discussed by Fahlander (1938). The general body structure is primitively organized with a distinct, compact, sclerous head and a multisegmented trunk that is flattened dorsoventrally. The head bears a pair of short, filiform antennae and prognathous mandibulate mouth parts. Two special organs of uncertain function (Tomosvary's and frontal organs) have been described. Each segment of the trunk bears one pair of jointed legs. Those of the first segment are strongly prehensile chelipeds, that bear poison glands and that are used in offense. All other legs are long and extend laterally from the trunk as oars did from the ancient slave galley. The body is actually suspended between the legs when the animal is walking. The single genital aperture is caudal. The tracheate respiratory system opens through segmentally paired spiracles on most segments of the trunk. Ventral sclerites have openings to hypodermal glands through which substances ooze which are toxic to the skin of man on contact.

Representatives of the class belong to the subclasses Epimorpha and Anamorpha. The former contains the large centipedes which have 25 or more segments in the trunk, while the Anamorpha have about 20 or fewer segments. The common house centipede, *Scutigera* sp. belongs to this subclass. Representatives of medical importance usually belong to the Epimorpha.

Chilopoda are found in forests either in the duff layers or under the loosened bark of dead trees. A few species occur in dwellings and other buildings which provide moist wood and ample cracks and crevices. Attems (1926–1930a) says that they shun light. They are active in the duff at all times, since natural light is often of low intensity there during the day. Some species are said to burrow in soil, but generally they live in natural lines of cleavages in duff and soil. A few tropical forms are provided with luminescent organs and glow in the dark. All are carnivorous and feed largely on other arthropods and worms, while some large species may attack lizards or other animals of similar size. Prey is impaled on the two stout opposable, chelate front legs and is then poisoned by secretions from glands. No parasitic species are known. When centipedes use their chelipeds as offensive weapons on man, they cause symptoms described elsewhere in the book (see p. 196). Chilopoda accompany millipedes that are moving in hordes, according to Cloudsley-Thompson. Possibly they prey on the hapless millipedes or on other arthropods that may be in the company.

CRUSTACEA

Crustacea is a class containing large numbers of species, most of which are marine. The oceans are teeming with these animals and some are said to occur at all depths wherever animals live. Medical significance of the group is minor because relatively few species cause injury to man or provide tissues hospitable to organisms pathogenic to him. They have an indirect importance in serving as hosts for some juvenile worms that attack vertebrates, including man.

Crustacea have a compact, rigid anterior part to the body and usually have a visibly segmented posterior part (Zimmer, 1926–1927). Two pairs of antennae occur anteriorly and three pairs of segmented appendages comprise the mouth parts. All body segments may bear a pair of jointed, biramous appendages. Certain forms add segments as they grow, and they may have seventy or more pairs of legs. All have closed respiratory systems with gills which provide the usual surfaces for external exchange of gases. This exchange is effected in some instances by way of the cuticula and the walls of the gut.

Representatives of the class have been variously grouped into eleven orders by most carcinologists, of which the five having some medical importance are shown in Table 2. The Branchiura, or fish

Table 2. Diagnostic Characteristics of Orders of Medically Important Crustacea (Adult Stage).

Characteristic	Euco-pepoda	Podo-copa	Bran-chiura	Iso-poda	Amphi-poda	Deca-poda
Length (in mm)	<4	<5	5–25	5–20	5–25	15–130
Free thoracic segments (number)	5	–	3	7	7	0
Abdominal segments (number)	3–5	0	0	0–6	6	6
Feeding appendages (number of pairs)	2	0	2	2	2	3
Abdominal appendages (number of pairs)	0	0	0	6	6	6
Telson	0	0	0	1	1	1

lice, are permanent parasites of fish. For details of the morphology of these groups the student is referred to Zimmer (1926–1927) and to Pennak (1953).

Copepods (Eucopepoda) (Fig. 3) are universally distributed as one species or another in static fresh water, particularly that of pools, ponds, lakes, and sluggish parts of streams. They usually feed by grazing along submerged surfaces and by filtration of plankton as do larvae of mosquitoes. All sorts of particulate matter may be swallowed, including immature stages of worms. A typical generation span completes, in order, an egg, six juvenile or nauplius stages, five copepodid stages, and the adult. Species likely to be consistently swallowed by man, waterfowl, fish, and amphibia may serve as hosts for juvenile worms.

Podocopa, or seed shrimp, inhabit all sorts of fresh water both static and flowing and are particularly adapted to life among exposed fibrous roots, algal mats, and debris. They have the appearance of tiny, bivalved mollusks because the carapace has grown laterally and downward to become shell-like. All vestiges of external segmentation have been lost. They feed on microbes and detritus and may be considered scavengers in the general sense. External respiration is largely cuticular. An egg stage and some eight juvenile instars precede the mature phase. Forms that are regularly eaten by fish are possible hosts for juvenile acanthocephalid worms (see p. 374).

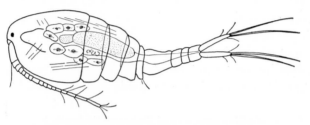

Fig. 3. *Cyclops* sp. (After Martini, 1923.)

Fresh-water Isopoda form only a small percentage of the order. They crawl on the bottoms of ponds, lakes, and deep, sluggish streams while some even inhabit subterranean waters. Wherever they live, they are scavengers on plant and animal remains. A few forms become hosts for juvenile acanthocephalid worms which live as adults in fish, amphibia, and bottom feeding water-fowl.

Amphipoda are largely marine, but a few live in fresh water that is unpolluted and well aerated. The fresh-water forms usually live on the bottom even at great depths. They are voracious feeders on both animal and vegetable matter, which they devour by first chewing off surface particles and then masticating those too large to be swallowed directly. Eggs are retained in a kind of pouch for incubation, and the young are released when the gravid female molts. Some are juvenile hosts for tapeworms, nematodes, trematodes, and acanthocephalids (see pp. 352–376).

Decapoda (Figs. 4 and 5) are the crayfishes, crabs, and shrimps of the world. They live on the bottoms of bodies of water and often at great depths. Many of the crayfish excavate burrows on waterlogged lands and extend the bottoms of their burrows down to the water table. Conspicuous claws on the front legs are their trademark. These animals eat many kinds of succulent vegetation and animal remains. They are seldom predacious, but some do ingest small swimming insects such as mosquito larvae, as any collector of

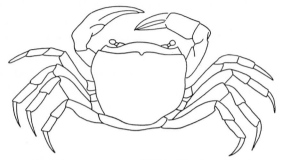

Fig. 4. *Potamon* sp. (After Martini, 1923.)

Fig. 5. A common crayfish. (Courtesy Illinois Natural History Survey.)

aquatic insects knows. Wherever people eat raw decapods, as is sometimes done in the Orient, several forms are hosts to a juvenile stage of lung flukes (see p. 353).

ARACHNIDA
(Scorpions, Spiders, Ticks, Mites)

The Arachnida, considered herein as a class, is rated by some as a subclass of Arachnoidea together with Merostomata (horseshoe crab, etc.) and Pycnogonida (sea spiders). Since agreement is lacking as to the exact relative phylogenetic position of the group, the more traditional grouping is used here. This class contains a large number of forms, though relatively few of them are well known.

Arachnida is the class of arthropods with especially remarkable adaptability to dry climates. This characteristic has enabled them to live in regions subject to both drought and cold. However, they are particularly successful in warmer parts of the world. This was among the first of the classes to become differentiated from the primeval arthropodan stock, and in time it has given rise to extensive, diverse speciation. Details relative to their evolutionary background may be found in Grassé (1949).

Distinctive characteristics of the class are as follows. Evolutionary lines for the group began without cephalization of the anterior segments into a head; hence the head as such is not distinguishable. The first post-oral somite retains a pair of appendages as chelicerae modified for stabbing or macerating food. No other oral appendages have developed. The second post-oral somite retains its appendages as pedipalpi which are variously modified for grasping, locomotion, or reception of stimuli. When these anterior segments form into a distinct section, it is the *gnathosoma*. Characteristically, each of post-oral somites 3–6 (*podosoma*) bears a pair of jointed legs. Twelve or thirteen somites comprise the caudal region or *opisthosoma*, but segmentation may or may not be visible externally. The anal opening is on the last segment. The genital aperture appears to be located on the first abdominal segment (since the true first segment is not visible). Some mites (Demodicidae), especially the males, show a secondary displacement of the genital opening. The respiratory system is characteristically tracheate, but many mites have lost all vestiges of such organs and respire externally directly through the cuticula. Visual organs range from none to eight ocelli.

The class Arachnida is represented by eight recognized orders of which three are of medical importance. The Scorpionida contains the true scorpions famous for their stinging propensities. Araneae are the spiders with some representatives well known as biters. The larger order and by far the more important medically is Acarina, commonly known as the ticks and mites. One order, Solfugae, contains the wind scorpions that are alleged to be able to broach human skin by a rending action. Diagnostic characteristics are given in Table 3.

Table 3. Diagnostic Characteristics of Medically Important Orders of Arachnida (Adult Stage).

Characteristic	Scorpionida	Araneae	Acarina	Solfugae
Podosoma	Segmented	Unsegmented	Unsegmented	Segmented
Pedicel	Absent	Present	Absent	Absent
Telson	Present	Absent	Absent	Absent
Pedipalps	Chelate	Unchelate	Usually chelate	Unchelate
Chelicerae	Small	Large	Small	Large
Opisthosoma	Segmented	Unsegmented *	Unsegmented	Segmented
Book lungs	Present	Present	Absent	Absent
Tracheae	Absent	Present	Present	Present

* Liphistriidae are the exception.

Scorpionida (Scorpions)

Scorpions are often recognized by the layman and are well known by residents in areas of their abundance. Their most characteristic feature is the general body form. The gnathosoma seems to be a part of the podosoma, and appears as a plump anterior unit. The podosoma is broadly joined to the opisthosoma which constricts to become a whip-like caudal element sometimes called post-abdomen. The body ends caudally in a telson with its thorn-like, rigid stinger. The post-abdomen in the offensive position is held over the back, so that the stinger is in front and above the body; otherwise the post-abdomen trails as a tail. The four pairs of walking legs are long and fairly stout. Each of the pedipalpi is elbowed forward and inward, and ends in two opposable chelae or claws. Both sexes have a "pectine" or comb on each side of the genital pore. The lamellae, or teeth of the comb, are richly supplied with nerves. Whatever may be the whole function of this pair of appendages, they certainly are vibratory receptors of great sensitivity (Cloudsley-Thompson, 1955). Respiratory organs consist of "book-lungs," or lamellate gills, which are in pouches in pre-abdominal segments. An epicuticular layer encases the body and is relatively impervious to the movement of water. Whip scorpions lack a stinger, but even so they are often confused with true scorpions by the layman.

Scorpions are most abundant in warm parts of the world which have long summers and either no winters or mild ones. Semiarid regions in or near the tropics are most suitable. When scorpions range into places having subfreezing temperatures, they secrete themselves in warmer crevices and lie dormant during cold interludes. They survive in situations which provide a dry microclimate such as cliffs, piles of rocks or other objects, sand dunes, and even loosened bark of dead trees. Though scorpions occur where the climate is usually dry, they require access to moisture because they drink water. Cloudsley-Thompson (1955a) pointed out that they have survived in a general semiarid climate because they inhabit crevices and are nocturnal. Species of Buthidae, for example, dig shallow crevices beneath rocks wherein they escape both diurnal heat and low moisture. Furthermore, specific sites occupied by them have moist microclimates easily available. Their crevices may be extended and connected to moist areas in the soil. Such extensions may go down the trunk of a dead tree to moisture. Some *Scorpio* spp., on the other hand, dig holes several feet deep in sandy wastes in order to reach a moist region.

A further adaptation of scorpions is the ability to withstand starvation for long periods. This characteristic is not uncommon among some arachnids such as ticks and some spiders. Survival without feeding for four to five months is common, and it has been reported for intervals bridging nine months. This adaptation is necessary since scorpions probably do not seek food; instead they lie in wait until some crawling insect comes near them. The exact means by which scorpions detect prey is unknown, though vision is thought to be unimportant since they feed in the dark. They can detect slight air movements, even those caused by passing insects, and they also detect minute vibrations. A scorpion bent on feeding moves about slowly with the chelae of the pedipalps spread and the stinger turned forward. When near the prey it blindly grasps with the chelae and simultaneously lashes its post-abdomen (Fig. 6). Scorpions are predacious on any and all small animals that come within range and can be subdued. Food consists largely of any available moving animal and includes insects, spiders, other arthropods, and even small mice (Cloudsley-Thompson, 1955a). Cockroaches are often used as food for caged scorpions. Presumably they do not differentiate between movements of potential prey and movements of persons, hence scorpions occasionally lash out with their post-abdomens and accidentally sting humans. Even though these animals may appear to be gregarious, they are actually antagonistic and keep their distance from each other except at mating time.

Baerg (1954) records the feeding act of one of the Buthidae from Jamaica as follows. Grasshoppers are clasped by the chelicerae and are repeatedly stung until they remain quiet. The chelicerae then pick a hole through an intersegmental membrane such as that of the neck region, and pluck out the internals. Since digestion is extra-oral, the material to be ingested is first made soupy in consistency.

Certain behavior patterns of scorpions seem to be characteristic of the entire group. Baerg (1954) and others before him have reported on their "courting performances." A male grasps the pedi-

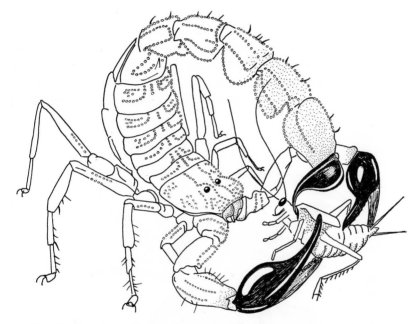

Fig. 6. Scorpion (*Androctonus* sp.) showing normal use of stinger. (After Vachon, 1953.)

palps of a receptive female with his pedipalps and the two walk together in a "backward and forward" sequence. This activity may continue for hours with some modification. During the latter part of the performance the male ejects a spermatophore which becomes dislodged (Alexander, 1956). The male then repeatedly drags the female over the spermatophore until there is contact with the genital pore. The female is then held in contact with the spermatophore until all sperms move into the pore. The embryos may be nourished by yolk in a self-contained egg, or they may be fed through the elaborate feeding organ in an ovariole that is connected to the mouth of the embryo (Vachon, 1953). Further maternal care of young scorpions continues for some days as the young swarm over the mother.

Millot and Vachon (1949) divided six families into about 600 species in the order; of these over 300 species are in the family Buthidae. Most of the families contain highly toxic species. Some of the more venomous genera are *Androctonus, Bothriurus, Buthacus, Buthus, Centruroides, Euscorpius, Leiurus, Prionurus, Scorpio,* and *Tityus* (for effects see p. 198).

Araneae (Spiders)

The order Araneae (see Table 3) is composed of three suborders: Liphistiomorpha, Mygalomorpha, and Araneomorpha, according to Millot (1949). The first one is of no medical importance, while the second suborder has only two families of significance, Theraphosidae

Fig. 7. Tarantula, *Eurypelma.* (After Savory, 1935.)

and Ctenizidae. Theraphosidae includes the big hairy spiders known in this country as tarantulas (Fig. 7), and Ctenizidae contains the trapdoor spiders and funnel-web weavers of Australia. Species in the genera *Acanthoscurria, Phormictopus, Selenocosmia,* and *Sericopelma* (Theraphosidae) of the tropics bite with varying degrees of severity. The last suborder and by far the largest one contains seven families and at least 14 genera having representatives of medical significance. Tropicopolitan species are in the genera *Heteropoda* (Fig. 8) and *Latrodectus* (see Fig. 9), both of which either voluntarily range or are transported into regions on both sides of the tropics. Bites of all species of both genera are very toxic. *Lycosa* species are cosmopolitan in temperate regions. *Loxosceles* species are in the Americas, and at least one ranges as far north as Missouri and Illinois. South America has species of *Ctenus*, *Chiracanthium*, *Mastophora*, and *Trechona* in addition to some of those

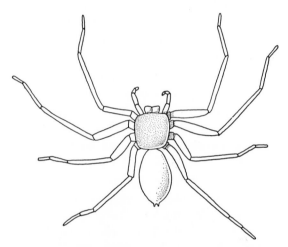

Fig. 8. A banana spider, *Heteropoda* sp. (After Comstock, 1912.)

listed above. *Segestria* and *Lycosa* are more common in Europe while others of lesser importance are occasionally encountered. The noxious species of Australia are included in the genus *Atrax*, and at least one is in *Latrodectus*.

Spiders are generally recognized by lay persons, particularly if a web is associated with them; however, few people know the diversity of form and habit that spiders may assume. Urbanization has not discouraged them, and forests and fields still have their share. In areas of spider abundance the air is sometimes a shimmering delight when the sunshine is reflected from the many strands of floating silk. This silk, called "angel's hair," is caught on trees, shrubs, wires, and aerials, and it may become a popular curiosity. The ever-present household spider with its constant supply of cobwebs is the bane of housekeepers. For the brighter side of spider life, the reader is referred to Gertsch (1949) and elsewhere. The purpose here is to discuss only those animals that may injure man, and fortunately the number of harmful spiders is small, though many persons are unaware of this.

Spiders are recognized by certain distinctive characteristics. The striking feature is the division of the body into roughly equal parts: a leg-bearing anterior portion (combined gnathosoma and podosoma) and the opisthosoma, or "abdomen" as it is often called. A marked constriction, the pedicel, connects the two parts. External segmentation is not visible except in primitive forms. The cuticula is entirely smooth and devoid of sutures except for joints on appendages and at places of their insertions on the body. Each chelicera ends in a curved, rigid fang which bears an opening to a poison duct near the apex. Pedipalpi are leg-like in the female and are apically specialized in the male as copulatory organs. Silk glands open on from 4 to 8 spinnerets placed caudally on the abdomen. Tracheae of the respiratory organs receive oxygen either through book-lungs in 2 to 4 ventral abdominal pouches or the spiracles or both. A tracheal net distributes oxygen to the cells. For greater morphological detail see Gerhardt and Kästner (1938).

Eggs of spiders are always placed in nurseries of silken cocoons which may hold several hundred eggs. Cocoons are laid down as sheets of silk on which the eggs are placed one at a time. The clutch is then covered by additional silk and the water-repellent cocoon is shaped as a disc or a hanging drop. These nurseries shield the eggs throughout incubation, and they may retain the juveniles for some months, if the young pass through winter in the cocoons.

Shortly after the young spiders escape their cocoons, they become air-borne with their strands of silk and thus are dispersed. First a spiderling climbs to a launching site suitably exposed to the wind. There it spins a tangled mass of web that is soon caught in air currents. When the lift of the breeze is sufficient, the silken mass with the attached spiderling is pulled from the site and drifts away. The spider may be supported for a long or short aerial trip, as the flight is passive and ends when the wind falls or when the web becomes entangled in wires or vegetation. This movement is known as ballooning. Household spiders and those likely to bite man disperse more often by walking than by ballooning.

All spiders are predacious and their prey is largely arthropodan. The food is caught by various means, and then impaled by the chelicerae and immobilized by venom secreted through the fangs. The better-known method used by spiders for obtaining food is the trapping of flying insects. The snares used are of infinite structural variety and intricacy but a webbing is always stretched across the likely routes of potential prey. The webs can be studied in Comstock's *Spider Book*. Some spiders are active hunters that stalk flies and other insects, while others passively wait in holes and crevices to waylay passing arthropods. In all cases the spider strikes swiftly, and the chelicerae are quickly jabbed into the prey. This is the pattern of attack when the victim is a large animal or even a person.

Toxic fluids come from the fangs and possibly from digestive fluids that can be forced out of the mouth. A neurotoxin is secreted through the fangs. Hemolytic fractions in the venom may also very well come from the fangs. Some species of spiders are known to emit digestive fluids from the mouth. These fluids are forced into the bodies of the victims by movements of the fangs, thereby enabling the spider to predigest the organs and tissues of its victims. The resulting magma is then sucked through the food tube.

Fluids sufficiently potent to digest organs and tissues of small animals could be necrotic and hemolytic to tissues of man. Spiders of the genera *Ctenus, Trechona,* and *Latrodectus* apparently do not flood the surfaces of feeding sites with digestive fluids since they produce only neurotoxins, while *Phormictopus, Segestria,* and *Loxosceles* produce both hemolytic and necrotic fractions. Unfortunately very little is known about the exact nature of the venoms beyond what was reported by Vellard (1936) and Pavlovsky (1927) (for effects see p. 195).

Table 4 contains 19 genera in some 11 families of spiders, any species of which may have medical significance. Some genera have several known species of importance. Most of the genera occur in the Western Hemisphere; however, much remains unknown about the distribution of poisonous spiders.

The ones best known for their medical importance are those of the genus *Latrodectus* (family: Theridiidae) that are commonly called widow spiders (Fig. 9). They live in tangled masses of their webbing and within the ranges of many crawling arthropods. Sites that are seldom disturbed as corners of out-buildings, piles of rubbish or rocks, folds of little used draped cloth or clothing, and the undersides of benches such as seats of privies are all suitable. In such obscure places these spiders spin their masses of open webs.

The bottom layers of the web are made of sticky threads of silk while the large mass of the webbing is composed of dry threads. The entire mass may be as large as a man's fist.

Table 4. Genera of Spiders Reported to Have Medical Significance.

| Genus | Family | Distribution of Venomous Species | |
		General	Local
Acanthoscurria	Theraphosidae	S. America	Debris
Aphonopelma	Theraphosidae	N. America	Under stones or logs
Atrax	Ctenizidae	Eastern Australia	Funnel-web, woods
Avicularia	Theraphosidae	N. America	Under stones or logs
Chiracanthium	Clubionidae	S. America	Vegetation
Ctenus	Ctenidae	S. America	Banana plantings, dwellings
Heteropoda	Sparassidae	Tropicopolitan	Domestic; warehouses
Latrodectus	Theridiidae	Tropicopolitan, warm temperate	Debris, privies, outbuildings
Loxosceles	Sicariidae	S. and N. America	Domestic
Lycosa	Lycosidae	Cosmopolitan temperate	Holes
Mastophora	Argiopidae	Andes	Tube-web in vines
Phormictopus	Theraphosidae	W. Indies	Rocks, logs
Plectreurys	Sicariidae	N. America	Vegetation, etc.
Polybetes	Sparassidae	Tropics	Tube-web in vegetation
Segestria	Segestriidae	Europe	Holes in ground
Selenocosmia	Theraphosidae	Indonesia	Under stones and logs
Sericopelma	Theraphosidae	Panama	Under stones and logs
Sicarius	Sicariidae	Brazil	Vegetation
Trechona	Dipluridae	Tropics and subtropics	Funnel-web, forest floor

Each web usually houses a female and several egg cocoons, and sometimes the lilliputian male lurks in some obscure part of the nest. The female clings in an inverted position to the tangled dry threads. When the web is vibrated ever so lightly as by a trapped fly or other small insect, the female darts to the site of the disturbance and quickly strikes the victim with the chelicerae. Usually the chelicerae are moved alternately in the manner of chewing and venom is injected at the same time. After hatching, the young spiderlings may literally fill the web before they wander away to make their own nests. The female may produce several egg cocoons and then die after a total life span of a few months; however, she does not live through winter. The eggs are able to withstand near-freezing temperatures for long periods. The male spider lives a lonely existence of short duration in the web of the female where it feeds little if at all. Sometimes the female hastens his demise by killing and devouring him immediately following copulation. Prolonged exposure to subfreezing temperatures seems to be a factor limiting the spread of the genus into cold climates.

The *Loxosceles* (family: Sicariidae) are spiders that usually live under bark of dead trees, and under stones. Domestic sites often provide a variety of attractive nesting places. These spiders build large irregular webs that are attached to a silken sac. They lie in the web to wait for prey, but they will retreat into a hideaway on provocation.

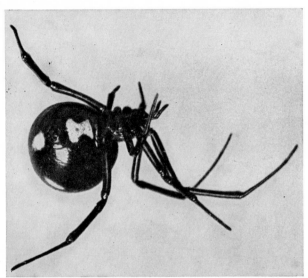

Fig. 9. Black widow spider, *Latrodectus mactans.* (Hour-glass mark on venter of abdomen is brick red.) (Courtesy Illinois Natural History Survey.)

The wolf or lycosid spiders (family: Lycosidae) are fairly large brown or gray spiders with distinctly long legs (Fig. 10). Species likely to harm man live in gardens and lawns, but they do not inhabit houses. They may be more aptly considered as burrowing spiders because they excavate tubes and then line them with silk. The burrows are dug by the chelicerae, and during the excavation the loose soil is wrapped in silk and then hauled out of the tube. Some kinds extend the silken lining an inch or two above the surface of the ground as a chimney or tower. These spiders often leave their burrows and wander about. Throughout the incubation period females carrying cocoons of eggs may be seen both in and out of the burrows. For several days after the spiderlings leave the cocoon, they cling to the body of the female.

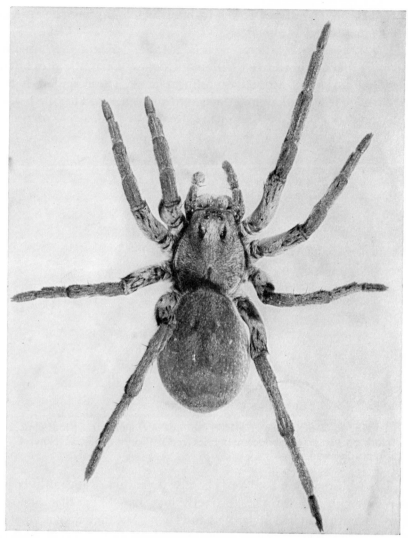

Fig. 10. A wolf spider, *Lycosa carolinensis*. (Courtesy Illinois Natural History Survey.)

McKeown (1952) has said that the spiders with the "darkest" reputation in Australia are the funnel-web spiders (*Atrax:* Cten-izidae, Fig. 11). At least two of the eight species that are widely distributed on the continent are the mygalomorph spiders that are related to the well-known trap-door spiders. These brownish spiders have stout, hairless bodies and short, hairy legs. A fully gravid female may have the abdomen distended to the size of a pigeon's egg. She will appropriate any suitable hole in the ground, such as one made and abandoned by a mouse, or she may dig a burrow. The entrance to this hole or burrow is not closed by a trap door as are those of its relatives; however, a silken lining extends upward beyond the opening as a kind of funnel. These spiders range away from the lair at night and feed on beetles and other insects active on the

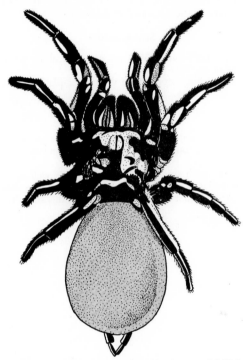

Fig. 11. *Atrax* sp. (After McKeown, 1952.)

ground. In attacking, they rear back with fore-legs and pedipalps elevated and chelicerae extended. The prey is buffeted by the legs and pedipalps as the chelicerae are brought into action. They display an abnormal belligerency and will readily attack a person. Apparently these spiders develop slowly and may live two or more years.

ADDITIONAL READINGS

General Morphology

SNODGRASS (1954) is an extensive account of morphology of insects in particular. It is intended for use of the advanced student. Any general textbook on entomology has one or more chapters on this subject.

IMMS (1957) discusses morphology of the other classes in the order as well.

Diplopoda and Chilopoda

ATTEMS (1926–1930 and 1926–1930a) must be seen for a comprehensive understanding of these classes. Both are well illustrated and are interesting. No comparable works have been written in English.

Crustacea

PENNAK (1953) has a comprehensive survey of this class. It is readable and can be used by the beginner and the advanced student alike.

Scorpionida

CLOUDSLEY-THOMPSON (1955 and 1955a) are accounts about morphology and habits and will provide clues to other papers.

VACHON (1953) is a well-illustrated article with color plates of several species. This is a semipopular presentation.

Araneae

COMSTOCK (1912) and the revision by GERTSCH (1948) are standard references (in English) to spiders. The books are well illustrated and deal with spiders in general.

McKEOWN (1952) deals with spiders of Australia. It is well illustrated with photographs. Some discussion is included about poisonous species, but there is no reference that brings together that which is known about this subject.

CHAPTER 3

Arachnida: Acarina

GENERAL

The order Acarina is one of the two most important orders of arthropods from the point of view of the epidemiologist. Their most common significance is as parasites which attach themselves to the skin of various animals. Many species cause diseases such as itch, mange, scab, and allergies. Others are normal hosts of agents that cause disease in vertebrates. In the case of pathogenic rickettsiae and viruses, acarine tissues are thought to be the basic ones. The range of genera most likely to be met by the medical entomologist are those shown in Table 5. While it is recognized that many of these may not harm man directly, the medical entomologist and medical practitioner may encounter them and needs to know those of clinical significance.

Acarina have proved to be adaptable to microenvironments of endless variety. They live in duff layers, in beds of moss, in patches of lichen, and in soil rich in humus. A great many species are generalized feeders on detritus of both vegetable and animal origin. A role parasitic on either plants or animals has been assumed by a large segment of the population. Those that parasitize animals live in close association with their hosts. Nests and lairs are occupied by some, while the vestiture of birds and mammals provides lodgment for others. A vast array of species lives in all sorts of vertebrates in every natural body opening as well as in the skin, in ducts, and in tissues below the skin. Study of these animals provides one of the most active fields for taxonomists, and, fortunately, a number of avid and dedicated investigators are collecting and systematizing the group. The layman knows representatives of this order under

33

Table 5. Genera of Mites Having One or More Species of Medical or Domestic Importance.

Genus	Family	Suborder	Medical or Domestic Importance of One or More Species
Acarus	Acaridae	Sarcoptiformes	Bite; invades lungs
Acomatacarus	Trombiculidae	Trombidiformes	Bite
Allodermanyssus	Dermanyssidae	Mesostigmata	Bite; vector
Apolonia	Trombiculidae	Trombidiformes	Bite; burrows in skin
Bryobia	Tetranychidae	Trombidiformes	Crawls
Carpoglyphus	Carpoglyphidae	Sarcoptiformes	Bite; invades lungs
Cheyletiella	Cheyletidae	Trombidiformes	Bite
Cheyletus	Cheyletidae	Trombidiformes	Bite; invades lungs
Chorioptes	Psoroptidae	Sarcoptiformes	Cattle scab
Demodex	Demodicidae	Trombidiformes	None; or cystic and pustular mange
Dermanyssus	Dermanyssidae	Mesostigmata	Bite; vector
Dermatophagoides	Epidermoptidae	Sarcoptiformes	Bite; invades lungs, urinary tract
Dermoglyphus	Dermoglyphidae	Sarcoptiformes	Invades quills
Echinolaelaps	Laelaptidae	Mesostigmata	Vector
Eulaelaps	Laelaptidae	Mesostigmata	Bite; vector
Glycyphagus	Glycyphagidae	Sarcoptiformes	Bite
Haemogamasus	Haemogamasidae	Mesostigmata	Bite
Haemolaelaps	Laelaptidae	Mesostigmata	Bite; vector
Hirstionyssus	Dermanyssidae	Mesostigmata	Vector
Holothyrus	Holothyridae	Onychopalpida	Gastric toxin
Knemidokoptes	Sarcoptidae	Sarcoptiformes	Cutaneous invader
Laelaps	Laelaptidae	Mesostigmata	Bite; vector
Neoschöngastia	Trombiculidae	Trombidiformes	Bite
Notoedres	Sarcoptidae	Sarcoptiformes	Bite
Ornithonyssus	Dermanyssidae	Mesostigmata	Bite; vector
Otodectes	Psoroptidae	Sarcoptiformes	Invades ears
Pneumonyssus	Halarachnidae	Mesostigmata	Invades air passages of primates, etc.
Psorergates	Cheyletidae	Trombidiformes	Invades skin
Psoroptes	Psoroptidae	Sarcoptiformes	Invades skin
Pyemotes	Pyemotidae	Trombidiformes	Bite
Sarcoptes	Sarcoptidae	Sarcoptiformes	Burrows in skin
Schöngastia	Trombiculidae	Trombidiformes	Bite; vector
Suidasia	Acaridae	Sarcoptiformes	Bite
Tarsonemus	Tarsonemidae	Trombidiformes	Bite; invades lungs
Trombicula	Trombiculidae	Trombidiformes	Bite; vector
Tyrophagus	Acaridae	Sarcoptiformes	Bite

the general name of ticks and mites. While these common names have little taxonomic value, they are widely used and must be retained in a general book. Most species of ticks attain a length of a centimeter or more at maturity; hence they are considered large. Most mites are a millimeter or less across the maximum dimension. However, exceptions to these general measurements are many.

MORPHOLOGY

The order has the following distinctive features in addition to those for the class and phylum. The body is composed of three regions that are distinguishable as is shown in Fig. 12. The anterior segments are fused to form the *gnathosoma* (called *capitulum* by some authors) bearing the chelicerae and pedipalps. The *podosoma* is a middle region of four segments that bears the legs. Behind the

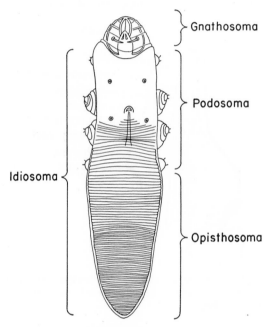

Fig. 12. *Demodex* sp. (dorsal view). (After Baker and Wharton, 1952.)

last pair of legs is the sac-like *opisthosoma* that is free of append-ages. The term *idiosoma* is often used to designate the part of the body behind the gnathosoma. The integument consists of a hypo-dermal layer of epithelium and a secreted cuticula of some four layers. A variety of sensillae, glandular openings, and sclerous areas mark the cuticula; however, evidence of segmentation is seldom visible. Four basic stages comprise a generation, namely egg, hexa-pod "larva," octapod "nymph," and adult. One or more instars may be completed in each of the post-embryonic juvenile stages.

The gnathosoma is the distinct anterior part. Usually it is fully exposed, but in some mites it is enclosed in an anterior cavity (*camerostome*) on the lower side of the idiosoma. The gnathosoma is usually covered dorsally by a plate called the *tectum* or *epistome*. The two chelicerae extend forward from below the tectum. Each chelicera terminates in two digits that are endlessly modified by emphasis, atrophy, or extension into cutting, clasping, or piercing organs. The pedipalps are laterad of the chelicerae and are variously modified from leg-like appendages to organs for attachment. The bases of the chelicerae together form the dorsal side of the pre-oral

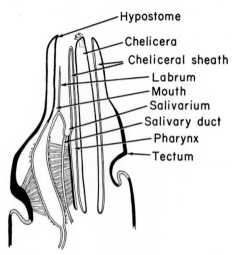

Fig. 13. Diagram of a median longitudinal section through the gnathosoma of an acarine showing mouth and oral appendages. (After Snodgrass, 1948.)

cavity (Fig. 13). An anteriorly projected cuticular flap, the *hypostome,* situated below the chelicerae becomes the ventral closure for this pre-oral cavity.

Most acarines are provided with three pairs of legs in the first post-embryonic (larval) stage and with four pairs of legs in subsequent stages. Legs may have become atrophied in the case of some present-day species until only 1 to 3 pairs of legs remain. Legs are usually simple and are used for creeping, crawling, burrowing, or jumping while some have become prehensile.

Internal systems for excretion, respiration, and coordination have some unique features. Excretion is carried on (1) by special glands called coxal glands that open near certain coxae, (2) by excretory tubules that open into the hind-gut, and (3) by epithelium of the mid-gut that exfoliates into the lumen. Nitrogenous wastes are largely guanin. There are characteristic variations in the number and placement of spiracles, that have taxonomic value. The central nervous system includes the usual nerves and a cephalized ganglionic mass about the esophagus.

SUBORDERS

The order Acarina is composed of such a large number of families that investigators feel a need for subordinal taxa. However, there is disagreement as to which groups should be called suborders. Baker and Wharton (1952) list five as suborders as follows: Onychopalpida, Mesostigmata, Ixodides, Trombidiformes, and Sarcoptiformes. The first three are very different from the last two, and the connecting link is currently unknown. For the purposes of this book these five entities are considered as one order despite the wide separation within the group (Table 6). Their suborder Onychopal-

Table 6. Diagnostic Morphological Characteristics for Medically Important Suborders of Acarina.

Characteristic	Onychopalpida	Mesostigmata	Ixodides	Trombidiformes	Sarcopti-formes
Haller's organ	None	None	Present	None	None
Pedipalpal coxa	Not fused dorsally	Fused	Fused	Fused	Fused
Body wall	Flexible	Flexible	Flexible	Flexible	Flexible or rigid
Stigmata	Ventral (1 or 2 pairs)	Near coxae (1 pair)	Near coxae (1 pair)	Near chelicerae or absent	Absent

pida includes the primitive mites which have claws on the pedipalpi and two or more pairs of spiracles on the idiosoma. Their suborder Mesostigmata is separated from Ixodides for convenience even though a close relationship seems to exist. These two are grouped as Parasitiformes by others. The mesostigmate mites have one pair of spiracles situated to the side of the legs and a poorly developed hypostome. Ixodides are the commonly called ticks and are similar to the preceding suborder except that the ticks have a well-developed hypostome and a special sense organ, called *Haller's organ* (described later), in the tarsus of the front legs. Included in Trombidiformes are the mites that usually have chelicerae for piercing and openings to the respiratory organs on or near the gnathosoma.

The plant-feeding forms (Tetrapodili) are included here. Representatives of the suborder Sarcoptiformes lack spiracles and usually have chelicerae modified for a sort of mastication of food. These mites include the free-living Oribatei of several authors. Various genera of medical importance are included in Table 5.

Onychopalpida

The primitive suborder Onychopalpida is represented by the genus *Holothyrus* that occurs on islands of the Indian Ocean and southeastward into Australia. These mites range in size up to 7 mm in length. Sometimes they are common in domestic situations where they have occasionally been known to poison children and domestic fowls that had swallowed them.

Mesostigmata

The suborder Mesostigmata is a large group of mites that contains representatives of four families of medical and domestic importance. These mites usually have brown, sclerotized plates or shields on the idiosoma. The families of importance are Dermanyssidae, Laelaptidae, Haemogamasidae, and Halarachnidae. The latter one is found endoparasitic in respiratory passages of mammals. Those of the genus *Pneumonyssus* live in wild primates, dogs, and other animals. They cause yellowish nodular lesions that could be confused with lesions of tuberculosis. None have been seen in man possibly because they are difficult to find except by autopsy. Members of the haemogamasid genus *Haemogamasus* are nest parasites of rodents, and they have been suspected of causing dermatitis of humans when populations develop in or near dwellings. Little is known about their bionomics.

Laelaptidae is a large family of hematophagous mites; however, the limits of the group are unclear and far from stable. These mammalian parasites are recognizable by bifurcate setae on the palps. Several are cosmopolitan parasites on a wide range of animals. Only those of the genera *Eulaelaps*, *Echinolaelaps*, and *Laelaps* are known well enough to mention here. These are all nest parasites of rodents and are of significance to medical entomology because of their potential in reservoirs of certain viruses and bacteria.

Mites of the family Dermanyssidae are of frequent concern to the medical entomologist because these invaders annoy persons in their homes. This is a very large family of mites of medium size. Their chelicerae are thread-like and each is chelate (often minutely so) at the end. Genera of these mites most commonly seen by the physician or medical entomologist are *Dermanyssus, Ornithonyssus, Allodermanyssus,* and *Hirstionyssus.* All of these are grayish in color and over 0.5 mm long. They become reddish and enlarge in diameter when engorged. All have striated cuticula and an anterior, dorsal sclerous plate on the body.

The common mite on chickens, *Dermanyssus gallinae,* is an inhabitant of the coop or nest and may be found in any building if the birds nest in or under it. These are invaders of dwellings and they may feed on man; however, removal of the nests of their avian hosts from the houses will cause the mites to disappear since they must have contact with fowls for food.

The so-called tropical rat mite (*Ornithonyssus bacoti*) is a cosmopolitan species of temperate and tropical regions that depends on domestic rats for maintenance of its population though it attacks man readily. Stages completed by these mites are egg, hexapod larva, protonymph, deutonymph, and adult. Of these only the protonymph and adult are hematophagous. The protonymph feeds only once and requires about 10 hours for repletion while the adult feeds repeatedly and requires about 10 minutes for each repletion. Adults feed every 2 to 5 days at room temperature. While feeding, the idiosoma is inclined at an angle of about 45° with the surface of the host. Some two to three weeks are required to complete all stages, and adults may live eight or more weeks. Bisexuality is normal; however, females may produce males parthenogenetically. While these mites spend most of their time away from their hosts, adults often remain in the fur of a rat for two days. These mites often infest warehouses, outbuildings, stores, and even theaters, and are especially troublesome in commercial buildings where rats are abundant. The mites become apparent to humans when populations of rats are suddenly depleted by sanitation measures or by migration.

The northern fowl mite (*O. sylviarum*) is a pest of birds and occasionally of man. These mites usually remain on birds but are often found in nests and elsewhere in chicken houses. Oviposition takes place on the birds as well as in nests. Eggs are cemented to the bases of feathers and to cracks and straw in the nests. They enter houses under the same conditions that encourage the chicken mite.

The tropical fowl mite (*O. bursa*) lives on birds in warmer parts of the world. It is particularly annoying to men in warehouses and dock buildings where birds roost and nest in large numbers; however, it rarely invades dwellings.

Allodermanyssus sanguineus, the apartment mite (Fig. 14), may live with burrowing mice in the wild, but it has come to be an inhabitant of suburban apartments. These mites are well suited to life with the house mouse wherever the rodents are abundant. They live in the nests and runs of both domestic mice and rats. Since the mites wander a great deal, they often invade various areas of apartment buildings where they may feed for a time on residents.

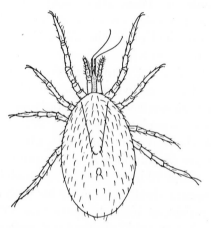

Fig. 14. *Allodermanyssus sanguineus.* (Modified from Baker, Evans, et al., 1956.)

Trombidiformes

Trombidiformes is a suborder containing species having diverse habits. The common phytophagous mites belong here; a large segment parasitizes arthropods in all stages, and the remainder parasitize vertebrates in one or more stages. Except for the primitive, predacious forms these mites have chelicerae modified for piercing tissues. Some lack tracheae, and those that have them also have the openings to them on the chelicerae or elsewhere on the gnathosoma. Families of mites in this suborder having some known medical importance are Pyemotidae, Tarsonemidae, Tetranychidae, Cheyletidae, Demodicidae, and Trombiculidae.

Pyemotidae are the mites that parasitize insects. Among the better known is the one of medical importance, *Pyemotes ventricosus,* a mite that pierces the skin of humans who have contact with infested materials. Female mites live as parasites on insects that infest such

stored plant products as grain, straw, and hay. Gravid females attach to suitable hosts, and as they feed, their abdomens become
greatly distended and bead-like. Eggs and juvenile forms develop
within this distended abdomen, and the offspring are produced vivip-
arously when sexually mature. Each female may produce 200 to
300 young during a lifetime.

Tarsonemid and tetranychid mites are secondary pests of man
that should be mentioned since at times medical attention is drawn
to them. Both are phytophagous mites, and both are casual invaders
of human habitations. The tarsonemid mites often attack house and
greenhouse plants, and they are occasionally inhaled by persons
working with infested plants. Tetranychid mites, especially *Bryobia*,
frequently invade dwellings near the sources of these acarines. The
houses may become hibernating sites, and sometimes the mites may
be seen crawling about windows on warm days of winter and spring.
While they are harmless to one's person, they are pests when crawling on the skin.

Cheyletidae on the whole are predators, and at least three genera
may be domestic pests. *Psorergates ovis* causes sheep itch and is a
minute species with short, stout, radially arranged legs. They may
be found in epidermal scrapings, particularly from Merino sheep.
Other species infest rodents. *Cheyletiella parasitivorax* lives in the
fur of rabbits and other animals infested with other species of mites,
and they may range onto persons who handle infested animals.
These are stout mites that seldom exceed 0.4 mm in length. Pedipalps are armed terminally by a recurved hook. *Cheyletus* spp. are
predators on mites in stored products; however, they may infest
man and cause localized cutaneous reactions.

Demodicid mites of the genus *Demodex* invade sebaceous pores
of the skin of man, also of dogs and other domestic animals. They
are very small and are difficult to see even in scrapings of tissue
known to contain them and at magnifications of 400×. They are 4–5
times as long as wide; the legs are mere stumps and the opisthosoma
is finely annulated (see Fig. 12). Most infestations of human skin
are benign even when the mites are abundant in pores around the
nose or eyelids or elsewhere. Mites of this group sometimes invade
the skin of dogs, and they may even penetrate to the lymph nodes.
When teamed with pus-forming bacteria, these mites cause mange,
an eruption on dogs, that may be recognized by its disagreeable
odor.

Trombiculidae are commonly known as chiggers or redbugs, or some name identified with the itch they cause, as scrub itch, ti itch, grass itch, or black-soil itch. Several hundred species are now known, and at least a score of these affect the health of man. All characteristically live outside domestic environments and attack humans only when the latter range into their haunts.

Trombiculids in all stages are reddish in color; however, the mites in active phases have the appearance of brilliant red velvet. Stages in order of occurrence are egg, *deutovum* (non-feeding), first

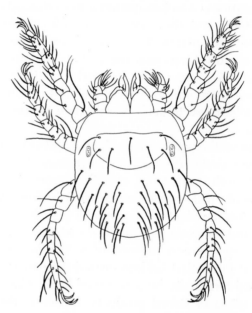

Fig. 15. Larva of *Trombicula autumnalis*. (After Savory, 1935.)

larva (or larva) (Fig. 15), *nymphochrysalis* (non-feeding), first nymph (or nymph), *imagochrysalis* (non-feeding), and adult (Michener, 1946). The larvae are best known to collectors, and relatively few of the advanced stages have been definitely identified with their larval stages. Taxonomy of the group is based largely on variations in the immature forms. Larvae are very small and barely visible to the unaided eye. The adults, on the other hand, may attain lengths of 1 mm. Details of the morphology have been summarized by Baker *et al.* (1956).

Life cycles of the several species of chiggers are similar in many ways. Eggs are deposited singly, and each is rolled about by the female until the surface is coated with pulverized detritus to prevent it from being eaten by mites in the vicinity. About six days after oviposition the shell of an egg splits equatorially to expose the granular cuticula of the *deutovum*. When about six days old, the deutovum changes into an active hexapod *larva*. In time it attaches to a reptile, bird, or mammal according to species of mite or availability of host. A larval mite requires attachment to a host from one to many days for feeding, and when replete it detaches from its host, falls to the ground, and becomes a quiescent, immobile *nymphochrysalis*. Very soon the active *nymph* emerges and begins to feed on eggs of small arthropods. When replete, a nymph, in turn, becomes immobilized as the bloated *imagochrysalis*. Finally the mite emerges as an *imago*. Like the nymph, the imago feeds on eggs of small arthropods such as those of Collembola. Insemination is accomplished by means of spermatophores in the manner of hydracharine mites (Lipovsky *et al.*, 1957). Males leave stalked spermatophores isolated on surfaces frequented by females, which in turn pick up the spermatophores while moving about. Gravid females place their eggs either on the surface of the soil or in its interstices.

Chiggers are notoriously erratic in distribution over their ranges. Some areas where they occur are heavily populated while there are spots within these areas that are devoid of them. The populated areas, called "mite islands," have distinctive characteristics (Harrison and Audy, 1951). These microcosms must provide an ample supply of arthropodan eggs for food during the last two stages, and they must be visited frequently by the vertebrate hosts of larvae. Since the larval host provides the only means for dispersal, the more specifically the principal larval host is tied to a site, the heavier the acarine population will be.

Interfaces, where margins of waste lands, seepage meadows, or narrow forests lie adjacent to some strikingly different vegetative pattern, provide ideal developmental sites. In the tropics, islands for *Trombicula akamushi* are vegetative mosaics that follow deforestation and human settlement. These interfacial situations permit the growth of populous colonies of species of *Rattus* amid dense populations of arthropodan hosts for later stages. Favorable sites for *T. alfreddugesi* in North America are located in and near blackberry thickets or certain shrubs where avian and reptilian hosts congregate (Williams, 1946). Chiggers rarely inhabit clipped lawns, parks, or cultivated fields. Calcareous soil is the common denominator for *T. autumnalis* in Europe (Keay, 1937). In one situation these chiggers were found on one side of a valley where the soil was chalky and were absent on the opposite side where the soil was sandy. Grasslands are favored in Britain, but infestations may occur in standing grain or even in grain stubble. Jones (1950) reported that thickets and strawberry beds were common island sites in Scotland.

Moisture most certainly affects both vertical and horizontal distribution of these mites. The surface of the soil must be moist but not continuously saturated. Warm weather and high humidity will cause mature mites to move to the soil surface while heavy rain, drought, or frost drive them into the soil. *T. autumnalis* may burrow downward into the soil for two or more feet (Richards, 1950). *Schöngastia indica* in Pacific Oceania and southern Asia lives in the moist debris found in rodent nests regardless of whether the nests are high in a coconut tree or hidden under a fallen log. In Tennessee, *T. lipovskyana* lives almost exclusively in moist situations provided by moss and occasionally in those provided by liverworts growing on logs (Penner *et al.*, 1954). Unfed larvae of most species live on the surface of the ground or in the vegetation debris which may be 2–3 inches above the actual soil surface.

Unfed larvae of chiggers often move about with surprising speed. The addition of any new object to their immediate environment increases their activity, and the chiggers will literally swarm over it. The rate of movement across a foreign body may exceed a foot a minute. Responses of larvae to such bodies are strongly and positively phototactic. The larvae ascend an object rapidly, and if it is a host, they continue ascending until an attachment site is located. Their habit of running upward has been utilized by persons in the field as a means for avoiding infestation. One may simply tuck the cuffs of trousers securely into the tops of boots or socks, hence the chiggers are easily shunted away from the legs and possible sites for lodgment to the outer surface of trousers. They climb upward on the outside of the clothing, and then drop off without harm to the person.

Little is known about specificity for hosts of each of the stages of trombiculid mites; in most instances larvae seem to have wide ranges. Larvae of *T. autumnalis* feed on rabbits, voles, hedgehogs, squirrels, ground birds, sparrows, and domestic fowl. In endemic areas one may see patches of other kinds of immature chiggers in the ears of rodents, or between the scales on the bellies of snakes, or on legs and necks of box turtles. Nymphs and adults are probably less specific for hosts than are the larvae. Critical hosts for nymphs and adults are virtually unknown, but eggs of Collembola very likely comprise an important constituent in the diet of many species.

It is thought that most chiggers in temperate regions pass the winter on their vertebrate hosts. Williams (1946) found *T. aka-mushi* in the ears of voles throughout the year. Larvae of *T. autum-*

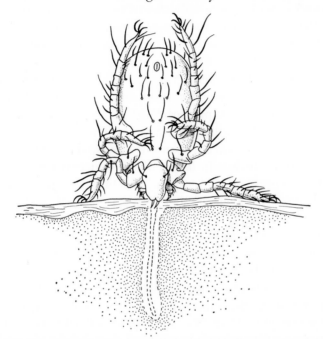

Fig. 16. Diagram of section through the skin showing attachment of a larval trombiculid and stylostome. (After Vitzthum, 1929.)

nalis live in the ears of rabbits and bank voles during the winter in Britain. Those of *T. alfreddugesi* have been collected from the heads of rabbits and from squirrels during the winter.

Vitzthum (1929) and later observers described the act of feeding of larval trombiculids, and all agree on essential aspects. The epidermis of a host is pierced by the chelicerae at some place where the skin is soft and relatively free of surface friction. A salivating mite digests a columnar mass of cells and stimulates the germinal layer of skin to grow a tubular wall about the mass of necrotic cells so that a discrete structure, or *stylostome*, is formed (Fig. 16). This stylostome ends blindly distally but is open where the mouth of the mite is appressed to the surface of the skin. The chigger ingests the digested cells within the stylostome. Neither blood nor solid matter is ingested. The feeding process lasts 3 to 5 days on man, but on rodents and possibly other animals it may last for some weeks or even months.

Sarcoptiformes

Sarcoptiformes is a large suborder of the chewing mites, so called because the mouth parts are adapted for tearing tissues. The two principal groups Acaridiae and Oribatei differ in the relative degree of sclerotization of the cuticula as the latter have such a heavy sclerous surface that they have acquired the name of armored mites. All the parasites of vertebrates, both casual and obligatory, belong to the former group. Representatives of the Oribatei may be in the series of hosts of anoplocephalid tapeworms.

The two groups evolved in moist, stratified media, and all the Oribatei continue to live in layers of moist detritus over wide latitudes. Representatives of Acaridiae live in stored products, in dry processed foods, in layers of scale insects on bark, under scales of vertebrates, and in the vestiture and skin of some vertebrates. All the media indicated are physically similar, though some are on the ground, others are on trees, and still others cover animals.

The mites of the suborder that live in dry processed foods include species of Acaridae, Glycyphagidae, and Carpoglyphidae. The better known of the first family are the cheese mites (*Acarus*), copra mites (*Tyrophagus*) (Fig. 17), and wheat pollard mites (*Suidasia*). Grocery mites (*Glycyphagus*) and dried fruit mites (*Carpoglyphus*) (Fig. 18) are the best known in the last two families. These are all small mites with short, stout legs ending in hooklike claws. One or another of them may be found in various kinds of layered plant parts, food stuffs, and even manure. Mushrooms, plant bulbs, humus, cheese, dried fruits, and grains provide common sites. All are non-parasitic but they cause allergic reactions on the skin of sensitized persons who handle infested products. Sometimes they invade the respiratory and urinary channels of man.

Several families of sarcoptiform mites live in the vestiture of birds and mammals. Some live in the hair and feed on surface exudates and detritus; others enter shafts of developing feathers and live on scales inside the quills, and some even invade the skin. One of the genera more noxious to man is *Dermatophagoides* of the family Epidermoptidae (Traver, 1951). All these mites are small, seldom exceeding 400 microns in length. Characteristically they have caruncles or suckers on all tarsi.

The families of Sarcoptidae and Psoroptidae contain tiny, obligate vertebrate parasites. These are globose mites whose surfaces are conspicuously marked by striae that often resemble fingerprints.

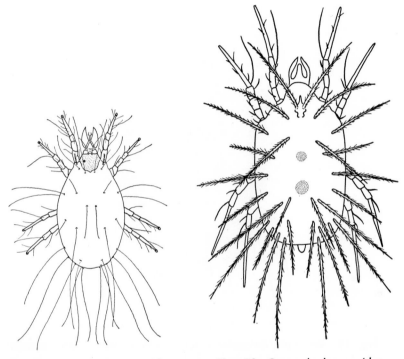

Fig. 17. *Tyrophagus* sp. (After Baker, Evans, *et al.*, 1956.)

Fig. 18. *Carpoglyphus* sp. (dorsal view). (After Martini, 1923.)

All stages are in permanent association with the skin of their hosts since they seldom survive more than a few hours when removed. The stages in sequence are egg, first larva (active), second larva (inactive), first nymph (active), second nymph (inactive), third nymph (active), fourth nymph (inactive), and adult (active). Speciation in both families is only partially understood for there seem to be few binomials and several trinomials based on physiological differences of each. More detailed comparative work is needed in this area.

Sarcoptid mites of the genus *Sarcoptes* (Fig. 19) live in burrows which they make in the superficial layers of the skin of mammals. Appendages of the gnathosoma and the forelegs are used to cut and tear the tissue as the tunnels are extended. Adult female mites are most active in burrowing into intact tissue while larvae, nymphs, and males tend to use old burrows or to move about over the skin surface and invade follicles. Eggs are casually deposited in tunnels. Presumably females are inseminated as older nymphs, and may dis-

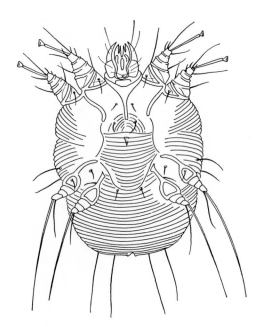

Fig. 19. Itch mite, *Sarcoptes scabiei* (ventral view). (After Martini, 1923.)

perse to new hosts when infested and non-infested animals come into bodily contact. The human parasite may be transmitted through contact with clothing or bed linen; however, most infections occur when people live in persistently crowded quarters, as in city slums, in jails, or during overcrowding in periods of calamity.

Johnson and Mellanby (1942) noted that the rate of infection in humans is low. In a large series of cases about half had less than six mites and less than 4 per cent had more than 50 mites; however, one patient had 511 mites. Little correlation exists between symptoms of scabies and incidence of mites. One reason seems to be that the mortality rate among juveniles is high. Seldom will more than 1 per cent of offspring reach maturity.

The two genera *Knemidokoptes* and *Notoedres* of the Sarcoptidae infest domestic animals; the former are found on fowls and the latter are usually on cats. Mites on fowls burrow beneath the leg scales and characteristically cause serum to exude and harden. In time, the scales become elevated, and the leg becomes sore and tender. Some species invade the comb and other parts of fowls. *Notoedres* sp. causes mange on cats, rabbits, rats, and dogs. These mites do not become established in human skin, but they will invade it. Repeated infections can cause a continuing symptomatology.

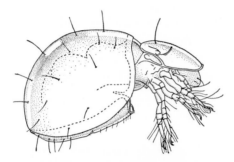

Fig. 20. Oribatid mite. (After Baker, Evans, *et al.*, 1956.)

Psoroptid mites of the genera *Psoroptes, Otodectes,* and *Chorioptes* may come to medical attention. With few exceptions, these mammalian parasites cause diseases known as scab and ear canker. Those of the genus *Psoroptes* live on the surface of the skin where they prick the skin and cause serum to accumulate and harden as a scab. The mites live under the edges of these scabs. Both *Psoroptes* and *Chorioptes* have physiological variants that seem to be naturally host-specific, but temporary crossing to exotic hosts takes place as with *Sarcoptes.* Sweatman (1957) has grown *Chorioptes* mites from several hosts in cages where they lived well and grew rapidly on "epidermic debris." Since *Otodectes* sp. live in the ears of dogs, cats, and wild canines, they may invade the inner ear and disturb the sense of equilibrium if the infestation is heavy. Human invasion is unlikely.

Oribatei are the oribatid or armored mites (Fig. 20) of pastures, fields and woods. They are often large and have a distinctive appearance. The cuticula has either heavily sclerotized, dark plates or it is very leathery. Tarsi end in claws and lack caruncles. Genital suckers are present. The gnathosoma is usually concealed. Wherever the soil surface provides a supply of decaying plant remains, these mites are present; and if the plant materials are in layers, the numbers of the mites may run into millions per acre. These animals avoid light and dryness, and congregate during the day in the shelter of sod or detritus. At night and on dark days they roam through grass and low vegetation. They browse over surfaces where they feed on spores and hyphae of fungi, decomposing plant parts, and fecal pellets of sheep, deer, and rabbits. Krull (1939) says they have gluttonous appetites and devour an enormous amount of material. As many as 619 mites per pound of forage have been taken from sheep pastures. These feeders on feces of ruminants, rabbits, and equines often ingest eggs of anoplocephaline tapeworms with the fecal material, and in doing so the mites become hosts for the juvenile stages of these worms. Infested mites may be eaten with grass by the vertebrate, and in turn the tapeworms are transmitted to the vertebrate host (see p. 356).

Ixodides

The term "tick" is properly restricted to representatives of this suborder. Stage for stage, ticks are usually larger than representatives of the other suborders. They have a remarkable capacity for enlargement during each instar as the cuticula has great elasticity. At least five structural characteristics serve to distinguish ticks from other acarines. (1) The gnathosoma is provided with a ventral, tongue-like, unsegmented, ventrally denticulated hypostome. (2) The chelicerae are two parallel, tubular extensions lying above the hypostome and bearing lateral teeth on the movable, apical digits. (3) The tarsus on each fore-leg bears on its dorsal surface a sensory pit called *Haller's organ* (Arthur, 1953) (Fig. 21). (4) Only two spiracles are present, and they are borne on the idiosoma above and behind coxae IV. (5) A specialized oviposition accessory called *Gené's organ* is present on all female ticks (Fig. 22). This is an eversible sac invaginated beneath a suture on the dorsal side of the idiosoma and located directly behind the gnathosoma.

As far as is known, all stages that feed at all do so exclusively on liquid from tissues of vertebrates. The actual mechanics of obtaining the blood is only partially known and is given in accounts of Arthur (1951), Foggie (1959), and Gregson (1960). Acts of pene-

trating the skin and attaching the mouth parts vary in detail according to stage and kind of tick. All cut the surface and deepen the
wound by slashing motions of the digits of the chelicerae, but only
the hypostome and the two chelicerae enter the wound. Once the

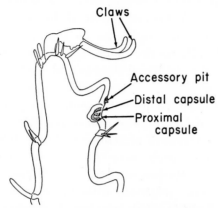

Fig. 21. Distal end of fore-leg of an argasid tick showing the relation
of parts of Haller's organ. (After Schulze, 1941.)

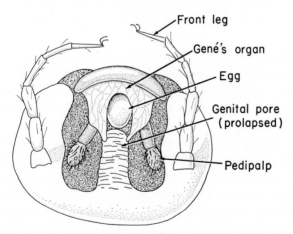

Fig. 22. Diagram of anterior portion of ixodid tick showing pro-
lapsed gonopore with egg extruded between the two lobes of Gené's
organ. (After Lewis, 1892.)

hypostome is fully inserted, movements of chelicerae cease in the
case of ixodid ticks, but the argasids continue slashing capillaries.
Within 24 hours after insertion of the hypostome by an ixodid tick,
a cement forms a plug which permeates the tissue on all sides of
the mouth parts. A kind of rigid binding results either by hardening

of the material or by a reaction of the tissue. The mouth parts are thus bound firmly to the skin. The apex of the hypostome projects beyond the encasement, and a sinus seems to be formed in the region beyond by the gradual liquefaction of the tissue.

Feeding begins after the mouth parts are fully anchored. Saliva is injected into the tissue beyond the tip of the hypostome. It digests the cells and erodes the capillaries so that a mixture of serum, erythrocytes, and cells results. This mass is ingested through the meatus formed by the cheliceral sheaths and the hypostome. Salivation and ingestion alternate at variable rates (Gregson, 1960). Foggie noted that red cells are not essential components of the diet for either nymphs or larvae. The rate of ingestion is slow or rapid according to the duration of attachment. Those ticks that ingest a great deal of blood in each instar do so over a period of several days during their one attachment to the host. Those that feed several times in an instar take relatively little blood each time and complete each feeding within a few minutes. Ticks that engorge slowly may ingest blood equal to many times their initial weight. This does not mean that the tick permanently increases its weight by this amount, as much of the water in the food is eliminated through the cuticle.

All arthropods that live on a sterile diet, as do ticks, have special cultures of symbiotes somewhere in the body. Ticks have rickettsia-like symbiotes which live in the malpighian tubules. They invade ovarian tissue and pass from one generation to the next (Jaschke, 1933).

Ingested food passes through the pharynx and esophagus into the multibranched intestine (Fig. 23). This elaborately branched organ becomes greatly distended while the tick is feeding, and it causes the body to enlarge many times the unengorged volume. Contents of the food tube are always near digestive cells as these are folded in and out of the magma. In the unengorged state the salivary glands fill a large part of the anterior of the hemocoel; however, they atrophy after engorgement. The gut in turn is replaced by the developing eggs as the food is utilized.

The ovary is a simple U-shaped tube of epithelium and it appears as a garland of ova having no follicular wall. One tick may produce thousands of eggs.

Reproduction normally involves two sexes, but instances are known in several genera where unisexuality is normal. Bremner

(1959) noted that the form of *Haemaphysalis bispinosa* occurring in Australia seems to lack males entirely.

Oviposition is an involved process in all ticks. Eggs are single cells covered by a simple secreted envelope and are very unlike those of insects. The shell is not impervious to water, and the process for changing this condition causes the complication. Eggs leave the genital pore as the pore is everted and directed anteriorly (see Fig. 22). As an egg appears, the gnathosoma bends downward and backward until the bifurcate membranous Gené's organ is exposed.

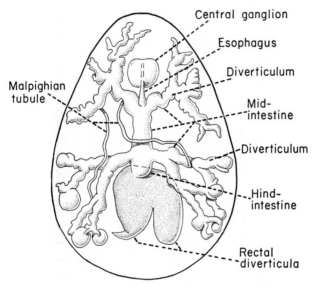

Fig. 23. Food tube of argasid tick (dorsal view). (After Patton and Cragg, 1913.)

It is everted by hemolymph until the tips of the organ enfold the new egg. The gonopore retracts and inverts, thereby leaving the egg adhering to Gené's organ, where it becomes coated with waxes and water-retaining layers. The organ then recedes as the gnathosoma assumes its normal position. Ultimately each egg is free among a mass of others anterior to the body. The process is repeated each time an egg is extruded (Lees and Beament, 1948).

Aeschlimann (1958) examined the coverings of the eggs of *Ornithodoros moubata* (Argasidae). From outer covering inward they are (1) lipoid layer, (2) exocuticle, (3) endocuticle, and (4) vitelline membrane. The layers seem to be continuous and without anything resembling a micropyle. How the genetic material of the sperm passes into an egg is in doubt.

In the suborder Ixodides there are only two families of any importance. They are Ixodidae or scutate ticks and Argasidae, the soft ticks. All stages of the former have a conspicuous sclerous shield, the scutum, on the dorsum of the idiosoma immediately posterior to the gnathosoma. Sexual dimorphism is apparent in the size of the scutum. That of the male forms a covering for the dorsum of the idiosoma, while that of the female is a mid-dorsal patch. Two sensory regions called porose areas appear as depressions on the dorsum of the gnathosoma of female ixodid ticks. The gnathosoma projects anteriorly and is wholly visible from above. Female ticks enlarge many fold during feeding, while the males feed little if at all. Juvenile stages following the egg are larva (1 instar) and nymph (1 instar). Argasidae, on the other hand, are not dimorphic, have no scutum, have a gnathosoma seldom visible from above and do not enlarge extensively as they engorge. The nymphal state of argasid ticks may have a variable number of instars.

Ixodidae (Fig. 24) are basically range parasites, that is, they live in sylvatic situations away from their hosts most of the time. A few groups board hosts as larvae and remain as permanent parasites until they engorge as adults. Some species have two serial hosts with an interlude for molting. The majority of ixodid ticks have a separation interval between each of the instars, and in the course of development these ticks live on three successive hosts. These three-host ticks leave their host at the end of each feeding period for molting and finally for oviposition.

Formal lists and keys to ticks from several parts of the world are now available as follows: Africa: Hoogstraal (1956); Russia: Serd-yukova (1955); China: Luh and Woo (1950); United States: various papers by Cooley and by Cooley and Kohls (see Bibliography).

The life history of ixodid ticks is briefly as follows. A gravid female drops from a host at some place over the range. It then finds a sheltered site where it deposits eggs over a period of two or more weeks. The eggs hatch in three to four weeks. Larvae climb to the tips of grass blades or twigs near a trail of some potential host. Often a cluster of larvae, from a dozen to a hundred or more, will cling together. Any vibration of this perch by a passing host will stimulate larvae to wave their legs about. Should the host animal brush against the perch, many or all of the ticks cling to the animal's hair. Larvae attach and begin to feed soon after getting on a host. One-host ticks remain on the host, where they molt and develop to maturity. Three-host ticks drop from the host to molt, and sometimes they remain over the winter as unfed nymphs. If they molt early in the season, they may crawl to a perch near a trail in quest of a host, as did the larvae. They too respond to vibrations and approaching large animals. They engorge in a few days, and then drop off the host to molt. Most species go through winter as unfed adults.

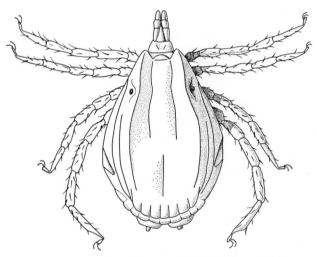

Fig. 24. *Hyalomma marginatum* ♂. (After Berlese, 1884.)

When ready for feeding, the tick locates a trail and selects a suitable perch close by, where it awaits a host. The waiting time may be as long as several weeks if there are few passing hosts.

The hundreds of species of ixodid ticks have been **arranged** in the following genera: *Amblyomma, Anocentor, Aponomma, Boophilus, Dermacentor, Haemaphysalis, Hyalomma, Ixodes, Margaropus, Rhipicentor, Cosminomma, Nosomma,* and *Rhipicephalus.* All of these contain some species of medical significance because they are hospitable to some pathogenic agent that may affect man or his domestic animals. While details for recognition are not possible for all, references to significant keys are given in the Appendix and the Bibliography. Descriptions of certain species are included herein as illustrative of the family.

Amblyomma americanum, the lone star tick, is representative of the genus. It is so named because of the prominent white dot on the scutum. Its common range follows the border of the Gulf of Mexico inland for 200–400 miles; however, it has been collected in Labrador and in northern South America. It is specifically adapted to well-drained woodland pastures where underbrush is dense. In the Ozark Mountains it is most abundant in hillside pastures that have a covering of disintegrated fragments of flint.

This is a three-host tick that has a wide range of hosts, which include ground birds, large rodents, ungulates, carnivores, and man (Bishopp and Trembley, 1945). Deer, dog, cow, and horse may be infested by all stages and in large numbers. Large rodents are undoubtedly factors in large populations. The ranges of hosts and frequency of occurrence on man gives this tick a high potential as a reservoir animal for pathogens.

Portman (1945) noted that the life cycle in the Ozark region requires about a year. Unfed adults lodge on ungulates primarily in April and May, and mating occurs on the host. After 3–7 days engorged, gravid females leave the hosts at their resting sites. During June and July each female deposits some 4,000 or more eggs. Larvae are present at all times during the summer. They often assemble on a blade of grass or twig near the ground as a compact aggregate of several hundred ticks. Any animal that brushes against the mass will pick up several or many of them. The ears of ungulates and hunting dogs often bear a hundred or more ticks. Early larvae give rise to nymphs, which feed and molt to adults the same season. Late nymphs and unfed adults hibernate in pastures during winter months; hence one and part of a second year is required for the maturity of the late nymphs.

Molting of both larvae and nymphs takes place while they are away from the host. An engorged tick secretes itself in the detritus on the ground, becomes quiescent, and even appears to be dead as the internal mass seems to shrivel and leave a clear area inside the cuticula. Finally the skin splits, and the flattened tick backs out of the bloated skin.

Each stage increases in weight several fold by the amount of blood ingested (Sacktor and Hutchinson, 1948). Most larvae are engorged within about five days and have increased in weight about 24 times. Upon molting the average weight drops from 1.05 to 0.4 mg. After about five days of feeding a nymph may gain weight to 8.9 mg for an increase of 37-fold. About one-third of the weight is lost on molting. A fully engorged female may have an average weight of 451 mg which is an increase of about 75 times the unengorged weight.

The Gulf Coast tick, *A. maculatum*, is similar in habits to the lone star tick except that birds are more significant for juvenile stages (Hixson, 1940). The meadow lark and the quail are the important hosts of nymphal ticks, but cotton rats are commonly attacked. Ungulates and carnivores are the more common hosts for adult ticks. These animals move their ears almost constantly while grazing. As a result, they often strike perches of questing ticks. Hence the place of attachment on ungulates is usually inside the pinna of the ears.

Boophilus species are one-host ticks that primarily attack ungulates. In favorable situations they may reach unbelievable numbers on cattle. Actually they may be so abundant on parts of an animal, particularly on the dewlap and the neck, that they overlap each other. This characteristic is of such common occurrence that the name "shingle tick" is commonly used. One observer noted that, when a cow was moved from a warm stall to a cool situation, the replete *B. decoloratus* dropped from her in such numbers as to make the sound of peas falling on paper. The genus has the outstanding distinction of having one species, *B. annulatus*, that was eradicated from a vast continental area. By systematic effort all of southern United States was freed from this tick and has remained free with the exception of certain small localities where wild hosts are abundant. Association of these ticks with the cause of cattle fever makes them forever a threat to livestock.

Ticks that belong to the genus *Dermacentor* are either one-host or three-host ticks. Characteristic of the first group are *D. albipictus, nigrolineatus,* and *nitens.* Those having three serial hosts include *D. andersoni, marginatus, occidentalis,* and *variabilis.* They all depend on specific combinations of wild animals for their maintenance, but several have adapted to domestic animals when the domestics have replaced their wild counterparts.

Dermacentor albipictus is a good example of the group that has a single host and has become a pest of livestock. It has a northerly range in the nearctic region extending from a latitude of about 36° northward into Canada. It ranges up to 7000 feet in altitude. Wild ungulates, particularly moose, elk, and mountain goat, constitute the normal hosts. In regions where bovines and equines have replaced wild ungulates, the ticks have continued. In the fall they board their hosts as larvae and remain with them until winter, thus acquiring the common name of winter tick. All stages are completed on the host, but oviposition takes place on the ground.

Dermacentor variabilis, the American dog tick, is characteristic of ticks having three serial hosts. Its range is over the United States east of the plains and even northward into Canada. It occurs wherever ranges of its serial hosts overlap. Larvae tend to feed on field mice and shrews; nymphs attack rodents and rabbits, and the adults are attracted to canines and other large mammals. Larvae quest along the runways of mice and attach to hosts as they pass, while unengorged nymphs congregate along runways of rabbits and similar rodents. Unengorged adults are the wanderers of the species; they disperse until they come to tracks of larger animals, paths, jeep trails, or roadways. These ticks may crawl a hundred yards or more before finding a suitable trail. When the dispersal urge ceases, the ticks perch on exposed blades of grass or other vegetation and await a passing host. Any dog, fox, ungulate, or even a person may stimulate the waiting ticks to extend their legs and grasp the passerby. The life history requires from one to almost three years depending on availability of hosts. Characteristically the ticks pass the winter as unfed nymphs or adults, but Hopla (1955a) has found that eggs deposited in nests of wood rats (*Neotoma*) may survive and hatch in the spring. Populations are largest in areas where hosts for larvae are abundant enough to provide adequate larval food, since it is this stage that is most susceptible to starvation. At present the areas of maximum abundance are (1) coastal land where diked salt marshes have become havens for field mice and (2) abandoned agricultural land in upland situations. These ticks are also abundant in overgrown fence rows and in vacant lots of urban areas. Even small increases in numbers of larval and nymphal hosts cause sharp upturns in abundance because of the great reproductive potential of this tick.

Haemaphysalid ticks are thought to have evolved early, in steppe and desert biotopes (Hoogstraal, 1956). The Asiatic *Haemaphysalis* sp. live on large desert mammals as adults and on small rodents or birds as juveniles (Hoogstraal, 1959a). North American species feed on a bird-rabbit complex, but some rodents may harbor them. Structurally primitive species, such as *H. inermis inermis,* as adults cling to their hosts all winter. Juveniles develop during the summer months characteristically (Hoogstraal, 1959). *H. leporis-palustris,* known as the rabbit tick in the United States, lives as larvae and nymphs on ground-feeding birds and on rabbits as adults. Over 29 species of birds may harbor juvenile ticks in Iowa (Joyce and Eddy, 1943). Cottontail rabbits are hosts for adult ticks in the southern part of their range, and snowshoe rabbits are dominant hosts for adults in Minnesota (Green *et al.*, 1943). The snowshoe rabbit and the ruffed grouse make the host complex in Minnesota and all other animals involved are secondary. Presumably the cottontail is insignificant in Minnesota because it lives in underground burrows much of the time. The species ranges from Argentina to Alaska as an effective parasite. Its role in the wild reservoirs of several agents of disease causes it to be particularly important to medical entomology.

Hyalomma ticks are in the sylvatic transmission chains of pathogens in Africa, Europe, and Asia. Hoogstraal and Kaiser (1958) have found larvae and nymphs on birds migrating across North Africa. Adults feed on rabbits and numerous burrowing rodents such as gerbils. Their ability to cling to migrating fowl and their close association with wild components in reservoirs of the agents of disease make this group medically important. Hoogstraal and Kaiser (1959) consider that ecologically *H. anatolicum* of the Near East is largely restricted to steppe lands, semi-desert lands, and oases. One of the forms (*excavatum*) does not range into the cultivated Nile valley, where another (*anatolicum*) is ubiquitous. Species of this genus are undoubtedly the most important of any from the medical and veterinary standpoint in the Near and Middle East (Hoogstraal and Kaiser, 1959a).

The genus *Ixodes* is a very large group of three-host ticks and the better-known ones attack carnivores, ungulates, and rodents. The Australian *I. holocyclus* (wattle tick) lives in open woods, where it parasitizes marsupials, rodents, and larger mammals including man. This tick has such a long hypostome (up to 1 mm) that, once it is attached, it is most difficult to remove. *I. persulcatus* of Asia is a product of animal populations in virgin, coniferous-hardwood forests in well-drained mountainous areas. It has disappeared in deforested areas. Small mammals and birds maintain the population, and cattle, goats, and dogs become infested while on ranges of the primary hosts. They are strictly range ticks and drop from domestic animals only on the range.

More information is available about *I. ricinus* than any other of the genus. This is a Eurasian species that commonly attacks sheep, other domestic animals, and even humans. It seems that ground-feeding birds, ungulates such as the roe deer, and rabbits maintain it in nature, while sheep replace wild ungulates in agricultural areas. High humidities are necessary for stages independent of the host; hence a good canopy of vegetation and a thick carpet layer of debris are requisites for high densities of populations. In Britain this tick is practically confined to hills and moorlands. Pastures overgrown with bracken provide a most favorable environment (Milne, 1952). In Russia the tick is invariably associated with wooded pastures that have replaced virgin pine forests (Pomerantzev, 1935).

This tick has a generation span of about three years while little more than an aggregate of three weeks is spent on a host. Bingham (1941) reports that adults may live in an unfed state for 21 to 31 months, and unfed larvae have lived 24 months. Winter may be passed either as fed or unfed larvae or nymphs. Adults are most active in the spring or in the fall. However, the level of humidity of the air during daylight hours has more influence on activity than does the season.

Since ticks of the genus *Rhipicephalus* are components of reservoirs of pathogens and are also parasites, they are of considerable medical significance. The genus is confined to tropic or tropic-like domestic situations in temperate regions. All are domiciliary parasites; that is, they leave the host while in burrows, dens, or living quarters rather than over the range. This characteristic habit has permitted *R. sanguineus* to extend its range out of the geographical tropics northward to 42° North or farther because heated dwellings provide a favorable climate. In the tropics it has a range of hosts among burrowing Insectivora, Carnivora, Lagomorpha, and Rodentia. In dwellings of temperate regions dogs are the hosts of importance, and man is only a rare host even when domestic populations of the ticks are high. *R. appendiculatus* and *R. bursa* are important components of reservoirs of pathogens.

Argasidae is a family containing the four genera *Argas, Ornithodoros, Antricola,* and *Otobius.* They look and behave as mites, but are called ticks because of their size and host relationships. They feed repetitively in all active instars as do most mites, and they also have several juvenile instars as mites. The gnathosoma is ventrad and is usually completely obscured when nymphs and adults are viewed from above. Unlike those of scutate ticks, the pedipalps have four prominent flexible segments. The cuticula of the idiosoma is slate-colored and is either wrinkled, tuberculated, or granulated. They are unlike ixodid ticks in that they lack a scutum, porose areas, festoons, and coxal spurs. Furthermore, the two sexes are similar.

Species in this group of ticks, with few exceptions, spend most of their time secreted in domiciles of their hosts and little time actually on the hosts. As a rule all but the hexapod stage climb on a host, feed, and leave it within minutes. Little blood is ingested with each feeding, and in the normal course of events the feedings are frequent. Some species are aggressive feeders, and others are

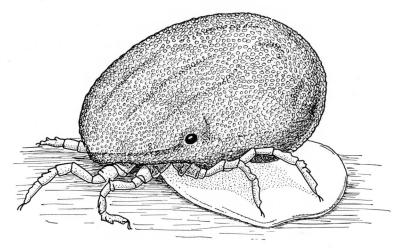

Fig. 25. *Ornithodoros* sp. with a drop of coxal fluid being extruded.
(After Jobling, 1925.)

almost seed-like in their passivity. Like other ticks, they may withstand starvation for extended periods; even a two-year starvation period is commonly endured. Pavlovsky and Skrunnik (1945) noted that caged *Ornithodoros tholozani* withstood starvation for 7½ years.

Argasids commonly empty their coxal glands while feeding or shortly thereafter. These glands collect a clear liquid containing wastes, such as chlorides, that may be emptied through fossae behind the anterior coxae (Boné, 1943, and Lees, 1946). The volume of liquid excreted as it pours out often forms a pool between the venter of the tick and the surface on which it is situated (Fig. 25). Evacuation of the contents of the glands makes room for new blood and helps keep the size of the animal fairly constant. Those that excrete coxal fluid on the surface of their hosts may contaminate them with pathogenic microbes.

Oviposition of most argasids is intermittent. Customarily a cluster of only a few eggs is deposited following a blood meal. The total number of eggs produced by one female may be one-fourth or less than those of ixodid ticks.

Species of *Argas* inhabit situations considered dry. Areas of low rainfall and dry niches in areas of higher rainfall are both favorable. The idiosoma is flattened dorsally even when the ticks are fully fed. The cuticula is wrinkled and pock-marked with circular "buttons" and a flattened marginal area is clearly defined around the idiosoma. Larvae have a habit of persisting on their hosts for several days, but subsequent stages remain on the hosts only a few minutes at each feeding. Around the world *Argas persica* is a parasite of domestic birds and lives in the houses of fowls. In very dry climates these ticks sometimes live in trees used by vultures and herons as roosting sites. Association between this group of ticks and specific spirochetes that attack fowls gives them a place in medical entomology.

Ticks of the genus *Ornithodoros* are of particular importance since they harbor certain spirochetes that attack man. Species of this genus are world-wide in distribution, but, like others of the family, they are more abundant in arid regions. The genus is recognizable by the absence of a flattened marginal area bounding the idiosoma and by the presence of mammillated or tuberculated knobs over the dorsum. No spines are present on the cuticula. Larvae apparently do not feed until they are in the second instar and some species require several days to engorge, instead of the usual few minutes. The great potential for long life and their capability as serial hosts of spirochetes for generations make species of this genus important components of reservoirs. Some of the South Asian ticks have lived 19 or more years in captivity. Excellent lists of species have been prepared by Davis (1942) for the Western Hemisphere, by Hoogstraal (1956) for northern Africa, and by Galouzo (1957) for Asia.

These ticks require sites that have a layer of dust covering the ground and are also sheltered from precipitation. Such places are caves, shelves under overhanging cliffs, burrows, crawl spaces under houses, and at times the interiors of dwellings. The ticks are so common in dry caves and rocky shelters that persons entering these places are advised to take precautions to prevent being bitten, as bites may cause very severe reactions. Several species live on bats, and secrete themselves in the dry guano under the roosts. When ticks invade bat roosts in houses, they may be seen crawling on walls and ceilings and are cause for concern by laymen.

Ornithodoros erraticus is probably the most important species of the genus in northern Africa, southwestern Europe, and the Middle East. Two variants, *erraticus* (large form) and *sonrai* (small form), are known. The former is especially abundant in burrows of more humid situations, while the small one inhabits dry burrows. All stages of both variants have been reared on toads commonly found in their range, but burrowing mammals such as rodents, hedgehogs, and the Egyptian fox are the usual hosts.

Ornithodoros moubata is a complex of at least five forms designated A to E by Walton (1959). Forms A to D occur in eastern Africa, while form E is a more southern one. Form A feeds on man in his huts in cool, damp situations. Form D lives in huts in hot dry climates and feeds on man and fowl indiscriminately. Form B feeds on fowls in native huts in damp climates. Burrows of wart hogs and porcupines harbor form C. The forms are all adapted to dry lairs or domestic sites where the floor is dusty or there are cracks in the walls, especially near the ground. The South African form is especially adapted to withstand severe desiccation. Buxton (1932) once reared 33 adults from 50 eggs placed in an atmosphere over calcium chloride. The existence of subspecific variants provides a partial explanation of erratic relations to spirochetes (see pp. 280–281).

Ticks of this complex are leisurely in all of their activities. They may feed infrequently and digestion of the blood proceeds slowly. Weitz and Buxton (1953) were able to identify the host animal on one occasion by examination of the blood taken by a tick 210 days previously. Identification was readily made 180 days after a blood meal. The ticks may live a long time and oviposit at a leisurely rate.

Ornithodoros parkeri lives in the mountainous areas of western United States. Specific sites are sandy floors of caves, burrows of rodents, and especially burrows of owls. These ticks live within a few feet of the burrow openings and are particularly abundant near the nesting area. The dry horse manure that is found in the burrows of owls adds much to the attractiveness for this tick (Jellison, 1940).

In Egypt the tick of fruit bats (*O. salahi*), when found near roosts of the basic host, is sometimes a pest of urban man. Both nymphs and adults readily feed on man (Hoogstraal, 1953). Their punctures may bleed freely for a half hour after feeding has ceased.

Ornithodoros tholozani is a very long-lived species of southwestern Asia. It is a complex of at least four variants: *crossi, pavlovskyi, persepoliensis,* and *tholozani,* according to Davis and Hoogstraal (1956).

Ornithodoros turicata is an occupant of dry caves having loose, sandy floors in southwestern United States. It has been a hazard to persons exploring caves or to those camping in the entrances of them. It is able to withstand starvation for years. Francis (1941) noted that over 10 per cent of a large population of these ticks withstood starvation for five years. Its long life, its resistance to starvation, its readiness to attack man, and its capacity for maintaining a specific spirochete serially make it an important tick over its range.

The genus *Otobius* differs from others of the family in several ways. Structurally these ticks are distinct. The idiosoma is without a marginal flattened band, and its cuticula is granulated and beset with short spines. The hypostome is vestigial. Unlike other argasids, larvae of this genus feed and molt on the host, and nymphs engorge before leaving the host. Larvae and nymphs usually live in the ears and may remain a hundred or more consecutive days on the host. Adults do not feed and never leave the site in which they molt. *O. megnini,* the spinose ear tick, lives on ungulates and occasionally attacks handlers of infected stock. Most of these ticks transform to adults on domestic animals, then subsequently live and oviposit beneath feed troughs or in protected areas where similar debris accumulates. Often oviposition begins 1–2 months after maturity, and it may continue for several weeks.

ADDITIONAL READINGS

Grassé (1949) must be consulted for the evolutionary background of Arachnida.
Baker *et al.* (1956) is a general compilation on mites. This group of arthropods is such a large one and is so little known that no one account gives information on all points that may be raised. Unfortunately systematics of the group is very unsettled and bids fair to be so for a long time.
Heilesen (1946) is an extensive account of scabies and is recommended for clinical aspects of the disease.
Arthur (1960) is a monograph of the ticks that contains morphological, taxonomic, and bibliographic information. It cites the literature of early in the century which contains basic information on morphology.

CHAPTER 4

Hexapoda

GENERAL MORPHOLOGY

The class Hexapoda (Insecta of some authors) is the group of arthropods most likely to affect the health and well-being of man and domestic animals. Representatives are very often hosts or carriers of organisms that cause disease. Sometimes they are carriers of microbes of medical importance between (1) wild animals, (2) wild animals and man or domestic hosts, (3) domestic hosts, (4) domestic hosts and man, and (5) human hosts. In addition many are themselves directly annoying to man. The annoyance factor alone is so great that the lay person often assumes that all insects are noxious. Indeed any numerically abundant species may justify this view. As sources of inhalant allergens, this range of noxious capabilities may be realized in proportion to the frequency of their contact with man or other animals.

The class is said to have evolved from a primordial arthropodan stock that had several of the anterior somites fused into a distinct *head*. One pair of pre-oral appendages persists as *antennae* while two pairs of post-oral ones persist as *mandibles* and *maxillae*. A third post-oral pair is fused to form the *labium*. Except where modified by later evolution, somites behind the head form two distinct regions known as the *thorax* and the *abdomen*. Three somites behind the head comprise the thorax, and on each a pair of legs is visible or may be accounted for. Wings, when present, are borne on the last two thoracic segments. The abdomen is composed of a number of somites that are usually identifiable externally. Legs are absent from the abdomen, but some primitive caudal appendages may persist about the genital orifice.

The *body wall* is composed of a secreted cuticula and two inner cellular layers. The noncellular cuticula is laminated as an *epicuticula, exocuticula,* and *endocuticula* of differing chemical and physical composition. All layers are secreted by the *hypodermal epithelium* and are structurally elaborate. For details see Richards and Korda (1948). The hypodermal layer of cells is made up principally of secretory cells, interspersed with numerous sensory ones. Inside the hypodermal layer is a thin sheet of connective tissue or the *basement membrane,* that is at once the wall of the hemocoel and the site of attachment of the hypodermis.

Insects have a basic set of visual organs called *ocelli* which are located on the head, and adults of most species have two additional *compound eyes.* Each of the ocelli has a single cuticular lens over a multicellular light-sensitive area. The compound eyes are covered by cuticular areas composed of numerous contiguous single lenses (*facets*) each of which typically focuses light on a single visual element. Ocelli permit insects to appraise minute differences in light intensity; the compound eyes are singularly adapted to the perception of form in motion.

The respiratory system of insects is a complex one of branching tubes (*tracheae*) through which oxygen and other gases are free to diffuse. The system is normally in contact with air outside the body through pores called *spiracles* located on the abdomen and thorax. In some cases spiracles are closed, and the tracheae end in *cuticular gills.* Linings of the functional tracheae are hydrofuge. At their tiny inner extremities, lumens of tracheae are extended as *tracheoles* or minute tubes of uniform diameter which have hydrophilic linings. Tracheolar liquid is said to advance or recede according to demands for oxygen from cells adjacent to a tracheole. Presumably oxygen reaches each cell as a gas directly from an adjacent tracheole.

Unlike those of Acarina, the *gonads* of female insects are complex, specialized organs. Eggs are produced in a series of tubes which are lined with a layer of cells. Some cells nourish the egg while others form the shell that covers it. Accessory to the female gonads are the *oviducts, glands,* and *spermathecae.* As an egg is deposited, it receives additions from these accessories.

Egg cells are enclosed with the yolk in a complex *shell* of maternal origin. The shell is laminated as an *exochorion, chorion,* and *endochorion* (Harwood and Horsfall, 1959). At the time of deposition, somewhere on the shell a portal for sperm called the *micropyle* is open. This pore closes after sperms have entered. Usually embryogeny takes place after deposition of eggs, but in some instances embryonic development, hatching, and even post-embryonic development may take place in the uterus of the female.

In their development insects progress through a sequence of three or more stages. All begin as *embryos* in an *egg stage*. After hatching, the insect is either a *nymph* or a *larva*. In the former instance the juvenile stage progressively comes to resemble the mature insect. The form of larva, on the other hand, even when fully grown, in no way suggests the form of the adult or *imago*. Instead of developing gradually, definitive imaginal appendages and parts exist as masses of cells, called imaginal discs, within the cuticula of a larva. Some time after a larva ceases feeding, development of the imaginal parts progresses rapidly so that when the final larval cuticula is shed, recognizable imaginal appendages appear externally. This stage, called the *pupa*, suggests the definitive appearance but is far from full development. When all parts are fully formed, the imago emerges from the pupal cuticula. For greater detail see Snodgrass (1954).

Insects are often medically important because some take vertebrate pathogens into their bodies and later transfer these pathogens to other vertebrates. Much of the exchange between vertebrate and arthropod is by way of the food tube; hence complete knowledge of its morphology and action is necessary. Most noxious microbes infect insects by being ingested. They may be transmitted to a vertebrate by (1) salivation, (2) regurgitation, (3) defecation, or (4) contamination.

Organs of insects essential for swallowing of food are the *pharynx* and *esophagus* acting in conjunction (Snodgrass, 1944). Each of these parts of the food tube has an expansible region or "pump" that is actuated by an elaborate musculature. The pharyngeal chamber, or *cibarium* (Fig. 26, upper), is dilated by contraction of a set of muscles attached to the clypeal region of the head capsule to permit food to be sucked into the chamber. As these muscles relax and allow the volume of the cibarium to diminish, other muscles attached to the esophagus (Fig. 26, lower) dilate it to permit ingested food to move backward in the tube and out of the pharynx. Contraction of both the esophagus and the cibarium causes food to move into the mid-intestine.

Before food can be swallowed, it may require some preparation or prior release. Either act is the work of the oral appendages or mouth parts. If the preparation is one of grinding or tearing, the mandibles are utilized. However, if it is one of probing through a surface and conducting food to the mouth, any of a number of parts may be involved. Fortunately the oral appendages have been genetically malleable, and endless adaptations have evolved for making food available.

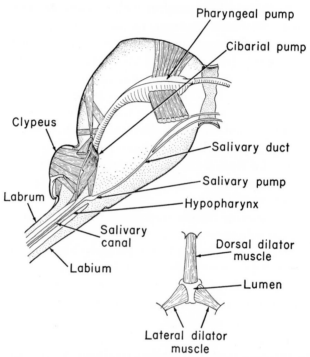

Fig. 26. *Upper:* Median longitudinal section of a head of a female mosquito (diagrammatic) showing anterior parts of the food tube. *Lower:* Cross-section of the esophageal pump of a female mosquito. (After Snodgrass, 1944.)

The actual mouth of an insect appears to be recessed in the head because it is surrounded by the mouth parts. Insects that chew their food have parts that are cupped or so articulated as to form a closure to the mouth. The mandibles in these cases are sclerous, opposable organs with cutting, rending, or grinding areas on the inner faces. The maxillae just posterior to the mandibles are elaborate, segmented organs, and each is provided with one finger-like palpus.

The labium is a complex flap which closes off the oral area behind, while an anterior flap, the labrum, closes the oral area on the front. The lower margin of the mouth proper, the hypopharynx, may be extended as a prominent lobe or blade enclosed by other parts. The dorsal lip of the mouth, the epipharynx, is usually short and indistinct.

Insects that feed on liquids must obtain their food on various surfaces or they must release it from the capillaries. Food obtained in either manner must be conducted to the mouth through a tube. Some treatment of food prior to ingestion may be required, since the food it not always in a physical state to be ingested, or since it may coagulate while being obtained. Saliva performs this function, and it is carried to the food through its own tube. Fortunately plasticity of the basic mouth parts has resulted in elongation, emphasis, and atrophy. Some of these adaptations are herewith indicated. A house fly feeds on surfaces and has the labium modified apically as a moist, flexible pad lined with minute hydrophilic capillary gutters (*pseudotracheae*) (Fig. 27). Liquid or semiliquid materials enter the pseudotracheae and converge in a pre-oral cavity. The somewhat tubular labrum extends into this cavity and acts as a relay to the cibarium. Closely related forms such as stable flies, that feed on blood below the surface of the skin, have the same structural characteristics for their mouth parts; however, the labium has become a sclerous tube ending in a labella which is an eversible membrane bearing prominent, retrorse, denticulate spines. The tissue is lacerated by alternately everting and retracting the labella while the teeth cling to the cutaneous tissue. Mosquitoes obtain food from capillaries by use of several elongated mouth parts. The labrum is a complex trough that conveys blood to the mouth from the punctured tissue. In this case the labium forms a trough with edges rolled forward and around the other parts, and the edges of this trough touch anteriorly for the length of the labium. The hypopharynx is a blade-like stylet through which saliva is conveyed into the feeding puncture. The maxillae and mandibles are hair-like blades with subapical serrations that cut cutaneous tissue and enter capillaries. The maxillae enter the epidermal and dermal tissue by a series of short, rapid cutting jabs. Six stylets (two maxillae, two mandibles, the labrum, and the hypopharynx) enter the incision between the lobes of the labella. As the stylets probe the capillary layer, the labial housing loops backward until the head nearly touches the labella. Fleas feed through a simple tube formed by the epipharynx and a part of each maxilla, which are drawn out as stylets. These are the basic patterns of mouth parts for insects which feed on liquid foods; however, modifications do exist, and further details are given in discussions of the species concerned.

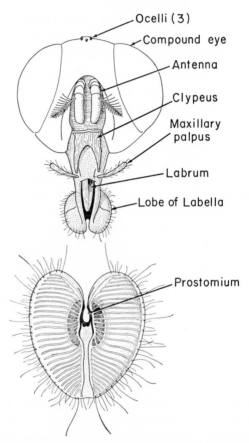

Ocelli (3)
Compound eye
Antenna
Clypeus
Maxillary palpus
Labrum
Lobe of Labella
Prostomium

Fig. 27. *Upper:* Cephalic view of head of muscid fly showing extended proboscis. *Lower:* Diagram of a distal view of the spread labella of a muscid. (After Snodgrass, 1944.)

Most insects of medical importance have similar intestinal tracts (Fig. 28) with some differences in detail. The pharynx and the esophagus (discussed above) and the proventriculus comprise the fore-intestine. These parts of the tube are lined with a cuticula similar to that covering the outside of the body. Sometimes the proventriculus is provided with spines and other sclerous projections in the lumen, as is the case with sand flies and fleas. The mid-intestine is usually a simple tube attached to a basement membrane that is lined with a layer of secretory epithelial cells. Sometimes pouches or caeca interrupt the wall anteriorly; sometimes mycetomes appear as special areas for enclosing symbiotic microbes. Often a tubular, veil-like, peritrophic membrane extends backward through the mid-gut from its ring of generative cells at the juncture of the fore- and mid-guts. A hind-gut lined with cuticula continues the food tube to the anus. Tubular excretory organs called malpighian tubules are

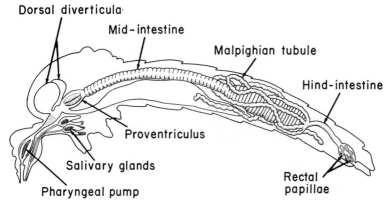

Fig. 28. Diagrammatic representation of the food tube of a female anopheline mosquito (lateral view). (After Fox, 1925.)

attached at the juncture of the mid- and hind-guts. These tubes float freely in the hemolymph and collect excretory wastes for discharge into the hind-gut. The unlined mid-gut and the malpighian tubules often become sites for lodgment of vertebrate pathogens ingested by insects. Many pathogens readily live either in the lumen of the gut or between its epithelial cells.

ORDERS

Almost any order of the class Hexapoda may contain representatives that have caused discomfort, injury, or disease for man, but only Phthiraptera, Hemiptera, Diptera, Siphonaptera, and Hymenoptera (Fig. 29) have numerous species with these specific capabilities. Cursoria, Dermaptera, Coleoptera, and Lepidoptera have few species that either affect man directly or provide lodgment for vertebrate pathogens. Trichoptera and Ephemeroptera, when very abundant, may be sources for inhalant allergens. These orders will be discussed as a whole and representatives of particular importance will be presented in some detail. No phylogenetic significance is intended by the order of discussion. For a general phylogenetic treatment see Ross (1956).

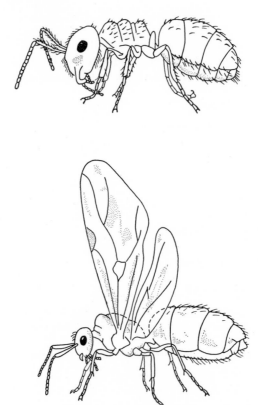

Fig. 29. *Lasius* sp. worker (*upper*) and female reproductive (*lower*). (After Cook, 1953.)

CURSORIA

Cursoria includes the cockroaches, mantids, and walkingsticks, and is a group that is frequently grouped with grasshoppers and their allies under the name of Orthoptera. The basic difference between this order and that of Orthoptera of some authors is that all Cursoria have running or walking legs, whence the name. Winged forms have two pairs of wings, the front pair of which is not folded and is thicker than the expanded, anal area of the caudal pair. The caudal wings are pleated from base to margin; the wings fold along the pleats when at rest. Development is gradual through a nymphal stage which has exogenous wings. Mouth parts are mandibulate. Only the cockroaches (Fig. 30) and possibly a mantid or two have any medical importance. Most species of domestic cockroaches are winged when mature, but some, notably the oriental cockroach, lack functional ones. All are flattened dorsoventrally and are usually a variant of brown in color. Typically they live in cracks and crevices

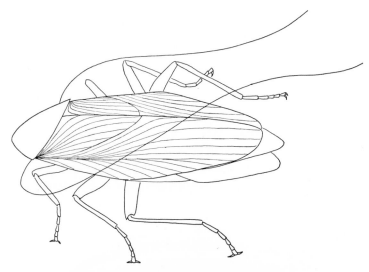

Fig. 30. American cockroach, *Periplaneta*.

where both dorsum and venter make contact with the surface. At night or during times of low light intensity, cockroaches leave their hideaways and run about.

The relations of cockroaches to human health have been reviewed by Roth and Willis (1957). These writers list 19 species in 12 genera as potential disseminators of enteric bacteria and other parasites. Enteric pathogens obtained from human wastes pass through roaches and remain viable in the feces. The semiliquid feces often fall on food, dishes, or kitchen utensils, where it adheres tightly after drying. Thus enteric pathogens of man may be carried to human foods by the roaches.

Eggs of cockroaches are deposited in packets (*oothecae*). Some species carry the packets in the genital aperture until shortly before the hatching, and some cement the oothecae to surfaces near their resting sites. The brown-banded roach secretes its eggs by cementing them to hidden surfaces especially those inside furniture. As a result of this habit, the roach is readily transported when people change their dwelling places.

Populations of cockroaches of one or more species have increased in urban situations because the common systems of sewage disposal provide all their basic needs. The American roach and others readily adapt to life in sewers, where manholes and vaulted passages provide escape from flooding, the food is ample, and the climate is ideal even in winter. Sewer pipes and channels provide routes for dispersal as well as easy access to dwellings (Jackson and Maier, 1955). Chances for contamination of roaches with enteric pathogens is very great because of frequent contact with human wastes.

COLEOPTERA

Coleoptera or beetles (Fig. 31) are of medical importance usually because of accidental or casual association with humans. Coprophagous species have been swallowed; saprophagous species may live for a time in matter accumulated about the perianal region of filthy persons or other animals; some crushed beetles release

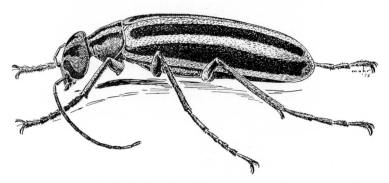

Fig. 31. Striped blister beetle, *Epicauta* sp. (Courtesy Dr. Carl Mohr, Berkeley, California.)

material toxic to skin; some provide hairs or scales that cause allergic reactions on either contact or inhalation, and a few beetles support juvenile stages of certain worms. Families of Coleoptera that may have species of medical importance are shown in Table 7.

While the Coleoptera are very numerous (over one-quarter million species), representatives are surprisingly similar in structure and development. Adult appendages develop endogenously in the

Table 7. Coleoptera of Concern to Health of Man and Animals.

Family	Genus	Possible Relationship to Vertebrate
Carabidae	*Acinopus*	Invasion of gut
Cleridae	*Opilio*	Invasion of gut
	Necrobia	Invasion of gut
Curculionidae	*Otiorrhynchus*	Invasion of gut, inhalant allergen
Dermestidae	*Dermestes*, etc.	Inhalant allergen
	Attagenus	Invasion of gut
Elateridae	*Adelocera*	Invasion of gut
Histeridae	*Saprinus*	Invasion of gut
Leptinidae	*Leptinellus*	Fur parasite of beaver
	Leptinus	Fur parasite of rodents
	Platypsyllus	Fur parasite of beaver
	Silphopsyllus	Fur parasite of muskrat
Meloidae	*Epicauta*	Dermal toxicant
	Lytta	Dermal toxicant
	Mylabris	Dermal toxicant
	Pyrota	Dermal toxicant
Nitidulidae	Any	Invasion of gut
Oedemeridae	*Alloxacis*	Dermal toxicant
	Oxacis	Dermal toxicant
Ptinidae	*Niptus*	Invasion of gut
	Ptinus	Invasion of gut
Scarabaeidae	Several	Host of juvenile acanthocephalids
	Caccobius	Invasion of gut
	Canthon	Perianal resident
	Macrocopris	Fur parasite of kangaroo
	Onthophagus	Invasion of gut
	Trichillum	Perianal resident of sloth
Staphylinidae	*Paederus*	Dermal toxicant

larval stages and become everted in the pupal stage; hence, the order is said to have a complete metamorphosis. Adult beetles usually have two pairs of wings; the metathoracic pair is membranous and developed for flying. The anterior wings are rigid and shell-like, and encase the posterior ones when not in flight. All parts of the body are usually heavily sclerotized. The mouth parts are mandibulate in both adults and larvae. Larvae have elongate, tubular bodies clearly segmented and flexible. They have three pairs of short thoracic legs and no abdominal legs.

Coleoptera live in many kinds of situations, and as larvae many burrow in masses of various materials. Some live in decaying animal and plant remains or in media that contains such remains. Some live in foods eaten by man and may be swallowed along with food. Others develop in media where they are regularly eaten by certain domestic animals as pigs and rodents, and some of the animals serve as hosts for juvenile stages of enteric worms. The segment of the order evolving into the majority of the quarter million species lives on and in more recently evolved plants. Another large segment of the order has become predacious on other insects. The ones most important to man provide inhalant allergens or dermal toxicants.

DERMAPTERA

Dermaptera or "earwigs" are elongated insects. Their most characteristic feature is a pair of short, sclerous, caudal appendages or "forceps" that project to the rear, either as parallel fingers or as curved projections, which have apices that are opposable. Wings, if present, are four in number. The upper pair are short elytra beyond which most of the abdomen is extended. The hind pair are membranous and, when not in use, lie in complicated folds beneath the upper pair. Appendages of adult Dermaptera develop exogenously (as is the case with true bugs), and metamorphosis is said to be gradual. Some earwigs may be as much as 15 mm in length.

Two families of this order, Arixeniidae and Hemimeridae, have parasitic relationships with Chiroptera and Rodentia. Food of both seems to be scurf and debris that is obtained in the manner of some of the biting lice. One species, *Arixenia esau*, is found in the pectoral sac of a bat in Sarawak while others of this family live in the guano. Species in the genus *Hemimerus* resemble cockroaches and infest the fur of rodents. In Tanganyika, Deoras (1941) found fungal spores, epidermal scurf, and amorphous material that could have been blood in the food tube of one specimen. Rodents infested with cutaneous fungi were often hosts to those pests.

LEPIDOPTERA

Lepidoptera, which are commonly known as moths or butterflies as adults and caterpillars as larvae, have few species of medical importance. This is the great phytophagous order. Adults have expansive, flat wings usually covered with minute scales. Mouth parts of the adults are the pair of maxillae which adhere throughout

their length to form a thread-like sucking tube between them.
Some species are covered with masses of hairs that may become
inhalant allergens when dislodged and air-borne. Caterpillars (Figs.
32 and 33) or larvae are of tubular shape and wholly unlike their

Fig. 32. An aggregation of larvae of the walnut caterpillar, *Datana*
sp. (Courtesy Illinois Natural History Survey.)

imagoes. Their creeping is accomplished by lengthening and shortening of the body. Three pairs of short thoracic legs are for clinging
and locomotion. Several abdominal segments have dual patches of
ventral hooks on the surface or on fleshy protuberances called prolegs. All caterpillars have mandibulate mouth parts.

Lepidoptera are pests largely because (1) larvae and imagoes shed hairs into the air and (2) several species of larvae bear nettling hairs that may cause dermatitis on contact with human skin. Moths are very rarely parasites. Larvae of one pyralidid (*Brachypodicola*) are surface parasites on a sloth, where they feed on epidermal secretions (Séguy, 1944).

Fig. 33. Larval tussock moth, *Hemerocampa* sp., showing four dorsal patches of toxic hairs. (Courtesy Illinois Natural History Survey.)

TRICHOPTERA

Trichoptera or caddisflies are moth-like insects numbering about 5000 species and exhibiting a remarkable diversity in form and habits. Adults characteristically have two pairs of membranous wings that are more or less densely clothed with silky hairs. On an insect at rest the wings are held as an inverted V over the dorsum. Bodies of these insects are soft, as are those of small moths. Antennae project conspicuously as long filaments. Mouth parts of the adult are vestigial except the maxillary palpi and labium.

Larval Trichoptera, or caddisworms, resemble caterpillars and live in silken cases or lairs in water. Most species live in portable, tubular cases of silk to which are attached pebbles or detritus selected from the bottom. Larvae have chewing mouth parts well developed for feeding on particulate organic material. Representatives of a few genera are predacious. When mature, the larvae pupate in their cases or in silken cocoons under water. Mature pupae have sharp mandibles with which they cut an exit in the pupal chamber. While still a pupa, the insect escapes from the chamber, rises to the surface of the water, and climbs onto some object and then molts. Ross (1944) gives a detailed account of this order.

EPHEMEROPTERA

Ephemeroptera, the mayflies, are insects with soft, slender bodies that characteristically bear two pairs of triangular, reticulated, membranous wings devoid of both scales and hairs (Fig. 34). Metathoracic wings are much smaller than the mesothoracic ones. When

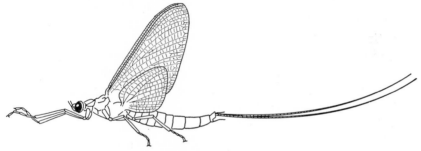

Fig. 34. Mayfly.

at rest, wings are held, dorsal faces together, over the back. Mouth parts of adults are vestigial, and the mature insects take no food. Antennae are inconspicuous, hair-like projections between the laterally protruding eyes. Two elongate, hair-like cerci extend laterally or caudally from the end of the abdomen. Some species bear a third caudal filament similar to the cerci.

The immature forms are aquatic. Mouth parts are mandibulate, and tracheae end in cuticular gills externally. When fully grown, nymphs crawl above the water surface and emerge as winged, aerial insects. A day or two after emergence, the insect molts once again, and the sexually mature imago appears. Exuviae left by the emerging adults become fragmented and when air-borne may become inhalant allergens. The numbers are so massive at times, especially near large bodies of fresh water, that layers of skins cover large areas. The dead bodies of adults sometimes drift onto shores and dry out and when fragmented become wind-borne, inhalant allergens.

HYMENOPTERA

The order Hymenoptera is a diverse group of insects. The better known ones are the ants, bees, and wasps, but the less familiar ones, such as plant feeders and parasites of insects, are much more numerous species-wise. The former groups include the species that are of medical importance because they inject venoms by stinging. This order is difficult to characterize, as there is great diversity of forms. A common set of characteristics would be useless as an aid to recognition. By restricting these so as to include bees, ants, and wasps, some common characteristics do emerge that are useful.

Adults of these groups have elongate bodies that are markedly constricted just behind the last pair of legs. This hinder part, the *gaster,* is freely movable at the constriction. From the caudal end of the gaster, the females of most species can project a pointed sclerous sting or can secrete a venom. Mandibles are short and broad and are often adapted for functions other than preparation of food. Polymorphism is a common feature. Not only are the sexes different from each other, but one or both sexes may have forms that vary in size, in emphasis of parts, or in atrophy of parts. Bees and wasps normally have four wings and ants have wings on some of the forms. All wings are membranous and only slightly veined.

Larval forms of bees, ants, and wasps are legless, whitish grubs incapable of living independently. The larvae live in cells or cavities preformed by the adults, and food is supplied to them by the adults. Some larvae masticate food, but the majority live on a semi-liquid diet.

Ants are social insects and live in colonies of diverse forms. Individuals in a colony vary in number from a hundred or fewer to over a quarter million in some instances. Ants most commonly seen by the layman are the wingless *workers.* These invade houses, annoy picnickers, and climb over flowers, shrubs, and garden plants. Once in a while masses of winged ants crawl about and fly away. These are the dispersal castes called *winged reproductives.* Other reproductives are wingless and never leave a nest. The caste comprising the majority of a colony is the worker caste. For a full account of social structure of ants the reader is referred to Wheeler (1930) and to Michener and Michener (1951).

Ants establish their nests in every conceivable dry medium. Many excavate a labyrinth of chambers and tunnels in soil. Others mine in wood or appropriate tunnels made by other insects. Some occupy natural and artificial cavities under rocks and surface debris on the ground, under bark, in spines and seed pods, and elsewhere. Some even create cavities by "sewing" leaves together with silk which their own larvae generate.

Ants tend to be transients. Within a nest they move the brood about restlessly, and on the slightest provocation they abandon a nest and carry all of the brood to a new location. Some species are so transient that they occupy nests for only a few hours at a time, as at night.

One species, the imported fire ant (*Solenopsis saevissima richteri*), because of its sting, has come to be a serious pest of man, since 1950 in southeastern United States (see p. 197). This is a mound-building species. Mounds are about 15 inches in diameter and up to 10 inches high. In low or marshy situations mounds may be three feet or more in height. These ants are omnivores that feed on other insects, young or helpless vertebrates, honeydew, and seeds of many plants. Whatever the form of food, it is ingested in a fluid state.

Wasps are Hymenoptera that feed their young on animal matter. They gather insects and spiders and provision each chamber in the nest before placing an egg in the chamber, or else they feed their larvae in open cells (progressive feeding). Wasps are winged and have slender bodies. The hornets represent the more robust kinds.

Nests of wasps are molded out of wood pulp or mud. Those that use wood pulp build single or multi-tiered rows of cells in some place that is protected from beating rains. Yellow jackets dig a cavity in the soil that is entered by way of a small hole. A nest is suspended from the roof of the cavity. Hornets build a similar nest that usually hangs from a tree or part of a house. A paper wall is maintained all around it as weather-proofing. The wood pulp is collected from weathered wood or dried stems and then is worked with saliva and tamped in place with the mandibles. A thin mottled gray paper results. Potter and dauber wasps mold cells out of wet soil by means of the mandibles.

The diet of wasps, like that of ants, is liquid, but it is more restricted. Adults eat juices of fruits, nectar, and honeydew for the most part. Larval food is macerated animal remains. Insects, spiders, and dead vertebrates are used by different wasps. Some nectar is fed larvae when progressive feeding is practiced.

Bees are associated with flowers because they derive all nourishment from either pollen or nectar. They have plumed or branched hairs over the body for collecting pollen and an elongate maxillary-labial complex for channeling nectar into the mouth. The velvety covering of the body and the compactness of form serve to identify bees. All are winged. Most have a sting that is used in offense only. While the better-known bees are social, actually only a few of the species are so.

The broods are reared in cells either by prior provisioning or by progressive feeding. Solitary bees usually fashion nests in the soil or in plant parts. More advanced techniques of nest-building involve wax as the structural material. The wax is a secretion from glands in the abdomen of the females.

Bees seldom sting a person except for provocation such as disturbing a nest or during swarming or some other unusually active period. When provoked, however, a worker bee will devote full attention to the attack. Some will sting repeatedly as does the bumble bee. The honey bee will sting only once because when the stinger is inserted it cannot be withdrawn but is wrenched from the body as the bee flies away. For effects of stings, see pp. 196–197.

PHTHIRAPTERA
(Lice)

All the surface parasites of birds and mammals called lice are placed in the order Phthiraptera in agreement with Weber (1939) and Hopkins (1949). Lice have been placed by others in orders named Siphunculata, Mallophaga, or Anoplura; however, comparative morphologies suggest that such separations are the more artificial. Unfortunately the terms "sucking lice" and "chewing lice" have been accepted as indicative of profound differences between groups of lice. Since several of the so-called chewing lice live on liquids, the term chewing lice is questionable. Actually mouth parts of lice seem to be highly plastic, and differences based on these parts do not reflect fundamental phylogeny. Harrison (1916) has called attention to the fact that sucking lice resemble members of one of the suborders of the so-called chewing lice more closely than the two suborders of chewing lice resemble each other. In this Hopkins and Weber agree. Since ordinal names are apparently a matter of choice, the name Phthiraptera has been chosen, as it permits a more realistic grouping of the forms.

Features common to all lice are as follows: (1) body and head are flattened dorsoventrally; (2) neither wings nor their vestiges are present; (3) antennae are composed of 3–5 segments; (4) spiracles are in a dorsolateral position on the abdomen; (5) tarsi have 1 or 2 segments; and (6) ocelli are absent. They are all small insects, immature and imaginal forms of which appear to be alike superficially except for size. Their legs are so attached and work in such a plane that the lice may be closely appressed to surfaces such as hairs or feathers. Table 8 provides an analysis of comparative anatomy of members of this order.

Table 8. Comparative Anatomy of Suborders of Phthiraptera.

Feature	Amblycera	Ischnocera	Rhyncophthirina	Anoplura
Head length	Normal	Normal	Elongate	Elongate
Antenna	Capitate	Linear	Linear	Linear
Mandibles	Horizontal	Vertical	Revolved 180°	Absent or fused
Maxillary palpi	Present	Absent	Absent	Absent
Visible thoracic segments	3	2	2	1
Tarsal segments	2	1	1	1
Tibial thumb	Absent	Absent	Absent	Present
Weber's organ	Absent	Absent	Present	Absent
Ovarian follicles	6	10	10	10
Testes (pairs)	3	4	4	4
Follicular epithelium	Binucleate	Binucleate	Binucleate	Uninucleate
Mycetome	Primitively absent	Primitively present	Present	Present
Spiracular glands	Absent	Present	Present	Present
Gonapophyses	Absent	Primitively absent	Present	Present

Similar habits characterize representatives of the order. All stages live permanently in the vestiture of their hosts. While lice are agile in the vestiture, they are loath to move from host to host unless there is intimate contact, as in case of the young with mother, or flocks that roost or rest in close contact. A marked specificity for hosts or even for limited areas on hosts has been seen and reported by various observers since about 1841. One of the obvious causes of specificity is that transfer is dependent on contact between infested and potential hosts, and such contact is rare or transient except within a species. When several species of birds roost together as do domestic fowls, specificity of hosts is not so apparent.

Specificity of site on a host is also well known. One reason for this tendency is that birds and mammals are capable of dislodging parasites on body parts easily accessible to claw or mouth; hence those parasites least molested by the host have a better chance for surviving. In addition to molestation, distribution is regulated by aggregations for mating and for nymphal feeding. Body temperature of the host is another factor affecting distribution, since lice come to occupy parts of a host where a tolerable temperature is found. The skin temperature is usually in excess of that tolerated for long by a louse. Air temperature also may be above or below a suitable range. Seasonal changes in vestiture of the host cause changes in environment. This factor is particularly evident in temperate climates in the case of lice on ungulates for there is a complete change in the layer of hair between summer and winter.

Populations of lice on an animal may oscillate within wide extremes both seasonally and according to host reaction. Eichler (1940) put 200 lice on an ailing fox and within 80 days he recovered some 14,000. Cattlemen recognize that cattle lice may build large populations on the cattle in winter, and the lice may completely disappear from the cattle during the summer. Heat becomes a hazard when the temperature of both skin and air is in excess of that tolerated by lice.

The order Phthiraptera is probably a descendant from psocopteroid stock and is composed of four clearly separable suborders. That of Amblycera seems to have appeared as an early specialization toward horizontal mandibles. The stem for the other three suborders had mandibles so hinged that they opened differently or became atrophied. Mouth parts of Ischnocera became strictly stabilized for chewing with mandibles hung vertically (Fig. 35). Rhynchophthirina showed continued rotation of mouth parts until the ental face of the mandibles turned outward on the end of an elongated head. The Anoplura have further evolved the mandibles by atrophy and fusion. All suborders have the hypopharynx well developed, with the most elaborate modification occurring in the Anoplura and Amblycera. Evolution of the four suborders was apparently completed in the late Jurassic and early Cretaceous periods. Hopkins (1949) gives an account of the evolution of the order in some detail.

Host associations of the four suborders indicate that lice evolved coincident with birds and mammals. Members of the Amblycera are natural parasites of birds and marsupials, and have adapted secondarily to rodents. Of the six families listed by Hopkins and Clay (1952), only two infest mammals. Those of Ischnocera infest birds and placental mammals, while none infests marsupials. Species of Anoplura infest only placental mammals and presumably represent the latest direction of evolution. Only one species comprises the Rhynchophthirina, and it feeds on elephants and wart hogs, which are, of course, placental mammals.

While the Amblycera have no direct medical significance, some are important as pests of domestic animals, particularly fowls, and several illustrate significant evolutionary details. Among the six families, two, Menoponidae and Gyropidae, attack domestic animals. The former contains a large number of genera, all of which live on birds. The latter contains some seven genera that live on mammals.

Species of Amblycera seem to subsist on mixed diets of solids and liquids, or on liquids alone. Ewing (1924) called attention to the liquid diet for Gyropidae and reviewed the earlier literature. Wilson (1933) and Colas-Belcour and Nicolle (1938) considered blood to be a regular component of the diet of Menoponidae. The

Fig. 35. A chewing louse, *Anatoecus dentatus*, from a wood duck. (Courtesy Illinois Natural History Survey.)

blood is obtained from capillaries in the case of Menoponidae. Wilson found this was true of *Menacanthus stramineus*, where mandibles were sunk deeply into the quill of a developing feather. When the louse was detached, blood flowed from the punctures. Quills so injured bore evidence of two punctures with a slash between them. Punctures represented sites of entrance of the pointed mandibles, while the slit skin was caused by the knife-like ental surface of the mandibles. Scars from previous wounds were abundant on the chicken, suggesting that this type of feeding is habitual. Blood has been found in the gut of other genera of Menoponidae and Trimenoponidae according to Colas-Belcour and Nicolle. The well-developed pumps in the food tube suggest that a liquid diet is normal. Much solid material is ingested and parts of feathers are cut into short lengths and swallowed.

Gropidae have a type of "lancing" mouth part described by Mjöberg (1910). The puncturing part is the hypopharynx modified as two stylets and equipped with muscles for insertion and withdrawal. Mjöberg suggested that lice probe into hair follicles and abrade the surface. Some species ingest serum, while others may also take blood; however, the diet is always liquid.

Clay (1949) has shown that a louse of hummingbirds, an amblyceran of the family Ricinidae, has piercing mouth parts. The mandibles are lightly sclerotized and dimorphic. Three extrusible stylets have been created from the hypopharynx, very much as they have been among Anoplura, to which it is only distantly related. This evidence suggests that mouth parts of Phthiraptera are very plastic and are not useful for separation of higher categories.

Ischnocera have little medical significance beyond annoyance of domestic birds and mammals and serving as hosts for juvenile stages of some tapeworms. The habit of feeding on solid materials of varied sorts makes possible their ingesting eggs of worms. Apparently lice of this suborder rely on the vestiture (hair or feathers) for their basic food. Some have been reared in cages on such a diet. Those parasitic on birds snip barbules from feathers and often convey them to the mouth with the fore-legs. Pieces of barbules are clipped off by the mandibles and collected in the pouch above the mandibles prior to being swallowed. Many lice ingest only specialized parts of feathers. The shaft louse of chickens feeds exclusively on barbs and barbules, while the wing louse feeds largely on the hooklets of the primary and secondary wing feathers (Crutchfield and Hixson, 1943). Waterston (1926) noted that philopterid lice swallowed sections of feather barbs and then broke the sections into even smaller pieces by action of the rasp-like crop. The midgut seems to contain only a homogenous mixture including all sorts of detritus such as mineral dust in addition to food.

The families Trichodectidae, Philopteridae, and Heptapsogasteridae comprise the suborder Ischnocera. All these families are largely composed of species that live in the vestiture of birds. Of the nearly 100 genera of Philopteridae all except the genus *Trichophilopterus* live on birds, and the species of *Trichophilopterus* live on lemurs. Two genera of Trichodectidae feed on mammals, while seven have avian hosts. Canine and bovine hosts are chosen by the two genera.

Ischnocera have the habit of clinging to objects with their mandibles, which is unique to this group. When an infested host dies, the lice fasten their mandibles to a hair or feather, and they in turn die in place. They may crawl outward on feathers or even to the head of the animal before the final fastening. Individual lice may attach to a hair on a flat fly (Hippoboscidae) or some other parasitic arthropod and then be transported to another host.

Rhyncophthirina is represented by only one known species, *Haematomyzus elephantis*, taken from the Indian elephant, the African elephant, and the wart hog (Hoogstraal, 1958). Ordinal status is urged by some writers for this species because it has a strange combination of primitive and specialized structures.

The elephant louse uses its uniquely rotated mandibles (see above) for clinging to a host and possibly for abrading the folds of skin prior to feeding. The denticulate ental faces of the mandibles are rotated 180° so that they are directed outward and, when spread, become wedged in a fold of skin. By a scratching motion the skin deep in a fold is abraded. Exudates of serum from the abrasions are ingested.

Mukerji and Sen-Sarma (1955) have given a good description of Weber's organ, a unique structure of unknown function in the dorsum of the head of Rhyncophthirina. It consists of two ovoid sacs, each of which contains separate chitinous spheroids. Each spheroid is made of several concentric spheres of chitinous material surrounded by a layer of flattened epithelial cells. A duct-like strand leads from each spheroid to a common strand that in turn is attached to the food tube in the head.

Anoplura (syn. Inrostrata) is a group of obligate parasites restricted to placental mammals. The species number less than 300 and are distributed among four families. Those of Echinophthiriidae (3 genera) parasitize some species of seals and their relatives. Species of Haematopinidae comprise about three-fourths of the suborder, and they feed on ungulates, carnivores, and rodents. Pediculidae feed only on primates. The family Neolinognathidae is represented by only one genus, which feeds on Insectivora. These lice are sufficiently host-specific to indicate relationship among wild animals.

Lice in this suborder are superficially very unlike the others. They are provided with stout tick-like legs projecting laterally. Each leg terminates in a prominent tarsal claw that curves anteriorly and meets a projection of the tibia. An elongate, tubular head with no externally visible mouth parts is a conspicuous feature. Superficially the mouth parts seem to be very different from others of the order because of emphasis, atrophy, and their retraction into a stylet sac inside the head. Actually the parts themselves are not greatly different from those of some Amblycera. Schölzel (1937) outlines the

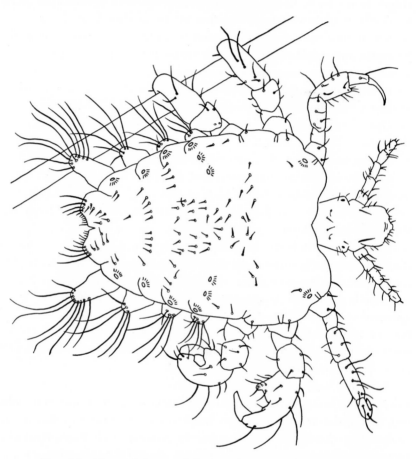

Fig. 36. The crab louse, *Phthirus pubis*. (After Martini, 1923.)

embryology of the oral structures and shows the origin of the several parts. Part of the labium forms a ventral tubular stylet. Most elaborate of all is the hypopharynx, that forms two stylets, a salivary one (called intermediate stylet) and a sucking one (called dorsal stylet), and a stylet-like extension from the venter of the pharynx (Snodgrass, 1944). The only externally visible part of the oral

appendages is the prostomium and anterior hood that is open apically and slit ventrally. The prostomium is supplied on its inner
face with recurved hooks which serve to anchor the louse to the
skin of its host while feeding.

Anoplura, like all others of the order, live in the vestiture in all
stages. One of the human parasites has even become adapted to life
in clothing of certain sorts which is an artificial vestiture. Eggs
remain in the hair or clothing because they are cemented in place.

Nymphs and adults cling to individual
hairs with the strong prehensile claw on
each leg. When the claw is apposed
against an elongation of the ental face of
the apex of the tibia, it encompasses an
area the size and shape of the cross-
section of the hair of the host. Any dis-
crepancies in size are compensated for
by the spinose, stalked tibial plate.

Humans may be infested by two
species of lice. *Phthirus pubis* (Fig. 36),
or crab louse, infests hairy parts of
the body other than the scalp. The other
species, *Pediculus humanus* (Fig. 37),
has two variants with specificity as to
aggregation sites. One normally infests
hair of the scalp, and the other infests
wool clothing worn near the body surface. While these forms are structurally
similar, they behave differently and have

Fig. 37. Body louse, *Pediculus humanus* (ventral view).
(After Fox, 1925.)

been called *P. humanus humanus,* or body louse, when on the clothing, and *P. humanus capitis,* or head louse, when in the hair of the
scalp. The two forms are regarded by some as varieties which may
regenerate from time to time. They may hybridize freely when in
mixed populations.

Body lice are strictly parasites of humans in nature and do not
readily adapt to life on other animals, but selections have been
found that are adapted. Snyder and Wheeler (1945) in a review of
colonization in a laboratory noted that a number of animals may
nourish these lice. Monkey, guinea pig, dog, cat, mouse, young pig,
and rabbit have been used as hosts since about 1916. Haddow
(1956) maintained colonies for a time in the absence of a host by

feeding the lice on sterile, defibrinated, hemolyzed human blood through an artificial membrane.

When human populations are exposed to natural infestation, the numbers of head lice vary from person to person according to the amount of hair more than any other factor (Buxton, 1941). In one prison group, only about 14 per cent were infested when the weight of hair on each inmate was less than 10 gm, while among prisoners in another group having over 20 gm of hair each, over 55 per cent were infested. Roy and Ghosh (1945) found that (1) children under 11 years of age had lower rates of infestation than others, (2) frequent combing and oiling of hair had no effect on populations, and (3) an infestation spread from person to person through actual contact. These observers noted that the individual infestation rate was an average of about 130 adult lice and 420 juveniles each. The maximum count from one head was 1,434 imagoes and 4,260 juveniles.

Infestations with head lice are highest when over a period of time persons are crowded into sleeping quarters and where facilities for bathing and washing clothes are minimal. Children in slums may show an incidence of infestation in excess of 50 per cent, and girls are more often infested than boys. Troops on the stalemated Western Front of World War I were said to have been universally infested after six months in the line. Crowding of people in London during the phase of saturation bombing during World War II increased louse infestation by 5 to 10 times the rate in rural England (Mellanby, 1942). In the United States head lice are a problem largely in primary public schools because many children play together in close contact. Infested children impart their lice to uninfested ones, who in turn often transfer the pests to members of their families at home. (For effects see pp. 187–188.)

Body lice are related more to clothing and climate than seems apparent with head lice (Nuttall, 1917). In areas where wool clothing of several layers is worn more or less continuously, infestations reach a peak in winter. In tropical climates these lice disappear even though head lice may remain. A situation that once existed in southern Mexico illustrates this effect of climate. Residents of a high plateau region were reported to be commonly infested with body lice since woolens were usually worn and bathing was rare. In the warm climate of a nearby coastal city, where woolens were not worn, body lice were said to be absent from residents whether or not they bathed regularly. Migrants from the plateau into the city lost their lice within a few days after their wool clothing was shed. Nuttall (1917) has explained the relation between abundance of lice and kind of clothing as follows. The temperature of the skin over the human body (when comfortably clothed) is 30–32° C. The temperature between successive layers of clothing falls near the exposed outside layers. In the layers near the skin the temperature is high and the humidity is low. Moisture evaporating from the skin is cooled in the outer layers of clothing and the relative humidity is higher at a point farther from the skin than at the surface of the body. In summer both skin and clothing have a moisture content often in excess of that tolerable to lice so they are forced to move outside the clothing and their eggs are thus killed. Louse populations decline or completely vanish either because of death of lice or because outer garments are changed.

Body lice are more frequently separated from persons than are head lice. They cling to clothing when it is removed, and some may leave the body and range over bed clothing. These parasites are common on beds in carelessly managed rooming houses. The more frequently such beds are occupied by different persons, the more likely they are to become infested. Separation of nymphs or adults from humans may be tolerated for as many as five days at 24° C, and 10 days at 15° C (Leeson, 1941). Eggs may remain viable up to 14 days at 23° C, but for much less time at 15° C.

Suckling lice feed in a manner unique to the order. When in a feeding position the louse appresses the ental surface of the prostomium to the skin, thereby bringing the tips of the fascicle into contact. The *dorsal stylet* forms a tube from two trough-like blades that adhere to each other apically. The tiny, tubular *intermediate stylet* lies immediately below the dorsal one and fits into a median groove of the *ventral stylet*. This latter one acts as a channel for the other two. All three are in a cavity below the pharynx and are extruded or retracted by extensor and flexor muscles attached to their bases. Saliva is injected through the intermediate stylet, and blood is drawn by the cibarium along the route of the stylets. Stojanovich (1945) stated that the blood appears to flow through the space around the stylets instead of through any tube formed by the mouth parts.

Populations of head lice vary in composition as to sex according to the stability of an infestation. A newly introduced population or one that is expanding will have females exceed males. Under more stable conditions the males tend to be in excess. Buxton (1940) attributes this majority of males to repeated copulations which could injure the females and curtail their longevity.

The crab louse, *Phthirus pubis*, is a parasite that lives in body hair rather than on hair of the scalp. The pubic and perianal regions are usual sites for this species; however they may spread to hair on the chest under the arms, to the beard, and even to the eyebrows. Infestation is said to result most often from contact during coitus, but there is little doubt that the crowding of clothing in locker rooms and gymnasiums also provides a means for transfer. These lice inhabit adult persons most commonly and are absent from children prior to puberty.

HEMIPTERA

General

Hemiptera is a diverse group of insects numbering thousands of species, but as an order of medical importance, the species concerned are few and numerically comparable to those of the Phthiraptera. Only two families, Cimicidae and Reduviidae, are directly important to man and domestic animals. The Polyctenidae is a small family of hematophagous parasites of bats.

The order is characterized by the following features. Mouth parts form a proboscis composed of a jointed labial trough, a short labrum, and four stylets representing the maxillae and mandibles. Two pairs of wings are basic although they may be atrophied or absent. The wings have entire margins and simple venation, and the front ones are as large or larger than the hind pair. Typically the bases of the front wings are more sclerous and thicker than the apical parts, which are both membranous and veined. Development is gradual, and wings are produced exogenously. The order derives its name from the structure of the front wings, which is peculiar to many families. The suborder Heteroptera, or the true bugs, contains the families of medical importance. Species in it have (1) antennae with 4 or 5 long segments, (2) a labium with 3 or 4 segments that is attached to the front of the head, (3) wings (when present) that lie scissor-like and flat on the dorsum, (4) stink glands in abdomens of nymphs, (5) compound eyes well developed except in the ectoparasitic Polyctenidae, and (6) a conspicuous scutum that is usually triangular and lies between the bases of the wings or forms a partial covering for them.

Cimicidae

Representatives of this family have dark brown, ovoid depressed bodies with abbreviated fore-wings (Fig. 38). They have a proboscis that lies appressed to the under side of the head and thorax in a mid-ventral groove. Ocelli are absent, and tarsi have three segments. A classification of the family as expressed by Kassianoff (1937) lists the few species as belonging to the genus *Cimex*, but it is probable that three or four genera noted by others are valid. All of the species are domiciliary parasites in the sense that they secrete themselves in the habitations of animals and feed while the host is at home. *Cimex lectularius* is the principal domestic pest in temperate climates, and *C. rotundatus* is more commonly annoying in the tropics. The human bed bugs will illustrate the habits of the group.

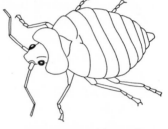

Fig. 38. Bed bug, *Cimex lectularius.*

The bed bug of the temperate region, *Cimex lectularius*, is an associate of long standing with man and is well adapted to domestic life. It finds many suitable sites for both oviposition and hiding in either crevices of furniture or in dwellings. Most cultures are afflicted with these bugs, and some people have them as universal associates. Commercial transport and public buildings such as theaters may become infested and the infestations sometimes become vast before being recognized. Myths regarding sources of infestations are common. New pine lumber is claimed to be a source, and houses built of it will surely be infested according to legend. Various animals, especially bats, are popularly supposed to introduce them to dwellings. One reason for myths regarding bed bugs is that these pests may live a very long time without taking food. Starvation for a year has been reported. As with all other insects, any household population must come from infestations in other dwellings. They are easily introduced among articles of clothing or other fabrics that are moved from an infested house.

Bed bugs may complete a generation in the relatively short time of 30 days at 27° C (Jones, 1930). This span involves embryogeny of about six days and roughly five days for each of five nymphal instars. If five days are added for a normal pre-oviposition interval, a total of some five weeks is involved.

Development can proceed at temperatures as low as 13° C (Johnson, 1941). Actually these bugs have no truly latent capability although survival at temperatures even below 13° may be tolerated for short periods. Embryos in the eggs die if exposed to freezing temperatures for more than 15 days.

Blood is the sole diet of both nymphs and adults of all members of the family. It is obtained by puncturing of the skin and capillaries. The sucking apparatus is composed of the usual cibarial and esophageal pumps on the receiving end of a food tube (Fig. 39, upper) formed along the inner faces of the two elongated maxillae. Each hair-like maxilla has two parallel, longitudinal grooves on its inner face that match similar grooves of the other. The maxillae are so locked together that the grooves form two tubes throughout the length of the stylet (Fig. 39, lower). Through one tube the food passes inward and through the other saliva is extruded. Two smaller mandibular stylets lie beside the maxillary one to form a fascicle in a groove formed by the three-segmented labium. When the insect feeds, the labium bends backward as a loop. This action shortens the labium and exposes the tips of the fascicle. By a series of short jabs the stylets penetrate the skin and the capillary layer. Any one feeding interval requires only a short time, and each bug feeds many times during its life. Humans are primary hosts of *C. lectularius* and *C. rotundatus*, but rats, mice, and even birds may become hosts if the bugs are threatened with starvation.

Bed bugs ingest only sterile food, and like all such insects, they have symbiotic microbes that provide certain components essential for adequate nutrition. These microbes are permanent symbiotes that live in the fat body and in special mycetocytes connected with the gonads. They are able to pass from one generation to another by way of the cells in the ovarian follicles (see Reduviidae).

An unusual feature of the bionomics of bed bugs is the method of insemination (Davis, 1956). The female has the normal genital opening, located in the caudal position for the deposition of eggs, but it has no copulatory function. The copulatory cavity is located between the fifth and sixth sternites and appears as a notch to the right of the mid-line. During copulation the curved, sclerous aedeagus of the male is inserted into the notch and the cuticula literally ruptures. Sperm masses are introduced into a hypodermal cellular mass called *Berlese's organ*. Sperms then move from Berlese's organ to the adjacent oviducts, and in time they penetrate to the lumen of the oviduct. The eggs are fertilized while still in the ovarian follicles. Copulation is frequent, and the mass of sperms is far in excess of that needed for fertilization. This method of copulation occurs in the anthocorid genus *Xylocoris* and presumably

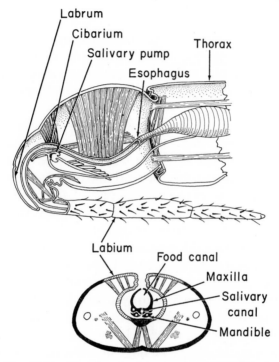

Fig. 39. Food tube of a bed bug. *Upper:* Median longitudinal section of the head. *Lower:* Cross-section of the proboscis through the distal part of the third segment. (After Snodgrass, 1944.)

in Polyctenidae. Carayon (1954) reported similar copulation in a bat cimicid (*Primicimex*) wherein dorsal intersegmental membranes of two or more segments may be penetrated.

Bed bugs are provided with a well-developed "stink apparatus" on the venter of the metathorax. Two sac-like glands open separately on the metasternum while a median chamber opens independently through a very fine metasternal pore. The so-called "buggy odor" of infested premises is caused by secretions from these structures.

One of the most significant aspects of the bionomics of bed bugs is that while the bugs are suitable hosts for a number of spirochetes, bacteria, viruses, rickettsiae and even trypanosomes, in no instance are they known to be a primary vector or vector-host of any vertebrate pathogen. It is possible that they had a major role in propagation of pathogens in medieval Europe since at that time their numbers were enormous.

Reduviidae

Reduviidae is a family of predacious bugs that is represented by several hundred species. Most of them prey on insects, but members of one subfamily, the Triatominae, have a blood lust and feed on birds, mammals, and even toads. Hematophagous forms have many common names, as cone-nosed bugs, giant bed bugs, and cactus bugs. They are characterized as follows. Bodies are elongate and dorsally flattened. The head, too, is elongate so that a neck-like portion is seen beyond the eyes. The rounded margins of the abdomen are usually visible beyond the wings. Usinger (1944) made a detailed study of the Triatominae of the New World.

Triatominae (Fig. 40) are largely domiciliary parasites in the New World and representatives are common all over South America; some range across Central America, and a few extend into southwestern United States. They secrete themselves in crevices of sites that are dark, obscure, and near sources of blood. This usually means the sites are in nests, burrows, and huts, but some live in trees that serve as roosts for large numbers of birds. Cracked walls of inhabited adobe huts provide choice aggregation sites for *Triatoma* and others. Incidence of bugs in a hut may be very high at times, as shown by data of Dias and Zeledón (1955) who found over 4,600 bugs in one small mud hut where six persons were housed.

Domestic species are generally more active at night, but the actual hour may vary widely according to degree of starvation, intensity of light, and temperature in the structure (Wiesinger, 1956). When feeding was permitted only once in three weeks, accelerated activity followed each meal, and then a rest period followed the activity. Some time before the next meal a second period of nocturnal prowling was observed. Temperature of 20° C and "strong" light reduced activity of *Triatoma infestans*.

This species locates its host by reception of a series of stimuli (Wiesinger, 1956). Radiation of heat attracts bugs when the air temperature is 20–22° C. Addition of carbon dioxide to the warm air at a rate of 1:1 increases rate of attraction over that for warmed air alone; hence the face of a sleeping person is often bitten by these bugs, probably because of the increased carbon dioxide in warm humid air. Lavoipierre *et al.* (1959) have described the act of feeding in detail and a summary is herewith given. At the feeding site on the skin a bug swings its labium forward and

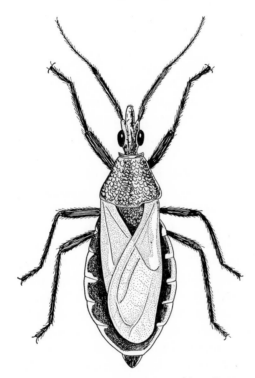

Fig. 40. A triatomine bug, Reduviidae. (After Patton and Cragg, 1913.)

touches it to the skin. Without either bending or telescoping the labium, the fascicle is extended from the apex. Penetration is initiated by rapid piston-like movements of the mandibles. Once through the outer skin the mandibles cease motion and the maxillary bundle is thrust forward, bending variously even up to 90°. The maxillary bundle exhibits a twisting motion particularly at the surface of the skin. The apex of the bundle lashes about in a whip-like fashion at times. Once the bundle enters a blood vessel of suitable caliber, probing suddenly ceases, a pulsation is evident, and the surrounding vessel collapses around the bundle. Feeding to repletion may take up to 15 minutes or more when the bugs are not disturbed.

The relation between feeding and defecation has an important bearing on the specific significance of triatomine bugs as vectors of trypanosomes to certain hosts. Wood (1951) stated that at a temperature of 33° C, *T. protracta* and *T. uhleri* will defecate within 10 minutes after feeding, and the latter species may defecate six times within an hour after feeding. The more frequent the deposition of feces and the shorter the time between feeding and defecation, the more significant a species is as a vector of trypanosomes.

Cannibalism is common among triatomine bugs (Ryckman, 1951). Instead of seeking a primary source of blood, some bugs seek engorged associates, which they tap. The nymphs particularly engage in this diversion.

Halff (1956) has isolated cultures of symbionts from *Triatoma* and tentatively considers them to be *Neocardia* sp. He reported that these microbes supplied the folic acid indispensable for normal development of the bugs (see Cimicidae).

Rhodnius prolixus is strictly a domestic species and is common in South America. Uribe (1926) reported that local residents believe the pests enter their huts on palm leaves. Palm thatch and cracks in adobe walls provide attractive sites for aggregation. These are avid feeders, and according to Buxton (1932), a single bug will ingest a total of something over a half gram of blood within the span of the six nymphal instars. When a dwelling harbors hundreds of these pests at one time, the residents will lose a considerable amount of blood each day. The bugs are commonly known as "pito" or "chinche de monte."

SIPHONAPTERA

Siphonaptera (=Aphaniptera, Suctoria) encompasses the fleas (Fig. 41) and is a group commonly recognized by laymen. Representatives of the adult stage are small, brown insects that are wingless and laterally flattened and have sclerous bodies. The head projects forward as a rounded shield dorsally, and is flat ventrally. The three-segmented, club-shaped antennae usually lie in lateral grooves of the head, but they may be brought to an erect position so as to resemble horns. Eyes, when present, are darkly pigmented ocelli and are located below each antennal fossa. Mouth parts are elongated and composed of (1) a labium which is channeled on the anterior face and bears a pair of palpi; (2) three stylets: a median anterior epipharynx and two apically serrated or denticulated maxillary laciniae; (3) maxillary palpi and lobes; and (4) a short labrum. The thorax of fleas is composed of three clearly recognizable segments each of which bears stout setae. The legs have prominent flat setae and five tarsal segments each. Larvae have a brownish head with mandibulate mouth parts and a whitish tubular, legless body. Pupae are whitish and laterally flattened in cocoons.

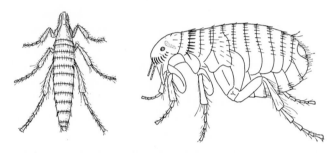

Fig. 41. *Ctenocephalides* sp. (dorsal and lateral views). (After Snodgrass, 1944.)

While fleas are thought to have developed coincidently with mammals, knowledge of their early history is incomplete. Primitive orders of mammals such as Insectivora are typically infested by primitive fleas (Holland, 1949). Specialization in mammals certainly coincides with specialization in fleas, and Holland considers fleas to have evolved with their hosts. The order is currently represented by several hundred species in some 17 families (Hopkins and Rothschild, 1953 and 1956).

Fleas are basically confined to animals that customarily have a den or recurrent resting place. Only the more advanced species have escaped this confinement. Insectivores and rodents are almost always infested because of their tendency to live in holes. When birds live in burrows, as do owls, or in colonies, as do swallows, or nest on the ground, as do chickens, pheasants, ducks, geese, and grebes, they may become heavily infested. Hares that live and reproduce above ground have far fewer fleas than *Sylvilagus* spp.

which inhabit burrows in the northern part of their range. Coyotes and foxes that live in dens, and other carnivores, such as bears, that hibernate in holes, are infested far more commonly than are ungulates and other roving animals. Muskrats, beavers, and other aquatic mammals have no characteristic fleas.

Wide variations in degree of host specificity is shown by fleas according to Holland (1949). Two species that feed on the rock rabbit are never found outside the range of this host, nor have they been reported from associated mammals. Other species may be dependent on one kind of mammal, yet they will range onto predator mammals such as weasel, skunk, or mink or onto associated mammals as rock rabbit and wood rat. Many similar examples could be cited. Very often the associated host does not provide conditions suitable for maintaining a population of fleas. Holland cites as an example *Orchopeas howardii,* the range of which coincides with that of the gray squirrel. This flea is frequently taken from the red squirrel of the same genus and from the flying squirrel, which belongs to a different genus, but only when ranges of these hosts overlap that of the gray squirrel.

Fleas vary in a tendency toward reproductive periodicity. Those having close association with one host have a periodicity coinciding with certain habits of the host. Bird fleas seem to copulate when the host is incubating eggs or when young are in the nest. The population of fleas on dogs, cats, and rats rises in summer and may decline to zero in winter when few or no adults are produced. Those parasitic on hibernating animals, on the other hand, are most active reproductively in winter when the host is constantly available, though larvae may not complete growth until warm weather. The common hen flea deposits eggs only in the spring and early summer, or during the primitive nesting season of the host.

Fleas are obligate associates of hosts that provide conditions in their nests or domiciles essential for larval development. The human flea, *Pulex irritans,* has always been a parasite when uncovered straw is regularly used as a bed. The dog flea, *Ctenocephalides canis* (Fig. 41), maintains itself where the dog sleeps on bedding of rags and fabrics that are not cleaned or replaced often. Fowls are afflicted by the sticktight flea if roosts are carelessly cleaned and layers of droppings accumulate. Rat fleas, *Xenopsylla cheopis,* live in littered burrows of domestic rats when they are made in sand. Another of the same genus, *X. vexabilis hawaiiensis,* lives in rat nests made of dried grass while other species live in nests of birds even though the sites are occupied by the hosts only once each year during the nesting seasons. Larval conditions for the avian parasites are satisfactory during nesting times, and adults withstand starvation during the intervening months. More details are needed about those factors which limit fleas to particular abodes.

The exact compositions of larval diets for different fleas are not completely known. Undoubtedly bits of dung, dead insects, scurf from the hosts, and dried blood are variously important. Some species are said to require parts of blood in the larval diet, but as larvae have no access to live animals they must find this food in abundance in nest materials. The source of most of the blood seems to be from the vertebrate occupant by way of the adult fleas. Since most adult fleas ingest far more blood than they utilize, much of it is squirted from the anus in small droplets. These blood droplets dry into tiny balls that fall to the floor of the nest or lair. Larvae grazing on the surface debris in the nest where the pellets fall ingest much of this dry blood. Certainly not all species require components of blood in the larval diet because they thrive on a diet which includes scales and scurf shed from the host animal. Bruce (1948) was able to rear 60 to 98 per cent of the cat flea on a synthetic diet containing yeast and no blood.

Adults seem to exercise no choice in the matter of oviposition site, and an egg ready for deposition is extruded wherever the female may be. Since they are in a nest or lair most of the time, oviposition is most frequent there. When oviposition occurs on the host, the eggs fall from the vestiture of the animal as there is no surface cement or physical feature that will hold them to the hair or feathers. Populations may build fast since progeny of a single female may be in excess of 500 eggs.

Siphonaptera may live as larvae or pupae from a few weeks to a year. The larval stage may be prolonged to a half year, but, whether the period is long or short, a larva passes through only four instars as do those of most Diptera. At the end of larval life a silken cocoon is spun in debris in the nest or lair. Pupation follows soon after cocooning, but a pupa in some instances may lie dormant for a year or even longer. Even the fully developed insect may not escape from a cocoon for months. Some vibration or the passing of a host may cause a dormant one to spring into action, escape from its cocoon, and cling to the host.

Blood is the only food known to be ingested by the adults. It is drawn from dermal capillaries through a canal formed by a fascicle of three stylets. The blood passes from the food canal through the fore-gut and into the mid-gut for digestion. At the entrance to the mid-gut is the proventriculus, a region of the fore-gut that is densely lined with a zone of several hundred prominent spines (Munshi, 1960). This zone becomes both a check valve that acts to prevent a return flow of blood from the mid-intestine during digestion and a means for triturating the red corpuscles. The spines project into the lumen of the tube and backward toward the mid-gut. After a flea has engorged, the proventriculus, through contraction, lessens its diameter and causes the spines to form a barrier to the return of blood to the fore-gut. Under some conditions, these spines have been said to block the normal flow of blood into the mid-gut, as is often the case when a culture of plague bacilli grows in the mass of spines. Much more blood may be imbibed than is retained for digestion, since fleas may feed continuously for two or more hours while passing the surplus blood on through the intestine and out the anus.

Deoras and Joshee (1959) confirmed the findings of others that the sex and age of fleas affect the degree of blocking that plague bacilli may cause. Apparently, as fleas get older, the number of spines in the proventriculus increases. Ratio between sex and number of spines is in favor of the females of *Xenopsylla* at least; therefore, females are more likely to be blocked than are males of the same age.

Some fleas have a remarkable ability to live a long time, at least in the laboratory. Their ability to fast increases their capability for survival for long periods. Rothschild and Clay (1952) noted that a rat flea was well fed and then lived 17 months with no additional food. Another instance is cited in which a human flea lived over 500 days when kept well fed. Whether such longevity is paralleled in nature is doubtful, though certainly numerous species representing several genera may live several months when well nourished (Burroughs, 1953).

While fleas are known to be strongly oriented toward nests or lairs of their hosts, different persons have made several observations which indicate that not all species are so limited. In some latitudes dispersal from abandoned lairs and nests is the rule. This type of dispersal by rat fleas is well known during times of epidemic disease in rats, and provides the means for contact between man and the fleas. These movements may have significant bearing on transmission of pathogens such as that causing plague. Diurnal movements take place in some instances. Fleas in burrows of ground squirrels move out at night and range over the nearby grassland, then they return to the burrows during the early part of the day. This phase of bionomics needs much more study.

The jumping propensities of these animals is of interest to the layman and was the subject of a series of observations by Mitzmain (1910). Adults of variants of *Pulex irritans* were able to leap as far as 13 inches over horizontal distances, while the highest leap was just under eight inches. *Xenopsylla cheopis* is less agile than *Pulex*.

Specific details of the bionomics of some common fleas are given herewith. These include the dog flea, *Ctenocephalides canis*, the sticktight flea, *Echidnophaga gallinacea*, the chigoe, *Tunga penetrans*, and the rat flea, *Xenopsylla cheopis*.

The dog flea (Pulicidae) is a common household pest if dogs are allowed in houses. Even an infested, transient dog may leave them in a house that it has visited. Any dog that lives indoors can become the cause of a flea outbreak at anytime. The usual time for such an outbreak in northern United States is during June, after basements become warm. Bacot (1914) has shown that temperatures of 24–26° C hasten their development and the completion of a generation. Basement temperatures ranging down to 7° C may retard all stages, and the pupal stage may be delayed up to 130 days. Often the winter's accumulation of pupae will transform to imagoes at about the same time, especially if the house is vacated for a time. When the human occupants return, the imagoes may emerge at once. The cat flea, *C. felis*, may be the more common in houses in some regions.

Temporary hosts for the dog flea may include rodents and opossums, but some canine, particularly the dog, is essential. Ewing and Fox (1943) believe that it lives on wild carnivores in areas remote from man. Since this flea must feed 5–12 hours daily in order to insure oviposition, it is virtually a continuous parasite during the feeding period.

This species is largely restricted to temperate climates. It tends to remain on a host once it gets aboard. When the parasites leave a host, they do so while the animal lies on a rug or is in its sleeping quarters. They are most likely to leave the host during the summer when the temperature is high enough to activate the fleas.

Oviposition takes place while fleas are on their hosts, without regard to season, possibly because the climate in the vesture of the host is more satisfactory in winter than it is in summer. Eggs deposited in winter may hatch slowly, and juvenile development is so retarded that new fleas seldom board hosts during cooler parts of the year. During the summer when dogs sleep out of doors, under porches, or in shrubbery, the eggs may fall onto soil in these sites and produce a generation away from a dwelling. As a result, there are frequent reports of fleas out of doors.

The sticktight flea (Pulicidae) is similar to the dog flea in all respects of its life history except in its choice of hosts and its method of feeding. All sorts of animals including man may act as hosts, but as an economic pest, fowls are most often involved. In the wild, rodents of all types may become hosts. The fleas attach to a host by the mouth parts, which are directed anteriorly at the time of feeding. Feeding, at least by the females, is continuous for several weeks; however, most of the blood passes through the fleas. Mules (1940) found that a female flea egested blood at a rate of 0.013 mg per feeding hour in the case of a related species, *Echidnophaga myrmecobii*. If each adult fed only half the time during attachment for the usual span of 50 days, a heavy infestation could easily cause severe anemia.

Xenopsylla cheopis, the rat flea of tropical domestic situations, is also a representative of Pulicidae. The peculiar domestic situation that encourages populations of it is the abundance of rat burrows under buildings, particularly in areas of sandy soils. Sharif (1949) suggested that the nature of the debris and soil in a burrow influences the development of early stages. Under laboratory conditions the texture of the sand used as a matrix for larval foods affects development. The proper combination of debris, sand, shelter, and air currents creates a stable climate suitable for the juvenile stages.

This flea has several features and habits that make it very important in the domestic propagation of plague bacilli. It is remarkably partial to feeding on rats in their burrows, but it will range out of burrows in the absence of a rodent host. Indeed it must often seek food, as its starvation interval is a matter of a few days. In the absence of rats it will feed on man in addition to other hosts.

The spines in the proventriculus seem to become easily clogged, re-sulting in a blockage that prevents normal intake of blood. Fleas so affected will repeatedly attack any available host in a vain effort to fill the mid-gut, which remains empty because of the proventricular block. When plague bacilli cause such blockage, conditions are ripe for transmitting the agent. This is discussed in the section dealing with plague.

Tunga penetrans or chigoe (Tungidae) (Fig. 42) is a tropi-copolitan flea that ranges some 10 to 12 degrees north and south from the tropics. It is a serious pest of man, pig, and dog over its range, and its wild hosts include burrowing mammals and owls.

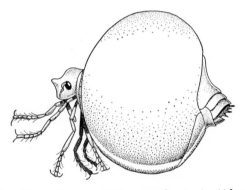

Fig. 42. The chigoe, *Tunga penetrans* (side view). (After Fox, 1925.)

It is a "burrowing" flea that imbeds itself in thick skin, such as on the feet, and it is known to cause severe crippling of its hosts in areas of the red loam soils in parts of Africa. Besides entering the soles of barefooted persons, these insects also burrow around the toenails. Scaly areas of skin, as on elbows and knees, may be at-tacked. Bruce (1942) noted that inseminated females slash the skin with the mouth parts, then insert the whole head and body until only the last two segments of the abdomen are exposed. Caudally directed spines on the abdominal segments anchor the fleas in place. The mouth parts ultimately extend to the capillary region of the dermal layer. The skin about the site of attachment becomes raised, and slight to moderate itching is experienced.

ADDITIONAL READINGS

Snodgrass (1952) should be examined for greater detail about morphology of insects. The short account in the present chapter must be considered as a guide to a much fuller discussion.

SNODGRASS (1954) is an extensive account of the kinds of development characteristic of insects. Various kinds of metamorphoses are compared, and details of origin of parts and appendages are given.

Cursoria

ROTH and WILLIS (1960) is a comprehensive treatment of the biotic associations of cockroaches. Information on where they are found, what they do, and how they affect man is well presented.

Other Orders

BORROR and DeLONG (1954) is a suitable reference for background information on American representatives. Keys to families and brief notes on habits of representative families are included.

IMMS (1957) is a general textbook of entomology that treats the class of insects in a manner that is helpful to one having some knowledge of invertebrates.

Phthiraptera

BUXTON (1947) is a full account of the bionomics of human lice. This should be helpful to both the student and the medical practitioner because of its completeness.

Hemiptera

JOHNSON (1941) is a good account of the ecology of bed bugs.

USINGER (1944) provides keys and taxonomic information for triatomine bugs. References in it will be helpful to one seeking additional literature to the group.

Siphonaptera

HOPKINS and ROTHSCHILD (1953, 1956) are helpful taxonomic references to fleas. Otherwise references are scattered.

CHAPTER 5

Diptera

GENERAL

Diptera is generally recognized as the order of arthropods of greatest direct importance by medical entomologists. Insects in this group affect more humans either by being pests or by carrying disease-causing agents than do all other species. Agents of the more serious arthropod-borne diseases of man usually have some dipteran to thank for their well-being. Frequency of adaptation to the hematophagous habit alone makes the order outstanding.

The combination of structural features characteristic of the order is as follows: Adults have one pair of mesothoracic membranous, functional, flying wings. The metathoracic wings have been transferred by evolution from flying to navigational status and are called *halteres*. They have evolved as small, knobbed outgrowths bearing receptors for the sense of equilibrium. Mouth parts of adults are suctorial; the labium is prominent, and other parts variously modified for obtaining liquids on or beneath surfaces. All larvae have tubular bodies sheathed in a flexible cuticula (see Fig. 50). They have mandibulate mouth parts and are devoid of legs and prolegs.

Systems for establishing subordinal categories utilize either two or three names depending on the features recognized as basic. Malloch (1917) recognized three as follows: Nematocera, Brachycera, and Cyclorrhapha. All are distinct, and each contains two or more families of flies of medical importance. Representatives of Nematocera have features as follows: The larva has a distinct head bearing opposable mandibles, and all four larval instars are active

ones. The pupa is free of an enclosing larval exuvia, and often the
pupae are active (example: mosquitoes). The imago has a long,
flagellar region on each antenna appearing to have seven or more
segments. Species of Brachycera as larvae have a head less distinct
than those of Nematocera, and they bear parallel mandibles that
move in a vertical plane. All larval instars are active as in the
case of Nematocera. The pupa is free of any enclosing larval exuvia
except rarely (Stratiomyidae), in which cases the larval exuvia becomes the case or puparium for the pupa. Such puparia rupture
in a dorsal, T-shaped slit as the imago emerges. The imago of a
species in this suborder has the flagellar region of the antenna more
compact than is the case with the Nematocera. Species of Cyclorrhapha more nearly resemble the Brachycera than they do the
species of Nematocera. The larva lacks a distinct head and has
similar parallel mandibles. The last larval instar is a non-feeding
one, and both it and the pupal stage are passed inside the rigid,
sclerous cuticula of the third larval instar called the *puparium*. An
anterior circular cap is forced off this puparium by the ptilinum of
the callow adult. The ptilinum is a membranous sac (see Fig. 58)
which is everted through a horizontal or semilunar slit to force off
the anterior end of the puparium. By alternate eversion and inversion it is used by the newly emerged adult to open an escape route
through the medium in which it has pupated.

Larvae of Diptera presumably evolved in a semiliquid medium
through which they burrowed and floundered. Some evolved in
more liquid media, and others came to live in solid and even dry
habitats. Keilin (1944) has said that larvae live in water that is
flowing or still, that is clear or foul, that is fresh or brackish, that is
cold or hot, and that is terrestrial or confined. A wide range of
larvae live in waterlogged soil, in excrement, piles of rotting
material, tissues of insects and vertebrates, and similar watery
masses. Some have taken to drier habitats as nests or lairs of birds,
mammals, wasps, bees, ants, and termites. Plant tissues of every
decription may be invaded by some dipterous larva. Lastly, larvae
of several families live in watery secretions of the uterus of the
female that produces them.

Adult dipterans, with few exceptions, have an active life as aerial
insects with freedom to fly about over a considerable range. They
fly readily, even swiftly, and some are known to migrate up to hundreds of miles. With few exceptions, flies are content to be centrip-

etally oriented within a small radius so that we may know that the presence of a pest species means that its sources are nearby.

Mouth parts of adult flies have evolved for fluid feeding. The labium has become a prominent proboscis ending in a pair of apical lobes, the *labella*. Lobes of the labella are pliable as is the entire labium in primitive Diptera. The labium other than labella is variously sclerous in Brachycera and Cyclorrhapha, becoming wholly rigid apically in many higher Diptera, where the labium becomes an organ for puncturing the skin. Among the Nematocera and Brachycera, the mandibles, maxillae, labrum, and hypopharynx are variously elongated to become puncturing stylets in hematophagous forms. The labrum and hypopharynx persist as tubular organs in higher Diptera. Liquids may be ingested through the trough-like labrum in Nematocera, but the labium as well as the labrum becomes part of the food canal in Brachycera and Cyclorrhapha. Details of feeding will be noted in discussion of the different families of flies. The families considered here are shown in Table 9.

Table 9. Families of Diptera of Medical Importance.

Suborder	Family	Representatives
Nematocera	Psychodidae	Sand flies, sewage gnats
	Ceratopogonidae	Punkies
	Culicidae	Mosquitoes
	Simuliidae	Black flies, buffalo gnats, etc.
Brachycera	Rhagionidae	Snipe flies
	Tabanidae	Horse flies, deer flies, gad flies
Cyclorrhapha	Chloropidae	Eye gnats
	Muscidae	House flies, stable flies, tsetse
	Calliphoridae	Blow flies, screw-worms, flesh flies
	Oestridae	Cattle grubs, bot flies, rodent grubs
	Hippoboscidae	Flat flies, sheep keds, louse flies

Nematocerous Diptera of common medical importance belong to the families Psychodidae, Culicidae, Ceratopogonidae, and Simuliidae. Others known as crane flies, midges, and gnats are seen occasionally by the non-professional person and have often been confused by him with species of one of the four groups of medical importance. For example, the large crane flies are often thought to be mosquitoes by the layman even though these flies are harmless, in fact if not in fancy. Any of a number of the smaller gnats may invade an eye or ear or may be sucked into the trachea and cause pain, but these groups are not considered here as such injury is casual and passive to a degree beyond the scope of this book.

PSYCHODIDAE

Psychodids are tiny flies with hairy bodies and wings (Fig. 43). Genera are grouped into subfamilies as follows: Psychodinae and Trichomyiinae (sewage gnats and moth flies without piercing mouth parts) and Phlebotominae or sand flies with piercing mouth parts (Fairchild, 1955). Species of the first two subfamilies may appear in swarms of sufficient numbers to yield allergens, but they

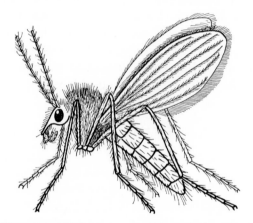

Fig. 43. *Phlebotomus* sp. (After Skaife, 1955.)

do not bite and have no known significance as vectors of pathogens. Representatives of Phlebotominae, on the other hand, may be annoying and may also have a vector status. Adults of this subfamily are recognizable as follows: bodies are linear, radial sector of wings is four-branched, labella is elongate, and palpi have five segments. Larvae are rarely seen, but they are tiny, legless maggots with sclerous tergal plates.

Sewage gnats develop on rocky surfaces that are kept wet by water which contains much organic matter in suspension. When the broken rocks of sewage filter beds are subjected to a continuous overload, clouds of these flies may be produced. The stones in such beds are kept wet but are not submerged, and the slime that accumulates on them is an ideal larval site at certain times during the year (Terry, 1956).

Sand flies are associated with dampness and a substrate high in nitrogenous wastes as urine and feces. Moist soil along cliffs, old stone walls, terrestrial coral scarps, brick linings of pit privies, cracks in dirt floors, edges of refuse piles, and the deep burrows of mammals all are common habitations of these flies. Whittington and Rook (1923) reported that the important *Phlebotomus papatasii* deposits its eggs in abundance in rich, loose earth such as wind-blown soil and at the foot of old stone walls where sticks, stones, and remains of insects may be littered. Young *et al.* (1926) found larvae along banks in recesses and cracks in soil that had a moisture content sufficient to hold the soil in shape when squeezed in the hand. Waterlogged soil is inimical to this species. Lewis and Kirk (1954) reported that some 37 species are adapted to arid regions in the Sudan, where they develop in cracking soil and burrows of animals. Large areas of this land are subject to extensive and deep cracking after the rainy season, and this massive "fissure environment" provides suitable sites for development during the long dry season. Elsewhere, domestic situations favor *P. papatasii, minutus, caucasicus,* and *sergenti* in sandy, arid regions. They live in caves, fissures, nests of birds, and burrows of mammals. *P. wenyoni* and *pavlovskyi* are strictly sylvatic. Burrows of porcupines are sufficiently deep and moist to permit the flies to emerge throughout the summer, while the shallow burrows of hedgehogs are too dry in summer in Turkmen SSR (Petrishcheva, 1935). *P. papatasii* continues to live in domestic situations when it supersedes wild biotopes. Mitra (1959) found six species in montane regions of northern India where adults were seasonal from May to October. Most flies live in the combined animal-human quarters.

Abonnenc *et al.* (1957) reared *P. freetownensis sudanicus* in the laboratory and compared the rates of development. A generation span from oviposition to appearance of the last adult was 39–41 days in the former and 25–30 days in the wet season.

Adults of *Phlebotomus* seem to find harborage during the day in burrows of animals, cracks in soil, in caves, in cavities of rocky ledges, and in dwellings. Hertig (1942) collected the Peruvian species *P. noguchii* and *verrucarum* relatively easily. Both were common in caves, while the former was more numerous if large mammals were absent, and the latter was dominant when some animal as a dog remained in the cave overnight. Pig pens and stables also sheltered *P. verrucarum*. Adobe houses are among the best diurnal harborages for sand flies. Crevices and fissures in rocky ledges harbor *P. noguchii* especially if small rodents are present.

Phlebotomus flies are nocturnal feeders particularly early in the night when the air is relatively still and the temperature is above 13° C. At 15° C Peruvian species are very active. A fly will readily approach a host that is inactive, but it tends to be wary of or to shun those that are active. In feeding, the fascicle of six stylets is quickly plunged into the capillary layer of the skin as the proboscis is elbowed backward, and the labella appressed to the surface. The blood flows along the labral groove to the mouth. The labella seals the area around the stylets and retains any blood that oozes to the surface.

Some degree of host selection is exercised. *P. noguchii* feeds largely on small rodents. *P. papatasii* prefers human blood whether collected in dwellings or elsewhere; however, it will feed on available livestock as well. *P. perniciosus* feeds to a large extent on cattle, but it also feeds on other domestic animals and man. Species elsewhere undoubtedly show similar dietary restrictions.

CULICIDAE

General

The family Culicidae is considered by writers to be divisible so as to include both the Chaoborinae, or gnats, and the Culicinae, the mosquitoes, or to include only the mosquitoes. While the former division is used in this book, only the latter subfamily is discussed. It is important to call attention at the outset to the need for recognizing the distinctions between the two subfamilies. In the case of the larvae, the distinctions must be known because certain of the larvae of the Chaoborinae resemble some mosquitoes so very closely that unwary observers may be confused. Larvae of Chaoborinae have antennae inserted near the mid-line of the head; if inserted elsewhere, the antennae are provided with prehensile hairs. Adults of this group have mouth parts no longer than the head. Larvae of Culicinae always have antennae inserted laterally on the head. The adults have mouth parts elongated so that they are several times longer than the head. Taxonomic understanding of the family Culicidae has been greatly extended since the earliest monograph by Theobald (1901). The catalogue of Stone *et al.* (1959) provides the most recent listings of species and synonomy.

The subfamily Culicinae is composed of some 30 genera of which 10 are of importance. *Anopheles, Aedes,* and *Culex* are the ones best known, and these groups contain over half of the known species. *Mansonia, Haemagogus,* and *Psorophora* have attained recognition as major genera only relatively recently. *Sabethes, Wyeomyia, Culiseta,* and *Armigeres* are gaining recognition because of their potentialities in reservoirs of pathogens. *Tripteroides* may become local pests at times. These genera will be discussed briefly in the following pages.

Among the hundreds of kinds of mosquitoes, some representative is capable of development in nearly every conceivable collection of water. Some may live at altitudes over 12,000 feet while others live in mines 3,000 feet or more below the earth's surface. Species range in latitudes northward from the tropics well into arctic regions and southward to the ends of the continents. There is no natural collection of water, whether fresh, saline, or foul, but that part of it may be occupied by some mosquito. No forest is so dense, and few areas are so barren, but that some mosquito may live there. A person may be annoyed by mosquitoes in the heart of a metropolitan district or on the most isolated island; he may be attacked on land and on ships at sea, or he may be disturbed at home and in camp. This is an amazingly adaptable group of insects.

The abundance of mosquitoes within an area is determined by numerous interacting factors of environment. Water is essential for growth of juvenile stages, and collections of transient water are especially productive. Broad acreages of poorly drained land and areas serially inundated yield maximum populations. Tidal marshes, flood plains of rivers, ponded areas on prairies, plains, and muskeg are sources of vast hordes of mosquitoes. Uneven or well-drained terrain provides sources for the very few that develop in ground water. Permanent bodies of shallow water having surface areas broken by plants or plant parts offer shelter to those occurring there since open water is wholly unfavorable. Streams and pools polluted by animal and various other wastes may yield hordes of certain species. Moderate summer temperatures stimulate populations in all situations, but the favorable temperatures are especially significant in increasing abundance of mosquitoes that may develop in permanent bodies of water. Lastly, ample larval food and sufficient food for adults near the larval sites are necessities for large populations.

Generations vary between one and many each year, and under adverse conditions some species are said to remain inactive for two or more years. Species that oviposit on water go through multiple generations each summer whereas those that oviposit elsewhere may have no more than one generation each summer. The former group normally requires about two weeks for completion of the aquatic stages under optimum conditions, and the latter group requires more or less time according to the air temperature at the time of hatching.

Eggs of mosquitoes may be found at the proper time of year in water or in debris on the ground, in depressions subject to inundation, or on the walls of both natural and domestic cavities and containers. The one essential that all sites must have is protection from wind and wave for the ovipositing female. Eggs that exist as rafts on open water occur only where winds do not sweep across the water's surface. Other eggs that lie singly on the water float into meniscuses about emergent vegetation or are cradled among mats of floating plants or debris. Some species glue their eggs to the lower sides of floating leaves. The majority of species put their eggs into nooks and crannies on moist surfaces that are subject to recurrent inundation. Hooke, Leeuwenhoek, Swammerdam, Bonanni, Reaumur, and Olivier of the seventeenth and eighteenth centuries knew that certain mosquitoes had floating rafts of eggs. Discoveries that eggs might lie either in debris or be attached to walls of containers were not made until early in this century.

Embryogeny requires only a few days regardless of species. Whether or not a fully formed larva breaks out of its shell immediately will vary from group to group. Species that oviposit on water vary from a few hours to a few days in time required between oviposition and hatching. On the other hand those placed elsewhere may not hatch for months or even a year or more. Larvae escape from eggs in much the same manner regardless of species. An egg burster on the dorsal part of the head is used to rupture the chorion with a circular rent made near the anterior end of the egg. A cap is forced off and the larva wriggles free.

With very few exceptions larvae of some species of mosquitoes may occur in all natural aquatic sites which may be reached by ovipositing females. The extensive sources of mosquitoes are transient and permanent ground pools. This means that broad and relatively flat terrain, subject to a high and variable water table yields maximum populations. Collections of water behind axils of leaves may be important and even dominant sources of some pest mosquitoes. Bromeliads are said to be one of the most common sources of larvae in parts of Jamaica. *Nepenthes* pitchers may contain larvae, and cavities in trees are very common sites. Growing bamboo stems, when broached from any cause, may house representatives of three genera in Brazil and six genera in Malaya. Thermal waters, of a temperature of 38° C or less, may contain larvae. Man's activities have had great influence on increasing incidence of mosquitoes. Careless construction of rights-of-way for transport passage and careless agricultural practices, especially in the opening of new areas to farming, have had vast effects on larval incidence.

Vertical distribution of larvae in their sites is extremely variable. Some larvae lie immediately below the surface film and have adaptive structures to support themselves in such places, while others hang from the water surface with the anterior end well below. These may descend at will to feed at all levels in the medium. There are species which spend most of their larval lives clinging to submerged surfaces or lying on their backs at the bottom of the pool. Lastly, some larvae burrow in muck on the bottom of permanent water pools. Numerous structural modifications obviously are required to permit life under such a variety of conditions, and these are discussed elsewhere.

Larvae propel themselves in numerous ways, and the mode of locomotion is often characteristic of the species. The familiar wriggling movement results when the abdomen lashes from side to side, and the larva is actually pushed caudal end first. At other times some larvae move themselves by simply vibrating their mouth brushes. Larvae break contact with the surface film and sink passively to the bottom with no exertion other than that required to close the siphon flaps. A fourth kind of movement is that of burrowing through soft debris. Actually this is a kind of lashing motion which results in a "head first" progression.

While solutes may be ingested, nutriment is basically particulate matter ranging in size from bacteria to clearly visible pieces collected by vibrating the labral brushes. Mosquito larvae ingest matter that (1) floats in the surface film, (2) is suspended throughout the water, (3) clings to submerged surfaces, and (4) is in the form of other animals that may be as large as themselves.

The mechanics of feeding has been investigated by a number of observers, from Reaumur in the eighteenth century to others in recent times. All agree that the act is a complex one. When suspended particulate matter is ingested, it is gathered to the mouth through the creation of a current across the mouth opening, where the repetitive pharyngeal suction forces the matter to flow into the mouth. Other brushes are composed of long, curved hairs, long, dense tufts on the apices of the maxillae, and a well-developed fringe on the ventral side of the mandibles. The parts vibrate at rates of several hundred times per minute according to the water temperature. As the cupped labral brushes swiftly close, they scoop water toward the mouth. The speed of movement creates the current.

Feeding on matter in the surface film is commonly done by *Anopheles* larvae and is occasionally done by culicine larvae. In the former case film seems to be drawn at times as a sheet toward a larva. On the other hand, culicine larvae, when feeding at the surface, bend the body in the shape of a U and vibrate the brushes in the film as the head describes spirals about the siphon as a pivot.

Grazing is a form of feeding common among culicines. If the potential food is an algal filament or matter too large for direct swallowing, it may be held in the vicinity of the mouth opening and then be subjected to trip-hammer blows of the sharp mandibular teeth while it is pressed against the sclerous dentate and serrate labium-hypopharynx. When the potential food is adherent to a submerged object, it may be dislodged when the stubby and stiff hairs of the mouth brushes are raked over the surface. Suction by the pharynx draws any dislodged particles into the mouth.

Predator species attack and ingest culicine larvae or other kinds of available insects. Prey is first impaled on the mandibles and then is literally packed into the mouth opening. The mouth brushes, when functional at all, are secondary, prehensile appendages.

The pupae, like those of most insects, are able to move the abdomen. Since these are suspended free in water, movements of the abdomen cause shifts in the insect's position. A pair of caudal flaps or paddles provides sculling surfaces, so that as the abdomen is repeatedly and quickly flexed, the insect may be spiraled end over end through the water. Various stimuli provoke a pupa to activity. Sudden changes in light intensity, which may result from a shadow passing over the water, will cause them to dive immediately. A disturbance of the surface film may produce a similar response.

Emergence begins as the pupal cuticula splits along the dorsum of the thorax at the water line. The split follows the inclusion of air inside the pupal skin by the enclosed imago. With no show of violent contortions the imago seems to float upward through the split skin. The thorax and head appear first, then the appendages are pulled free. While the hydrofuge legs are resting on the surface film, the abdomen is worked free by a kind of peristalsis. The entire change requires about five minutes.

The moment of emergence from an aquatic pupa to an aerial adult is a critical interval in the life of all mosquitoes. The water-air interface must remain stable throughout the interval of several minutes required for emergence. For this reason molting usually takes place at night, when the greatest stability is likely. Those species that develop in large bodies of water move to the undisturbed parts of the water-air interface before molting.

Adult mosquitoes of noxious species must span the distance from their larval sites to sources of blood before moving to a favorable site to oviposit. Dispersal takes place as (1) extensive and massive flights or (2) local, creeping flights. The former may be variously extensive up to several hundred miles, but such flights are thought to be characteristic of relatively few species. Local, creeping flights seem to be made by all species at some time, and they account for the presence of most of the annoying mosquitoes. As early as 1879 mosquitoes were reported to have traveled great distances over an area near the coast of Texas. Most accounts indicate that the mosquitoes traveled more than 50 feet above the ground; however, such flights may take place at elevations varying from a few feet up to a thousand or more feet. When migrations take place, the relation of wind to the movement seems to vary widely. Long flights seem to be in the same general direction as the wind, while the shorter flights may be in any direction. The proper influence of wind as a determiner may be more fully understood as knowledge of flight orientation becomes complete.

Creeping flights take place near the ground and apparently result in irregular patterns of distribution. These flights may be induced by stimuli that cause mosquitoes to (1) secrete themselves, (2) oviposit, (3) feed, (4) hibernate, or (5) swarm. Whatever the objective, distances covered during the flights are thought to be short, as the stopping place is near the starting point.

Female mosquitoes seeking blood find their prey through a combination of chemical and visual stimuli. They tend to fly upwind in the direction of odors emanating from humans or their waste products. Once in an environment permeated by human odor, as a room, visual stimuli dominate and orientation is then in the direction of a line separating light and shadow. This line of approach, if toward a human, brings the mosquito into range of a temperature or humidity gradient that permits the location of the person. Reports of various observers on the exact role of temperature in attracting mosquitoes are conflicting. Females locate a host at short range in the absence of an increasing gradient. The higher proportion of mosquitoes fed when temperatures of the environment and skin were similar. Warmth does not seem to be the attractant since radiant energy alone causes no effect, however a warm object (37° C) is more attractive than a cold one (27° C). Heat of convection with consequent air turbulence in the vicinity of the body is attractive. Both surface moisture and degree of absorption of light by the surface affect the landing rate of hungry, caged females (Brown *et al.*, 1951). When both moist and dry, black and white billiard balls were introduced into mosquito cages, landing rates varied widely. The landing rate on a moist, black ball was 4.6 times that on the moist white ball. Moist balls of either black or white stimulated landings over seven times more than dry balls. In moist air, carbon dioxide added nothing to attractiveness, but dry air containing carbon dioxide stimulated twice as many landings. In dry air, sweat increased the attack rate, but in humid air it decreased the landings.

Adult mosquitoes that take nourishment feed only on fluids, since the food canal in both sexes is a very fine capillary tube which permits passage of liquids only. Plants provide the most readily available food, as nectar, honeydew, fruit juices, and "oozes" from injured or diseased areas of the plant. There is little doubt that many species live exclusively on a vegetable diet, and males of all species seem to take no other food. Females of a great number of species may feed additionally on blood of living animals. Blood of man has been a recognized part of the diet of some species since the time of the earliest historic records. Warm-blooded animals other than man may be the most common sources of blood for many more species than those which choose man. Cold-blooded animals may be food sources for certain species. The avidity with which biting attacks are made on man has been a subject for the hardship tales of explorers and travelers who have gone to little-known places. The ferocity of the attacks on reindeer in northern Europe is said to be an important cause for migrations of this animal.

Feeding is made possible by means of an interacting group of six stylets (*fascicle*) and a trough-like proboscis. Prior to and after feeding the fascicle lies in the labial trough. During the act of feeding the labium is looped backward, opens along the anterior slit, and exposes the fascicle of stylets, which extends straight from the head into the host skin by way of the labella only. The path of the fascicle beneath the skin may be straight, curved, or even re-curved. The insect injects saliva into the wound by way of the hypopharynx, and blood flows into the head through a canal made by the trough-like labrum.

Disposition of ingested food has been the subject of considerable speculation and was somewhat clarified by observations of Trembley (1952) on a *Culex*, three species of *Anopheles*, and three *Aedes*. While the mosquitoes were feeding on blood through a membrane, all of them filled the mid-intestine, and nearly all had some blood in the diverticula. When blood was fed as a free liquid, most of them stored it in the mid-intestine and all had some blood in the diverticula. When glucose was fed both ways, all specimens had the liquid in the diverticula but showed wide variation as to its retention in the stomach. Marshall (1938) attributes the selective placement of the food to the stimulation imparted to the proventricular valve.

Swarming of male mosquitoes has fascinated both the professional worker and the layman for a long time. However, there is no general agreement as to its importance. Size and locations of swarms as well as periods of swarming vary widely among species. Some aggregations collect as small groups in the vicinity of warm-blooded animals, while others swarm as dense columns over prominent objects. Narrow, horizontal bands of mosquitoes several feet in height and extending for several miles along a railway road-bed have been recorded in areas of massive emergence.

Oviposition is a matter best considered according to the species, but some general aspects may be stated. For floodwater species water must be present as moisture on the soil surface, but standing water is required for other species. Those mosquitoes that deposit eggs as rafts always do so on standing water. Others attach eggs to masses of vegetation and deposit them on or barely beneath the surface of standing water. A number of species deposit single eggs on water or even on wet surfaces. Some select water surfaces and either drop their eggs while hovering or alight and drop them at random on the water. Several species oviposit at water-solid interfaces. Eggs of others are deposited only on very wet surfaces of soil in a zone immediately above the water line. The last category also includes those that oviposit on moist debris in depressions subject to inundation.

Adult mosquitoes may live from a few days to several months according to sex, species, climate, and weather. In any event, females tend to outlive males when subjected to the same conditions. In no case do males live more than a few weeks. Active females, on the other hand, may live two or more weeks in natural sites. Dormant mosquitoes of species capable of hibernating may live several months. As a rule species that hibernate as eggs rarely live more than 30 days during the warm parts of the year.

Anopheles

Anopheles (Fig. 44) is the best-known genus of mosquitoes and has one or more species that are vector-hosts of malaria parasites in each of the many tropical and temperate parts of the world. Bionomic details are well known for the most noxious ones. *Anopheles* species are usually considered as inhabitants of the broad, flat lands of the world. Indeed, they do abound on flood plains of great rivers, over prairies, and along coasts in the Americas, but a number of species may inhabit even mountainous terrain. Almost half of the species in India are indigenous to the submontane region; slightly fewer range the broad plains and deltas; and an even smaller number are montane. Records from the African tropics indicate a similar distribution according to terrain.

Eggs float singly on water surfaces of suitable larval sites. An entrapment of air in "floats" on the sides of each egg together with the combination of hydrophilic and hydrofuge areas on each causes an egg to remain properly oriented on the water. Since eggs float freely, and each has its own positive meniscus, they gravitate toward other positive meniscuses about stems, other eggs, or any object that breaks the surface film of water. If the surface of water that is bearing eggs is lowered, eggs may become stranded at the margins. Water subject to wave action loses most of its eggs at margins also, especially when the banks are shallow. Eggs are disposed variously on surfaces in characteristic ways that may be of taxonomic value to an ecologist.

Embryos mature rapidly. Incubation may require a week or more at temperatures near the threshold. In a few instances embryos develop so slowly that they survive during winter in eggs.

Anopheles larvae have become adapted to a variety of niches wherever water has a degree of permanence. Certain species require aerated water; others tolerate brackish water; some inhabit cavities or containers, while others live in recesses among epiphytes. Specific sites are small natural pools or puddles that either are stagnant or change slowly because of a constant or occasional trickle of water that runs through them. Shallow water, especially if there

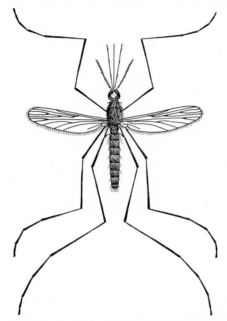

Fig. 44. Anopheles mosquito ♀. (Note palpi as long as proboscis.) (After Carpenter and LaCasse, 1955.)

is a good growth of green algae, seems to be almost universally infested. In India, populations of Anopheles have increased where (1) excavations have exposed the water table, (2) ground pools are formed in catchments, (3) obstructions prevent flow of water in ditches, drains, and streams, and (4) a system of newly graded canals becomes established.

A change from dry-land agriculture to one based on irrigation has always resulted in outbreaks of these mosquitoes. In India one serious problem originates when gravity irrigation from impounded rivers permits excessive watering without corresponding good drainage. Over the glaciated parts of the prairies of the American midwest, Anopheles populations were of massive proportions prior to the lowering of the water table for agricultural reasons.

General references to sites where adult mosquitoes may be found are of little help either to the sanitarian or to the biologist. In areas where the diurnal humidity of the air varies widely, sites are more restricted than in areas of high humidity. Apparently most species live in vegetation but have representatives that may stay in houses, especially in areas where humidity and temperature fluctuate greatly each day. In the wet tropics few adults may be seen because they disperse more widely out of doors. However, since most collection records are made either by sanitarians or are for their use, one might surmise from the literature that dwellings and animal quarters are the chief resting sites. Certainly most of those belonging to the subgenera *Myzomyia, Kerteszia,* and *Nyssorhynchus* live out of doors among vegetation or along banks of streams. Possibly this habitat is occupied by the subgenus *Anopheles* as well, but in this case the weight of the collector's evidence is in favor of quarters occupied by animals.

Anopheles, with few exceptions, feed at night or in subdued light. Apparently all feed on warm-blooded animals as some actively seek animals in enclosures while others feed on any available ones. Data on the nature and extent of host specificity have been collected mainly for use by sanitarians and for the most part show only relations to man and domestic animals.

Aedes

The genus *Aedes* is the dominant group of pest mosquitoes of the temperate and arctic world. It is the group that plagues man as a pioneer, soldier, laborer, and camper the world around. There are representatives in the woods, over the prairies, and even in towns and cities. Some from this group go high up in the mountains, others dominate muskeg and marshy areas of colder latitudes, and there are those that range into the densest forests.

The habit most characteristic of the genus is that of ovipositing on surfaces subject to flooding but above the water table at the time of deposition. Those that oviposit in cavities as rot holes in trees, axils of leaves, or domestic containers may attach their eggs to walls of the cavity just above the receding meniscus. Some representatives oviposit in debris or on the surface of the soil, but they do so where the surface is moist but not waterlogged. They are very likely to choose soil adjacent to sticks and leaf mold in preference to sites more exposed. They normally oviposit as the water recedes, but many of the eggs are deposited following heavy rains.

Eggs have a capacity for resisting exposure above the water table for months or a year or more. The shell of an embryonated egg is impervious to water and consequently very resistant to loss of water by evaporation. This is a necessary feature for all species since the eggs hatch only when submerged. After rain has filled depressions and cavities or caused streams and rivers to leave their banks, eggs are submerged and then hatch. Some embryos will hatch naturally only in cold water of early spring. These are often known as snow-pool mosquitoes, and they have but one generation each year. Other species may have multiple generations if repetitive flooding of an oviposition site occurs. Whether a species has one or several generations, its eggs must withstand periods of prolonged submergence or drying or even freezing. One or two species representative for typical responses to each of these conditions will be summarized herein.

Dormant eggs of *Aedes* have fully developed embryos inside them. After periods of first aging and then being submerged in water at hatching temperature, they may be induced to hatch by reducing the amount of oxygen in the medium adjacent to the egg. This is usually accomplished in nature by activities of microbes growing in the detritus which covers the eggs. The process may be accomplished in several ways in the laboratory.

Aedes stimulans is a species representative of the snow-pool group and has but one generation each year since it hatches in cold (11°C) water. Its range includes forested areas of North America east of the Great Plains and north of latitudes of about 36°. Eggs are placed in the leaf mold found high around the edges of woodland pools when the water table is near to them. Populations of this species will decline and then disappear from an accustomed site when drought prevails. At such times the water table falls well below the soil surface soon after adults emerge. Adults emerge within 4–6 weeks after hatching, and they may live for six weeks or longer in the woods near their source since they seldom range for any distance away from the woods. The snow-pool mosquitoes may be very annoying to persons who go into their territory, and they are well known as pests because of their enormous outbreaks in far northern areas.

Aedes sollicitans is characteristic of those species having multiple generations each year. It is a particularly good example because it tolerates saline water and shows repetitive generations during the summer months coincident with times of high tides. It may have

5–8 broods each year on the East Coast of the United States. Eggs are deposited in both coastal and inland sods and over soils that have a sulfurous odor. One of the areas of greatest abundance is in central United States where the effluvium from mining operations allows iron sulfides to accumulate over flood plains of streams and rivers. Over 50,000 eggs per square foot have been collected in such areas. Every time the regions bearing eggs are inundated by either sea water or fresh water, larvae hatch and develop to adults.

This and other summer, floodwater mosquitoes, unlike the snow-pool mosquitoes, may fly long distances and invade cities and towns. Specimens of the species have been taken at sea more than 110 miles off the East Coast of the United States. There is every reason to believe that this flight capability is matched or exceeded by others with extensive dispersal propensities, such as *A. vexans*.

Mating of this species and probably all other *Aedes* takes place in the vegetation before the individuals leave the locale of their larval development. Conditions that bring about copulation are not well known, and few species are successfully propagated in cages because they cannot be stimulated to mate. All species can be maintained as caged colonies by decapitating the males and immobilizing the female to induce mating (McDaniel and Horsfall, 1957).

Aedes aegypti is the best-known representative of the *Aedes* that develop in cavities. It is easy to rear in the laboratory and has received much attention because of its established significance as the vector-host of the virus yellow fever in urban situations. It deserves attention of medical entomologists now because of its status as a domestic pest in the tropics and adjacent warm temperate regions rather than for its former (and currently its potential) connection with yellow fever.

Adults oviposit on the walls of cavities lined with wood or wood products and just above the water line. Eggs are covered, in part at least, with an adhesive that holds them in place even after the site dries. They are very resistant to drying even at low atmospheric humidities.

In nature larvae live in dark cavities. They will descend into the detritus at the bottom of their cavities when stimulated by a shadow passing over the surface. Vibrations, too, cause this alarm reaction. They are grazers for the most part and live on microbiota and detritus found in their containers. Extensive microbial contamination is relished by the larvae; however, this is considered unfavorable for species that live in either ground pools or snow pools.

Adults of *Aedes aegypti* are active during the day. They are domestic and rarely travel any great distance from their sources, but they may go from house to house as far as 300 yards, or they may even fly to ships anchored a few hundred yards off shore. These mosquitoes flit about on porches and in and out of openings of the house. They hover near the floor and tend to feed on the ankles, legs, and bodies of persons.

Culex

The genus *Culex* has been separated into about 16 subgenera of distinct habits and characteristics. The subgenera *Culex* and *Melanoconion* are the ones of medical importance. Species of the former are more significant as human pests and vector-hosts, particularly in the tropics and warm temperate regions.

All members of this genus oviposit on surfaces of collections of water and are most numerous where suitable aquatic sites are maintained continuously. Eggs are deposited in compact masses on quiet water surfaces. Each egg in the mass or "raft" stands on end and is held to adjacent eggs since only the lower half of each egg is wet. The incubation interval of eggs is a matter of a day or two, and embryos have no appreciable rest period before hatching.

Larvae of the subgenus *Culex* (Fig. 45) live in water that either is foul or supports microbial activity, and they feed on the flocculent detritus always abundant in foul water. They withstand crowding to the point that there seems to be room for no more larvae; however, they are not disturbed by this close contact as is often the case with *Aedes*. Food is ample for them in this environment.

Culex pipiens is a complex of trinomial variants that is the best-known group of mosquitoes in the genus. Some of its variants may well be among the more important ones as they are vector-hosts of viruses, worms, and Protozoa of many sorts. Some of the variants feed readily on man. Blood of birds is the mainstay of the diet of the several species.

Some variant of this complex may be found the world around between the latitudes of 60° North and 40° South. *Culex pipiens pipiens* extends across Europe and Asia between 30° and 60° North and extends up the coast of Norway as far as the Arctic Circle. In the nearctic region this form occurs between 30° and 55° North. It

is found in eastern Africa, South Africa, and Dakar as island populations. This variant gives rise to a genetically recurrent population
called *C. pipiens molestus* which seems to appear from time to time
over the world for reasons not yet clear. It occurs as island populations over Europe, North America, and northern Asia, and is the
universal form around the Mediterranean, especially in areas border-

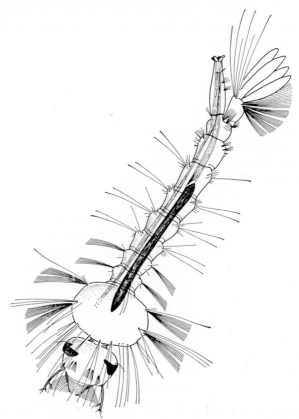

Fig. 45. Larva of *Culex* (dorsal view). (After Fox, 1925.)

ing the southern and eastern shore. Furthermore, it extends the
length of Africa along the eastern side. Since the beginning of
World War II, the form has been known along the east coast of
Australia. The form *C. pipiens pallens* occurs over the islands of the
Pacific from Japan south and also along the California coast in the
United States. *Culex pipiens fatigans* encircles the world in the
tropics and warmer temperate climates. It was doubtless transported
by sailing ships to all ports during the days of sailing. It now covers

the continents of Australia, Africa, and most of South America east of the Andes. Wherever ranges of the various forms overlap, natural hybrids occur and cause much confusion in identification.

Larval sites of variants of *Culex pipiens* seem to vary widely according to locality, season of the year, and population concerned. In the northern parts of the range, it occurs in ground water and artificial containers, while in the warm parts it occurs largely in containers. The form of *Culex pipiens pipiens* found along the New England seaboard may be abundant in polluted ground water. Populations of this mosquito are commonly collected from street drains, gutters, and domestic containers, especially when they hold foul water. During the heat of summer, collections of irrigation water in drains are a normal source. As a rule "slack water" supporting abundant algae is preferred, however, soapy water drains often hold large numbers of larvae. *Culex pipiens molestus* inhabits any stationary, polluted water that is accessible and situated in continuous or partial darkness. Populations of *Culex pipiens pallens* occur in artificial collections of water near or within human habitations. Such sites include water butts and discarded utensils as well as ground pools and ditches. The larvae are only rarely found in rot holes and bamboo stumps. Sites for *fatigans* may be water on the ground or in containers, provided it is neither foul nor subject to high surface temperature. When found in artificial containers and static ground pools, the sites chosen are protected from long exposure to intense sunlight. When larvae are present in the margins of moving ground water, as in drains, they may tolerate direct sun in some areas if the water movement prevents the surface from reaching an unfavorably high temperature.

Little has been published about local distribution of the variants of *Culex pipiens* as adults during the summer; however, records indicate that they may be collected during the day in dark, damp shelters. Those of *Culex pipiens pipiens* rest in cellars, lofts, and other dark places having fairly constant temperatures. Most of the females are found on walls and particularly on cobwebs. Similarly, adults of *fatigans* occur in occupied buildings. They have been taken in barns, outhouses, chicken houses, and dwellings, and both sexes have been found in abundance in basements of dormitories. Agreement is general that normal hibernating sites for all variants are dark, damp places sheltered from wind. After the middle of September, females move to dark cellars, basements, and unoccupied houses, where they cling to walls and remain with the heads pointing upward.

Under natural conditions adults of the variants feed only at night. La Face (1926) found considerable variation in feeding habits from locality to locality for the forms occurring in Italy. However, all will feed during the winter when the temperature is above 15° C.

Culex tarsalis has come to be recognized as an important vector-host of viruses of encephalitides, particularly in arid areas. This mosquito is suited to the Great Plains and arid areas in western North America. It extends from Canada southward into Mexico and eastward to the Mississippi River. Isolated records of occurrence are known from Indiana, Virginia, and southeastern United States. Jenkins (1950) reported it from northern Canada.

Larvae may be found in all sorts of ground pools containing emergent vegetation. They are commonly found in grassy marshes and especially in seeps and irrigation wastes. The form occurring near sea level in California develops primarily in foul water, but the one found in mountains often occurs in clear, cold, unpolluted water. The form in Utah may be collected in water that is clear or foul, fresh or alkaline, and found in ditches, hoofprints, ornamental pools and even rain barrels (Jenkins, 1950).

In California females may be collected during the summer from shelters inhabited by chickens and possibly other animals, while in southern California females have been found during the winter in nests of the wood rat. During the winter in Utah, females may be collected in basements, cellars, caves and outbuildings.

Mansonia

This genus is often referred to as *Taeniorhynchus* by both recent and earlier writers. Representatives of the genus are principally tropical, but some range well into temperate latitudes such as Tasmania on the south and Sweden on the north. Characteristically, it abounds in the "wet tropics." Species in all latitudes are well known for the prolonged aquatic interval so that often only one generation is produced annually in extreme northern latitudes, and there are very few even in the tropics.

Larvae may be found in situations where the water is permanent and the bottom is a deep mass of flocculent matter. Required associations are plants which have roots with abundant air cells that may be penetrated by the siphon. Some of the mosquitoes are very specific, while others attach to a variety of plants. Water lettuce, *Pistia stratiotes,* is the most commonly associated plant, especially of the subgenus *Mansonioides.* Larvae of some species burrow in bottom debris and ingest all sorts of particles, but the exact nature of material digested is not known. Those that cling to roots of plants in floating islands may be even more specific as to the nature of the food used.

Pupae of all species attach themselves to roots of plant associates by means of their pointed trumpets. These are inserted by a manipulation somewhat similar to the opening and closing of pliers. Some species of the pupae may attach only once, at pupation, because the spine-like apices of the trumpets absciss at the time of detachment, thus precluding reattachment. Other species have a fixed spine on each tube and may attach or detach at will.

Haemagogus

The genus *Haemagogus* ranges from its main source in the central region of South America northward across Central America, and into North America as far as the southern tip of Texas. It ranges southward into Argentina. The genus is most abundantly represented in the extensive forests from the eastern slopes of the Andes along the great water courses of Brazil. The forest belts at elevations of about 1000 feet in Central America are well suited for some species. Bamboo plantings, particularly those areas in which the plants have been cut and have stumps remaining, are excellent sources of some species. *H. spegazzinii* is ordinarily an inhabitant of the upper stories of tropical rain forests, but it may thrive at ground level if the forests have been thinned and cacao plantings provide the understory. The lower cacao trees produce a canopy near the ground very like that high in the uncut forest. *H. lucifer* lives in rain forests while *H. argyromeris* thrives in deciduous and second-growth forests. They all live in cavities as larvae in the manner of the subgenus *Stegomyia* in the genus *Aedes.* These mosquitoes are known to be the principal vector-hosts of the virus of yellow fever in sylvatic environments in the New World.

Psorophora

The genus *Psorophora* is the common floodwater mosquito of both the tropics and warmer temperate regions of North and South

America. Species reach their maximum abundance in vast flooded areas such as the rice-growing regions of south-central United States and the wooded flood plains of the great rivers and their tributaries. Representatives are better known for their capabilities as pests, but some are vector-hosts of pathogens in South America at least. *P. confinnis* and *P. discolor* are savanna species that have become the vastly abundant rice field mosquities. Woodland species that may become equally abundant are *P. varipes* and *P. ferox*. The woodland pasture species is *P. cyanescens*. Because of these different species, life is often made miserable for animals on pasture and for people whose activities require them to be among mosquitoes. In nearly all respects these mosquitoes behave as the floodwater species of *Aedes*.

Sabethine Mosquitoes

The genera *Sabethes* and *Wyeomyia* belong to the tribe Sabethini and have habits so similar that they may be considered together. Both have recently come under consideration because some species are sylvatic vector-hosts of the virus of yellow fever. Practically all species are found in American tropics. *Sabethes* larvae live in stumps of bamboo, in rot holes of trees, and to a lesser extent in axils of leaves of bromeliads. Larvae of *Wyeomyia* inhabit minute cavities in plants such as axils of leaves of bromeliads, bracts of *Heliconia*, and leaves of pitcher plants (*Sarracenia* spp.). A very few stray into domestic containers. Actually larvae of all species occur in cavities. Adults are, for the most part, sylvatic species.

Culiseta

The genus *Culiseta* (syn. *Theobaldia*) is a cosmopolitan one, and most species occur in cold water. Larvae are found in obviously foul water or in clear water over foul muck. Stable drainage containing urine and pools with malodorous muck on the bottoms are sites of abundance. Cattail marshes and collections of water beneath roost of blackbirds and waterfowl are choice sites. *Culiseta inornata* is a summer species in Minnesota, a spring and fall species in central Illinois and a winter one in southern Arkansas. *C. melanura* is a bog species found where and when the water is cold, as in natural springs, and the bottom is black muck. Adults of some species may feed on man, but birds are more common sources of food. The habit of living in close proximity to rookeries of migratory fowl places them in an excellent position to become vector-hosts for viral agents.

Armigeres

This is an Australasian genus that is particularly abundant in the Indian, Malayan, Indonesian, and Philippine regions. Larvae live in cavities and particularly in those containing foul water. Flooded pit privies, collections of water containing fecal material, and rotting coconut husks are often heavily infested. They have also been seen in rotting coconut meat that was slimy in consistency. These mosquitoes are often domestic and feed on domestic animals.

Tripteroides

This genus is represented by domestic and sylvatic species that feed near their larval sites on vertebrates including man. Some species have become pests in northwestern Australia where they invade houses. All species develop in various cavities that range from pitchers of *Nepenthes* to rot holes, coconut shells, bamboo stumps, and domestic containers. The water in a development site is relatively clear and is not foul in the same sense as the water in which most *Culex* live. Larvae usually stay submerged with dorsal side downward; however numerous multi-branched hairs may support them slightly above the bottom. They feed on arthropods or their remains in the water.

CERATOPOGONIDAE

Ceratopogonidae (syn. Heleidae) is represented in the medical group by the genus *Culicoides* (Fig. 46), a cosmopolitan one. Both *Leptoconops* and *Lasiohelea* are known to attack vertebrates (Fox, 1955). They are found along sea shores, the edges of streams, ponds, and mountain brooks. Some areas in Brazil and western Africa are made almost unbearable at times because of these tiny gnats. Since they are so small, they are often not seen even at the time they are biting; and for this reason they are known in parts of North America as "no-see-ums." Besides their proclivities as biters, they are vector-hosts for juvenile stages of a few filariid worms.

Larvae live in a waterlogged, dense medium such as mud or the algal mats in margins of ground pools, ponds, springs, creeks, and lakes. Wet rot holes in trees may be prolific sources, and slime-covered bark is also a source. Liquid manure and slimy collections of water are suitable larval sites for some species while the mucky edges of salt marshes and mangrove swamps are ideal for others. Sides of ditches through mangrove swamps support the greatest number of larvae of *C. dovei* per unit area. *C. austeni* of Africa develops in the slime on felled stems or stumps of banana. During the heat of summer larval sites are always in dense shade. Larvae are carnivorous and even cannibalistic. They lie buried except for the head, and when disturbed they quickly wriggle into the substrate.

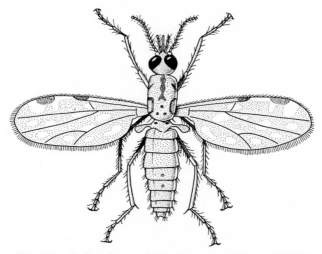

Fig. 46. *Culicoides* sp. (After Patton and Cragg, 1913.)

Gluchova (1958) noted that even though species of *Culicoides* are winged, two types of attack are known: hunting flights and waylaying attack. Hunting flights may take the flies considerable distances before a host is located. Those that waylay a host reach it by flying or crawling, but the host must come to the immediate environs of the fly. The crawlers move along the ground and onto the parts of the body in contact with the ground. The crawling attack is most common in windy or cold situations.

Jobling (1928) has described the mechanics of feeding of adult flies in the following manner. All apparently feed on blood of vertebrates. The blade-like mandibles slash the skin. Then the two apically spinose maxillae presumably abrade the interior of the wound. The labium is pressed to the surface of the wound as a kind of cup. The trough-like labrum is forced into the wound to provide the channel for the blood. Some species obtain blood vicariously by attaching to engorged mosquitoes.

Downes (1958) has written a review of the knowledge of this little-known group and should be consulted for greater detail.

SIMULIIDAE

This family includes gnats variously known as black flies, buffalo gnats, and turkey gnats. Wooded, mountainous areas and forested river valleys may have hordes of one or more species of these flies. Prairies and plains of northern latitudes may likewise produce

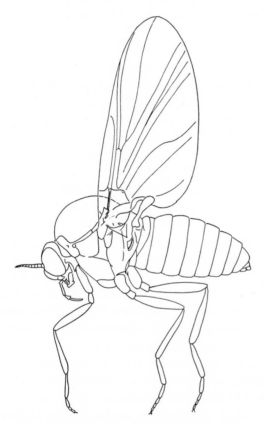

Fig. 47. *Simulium* sp. (After Smart, 1956.)

enormous numbers of one or more species. Their blood lust and sudden appearance in large numbers give them a significant place in medical entomology. Several species become vector-hosts for juvenile stages of filariid worms.

These insects are readily recognizable as larvae, pupae, and adults. Adults have short stout bodies with the mesonotum so arched that the head is almost under it (Fig. 47). Wings are short and broad, with veins crowded toward the costal margin. Larvae have elongate, black bodies that are somewhat bulbous posteriorly. A single median fleshy appendage extends toward the mouth from the venter of the thorax. A posterior patch of hooks on the venter provides the means for attaching a larva to the substrate. Mouth parts are similar to those of a larval mosquito. The pupa is encased in an upright cone-like cocoon. A pair of filamentous, branching, respiratory organs arises from the thorax and extends upward (anteriorly) as gills.

Species of this family tend toward one of two ecological groups: the riverine and the cold-water forms. The former may have a generation each year every time the river is in flood, whereas the latter usually has one generation in the spring but may have another in the fall. Regardless of species, they tend to live through the winter as larvae.

Eggs of black flies show two patterns of distribution: either the eggs are at the bottom of rivers and streams or they are attached to objects at or near the waters surface. Cold-water species release eggs on the bottoms of streams and rivers, where they may lie dormant under stationary stones and similar objects throughout the summer. Eggs of some species are said to withstand desiccation like those of floodwater mosquitoes. Riverine species deposit eggs in masses encased in an adhesive jelly. Any object standing erect in a stream may be a suitable site for attachment of eggs. Crosskey (1959) has shown that two important Canadian species (S. *hirtipes* and *venustum*) oviposit most often at dams or outfalls of lakes. Larvae drift downstream from these sites.

Larvae usually live in water that is relatively turbulent because the important factor seems to be availability of food. Crisp (1956) shows that those of *Simulium damnosum* were concentrated in water 6 to 18 inches deep in rivers in Ghana. The Golubatz fly of the Danube has two strains according to the depth to which its larvae descend. The form called *profundale* by Baranov (1939) attaches to stones on the river bed where the water varies from 13 to 65 feet in depth, and the current is very swift. The form called *litorale* attaches to submerged branches at depths from 8 to 14 inches. The minimum tolerable rate of flow for any species is about 0.5 foot per second while velocities of 4 to 6 feet per second are the more common. Few larvae live in water moving more than 7.5 feet per second. Philipson (1956) and others have stated that the significance of motion in water is one of pressure acting to keep the mouth brushes open so they may act as traps for suspended food. For each species there is probably a minimum current necessary to keep the mouth brushes spread. The upper limit on velocity is that which will permit attachment. Those that live in clear water which provides little suspended, edible detritus will tolerate the higher velocities needed to provide adequate food. Silt and similar indigestible detritus in quantity is inimical to larvae, and it may be a factor limiting distribution in some instances.

Larvae usually attach along the vertical sides of fairly stable objects found in the currents of water. Normally they range along the side of a stone, tree trunk, or log at the place where the current is turbulent as a result of being temporarily checked by the face of the submerged object. In such sites thousands of larvae may occur over a few square inches. For example, larvae of the buffalo gnat scraped from one submerged fence post more than filled a quart jar. In Kenya and Congo, S. *neavei* lives phoretically on larvae of mayflies (*Afronurus*) and a crab (*Potamonautes*), according to Van Someren and McMahon (1950). In Nigeria only crabs are known to be phoretic hosts. De Meillon (1957) quoted Wanson to the effect that eggs of this species are placed on vegetation and that the freshly hatched larvae seek the arthropods for attachment sites. They probably feed on the flocculent matter available in the water that surrounds the mouth parts of a feeding crab.

Larvae are remarkably able either to move about or to maintain a stationary position in torrents and rapids. They change position frequently and the chief reason for the shifting is that the velocity of the stream is unsatisfactory (Crisp, 1956). Holdfasts are discs made of silk that are attached to a solid surface. A larva clings to the disc either with the hooks on the apex of the pseudo-leg on the venter of the thorax or with those on the caudal end of the abdomen. A larva may move from one disc of silk to another in any direction depending on the current. While clinging to one disc with the caudal hooks, it may stretch out and spin a new disc with the labial spinnerets. The thoracic hooks are then used to cling to the new disc while the grasp on the old is released. This process may be repeated until a suitable location is reached. Progress downstream is rapid when the larva attaches a silken thread to a solid surface and then drifts downstream while spinning out new silk in the manner of a caterpillar or spider. Larvae feed on particulate material screened from the water by mouth parts elaborately modified in the manner of those of Culicidae. Unlike larval mosquitoes, however, they hold their labral brushes open to form two palmate sieves, and the rushing water is strained free of particles while the larva lies on its dorsum. At intervals the brushes are clapped over the mouth opening and combed free of detritus. The pharynx is opened and the mass is sucked in. The water is expelled through a complex mass of combs in the pharynx as is the case with the larvae of mosquitoes. Anything small enough to be swallowed will be taken in. Silt, diatoms, algal filaments, flocculent organic matter, and animal plankton may be swallowed; however, diatoms are sometimes more important components of the diet.

Pupation occurs in the open cones of silk attached to the sides of the rigid supports found at larval feeding sites. Sometimes the water recedes and leaves pupae exposed, but more often development is completed in turbulent water, and the adults emerge from such water. Species vary as to the methods employed in escaping from water. When imagoes emerge from the pupal pelt they have a hydrofuge surface that is surrounded by bubbles of air. They rise inside the bubbles, and with the bursting at the water surface the insects are virtually catapulted into the air and immediately take wing and fly away.

Practically all black flies travel several to many miles from their larval sources. The tropical *Simulium damnosum* travels 6–12 miles regularly, while flights of 45 miles have been reported. Short flights along the water courses of origin are normal. The Golubatz fly may leave its sources on the Danube and fly 60–160 miles within a few hours following the period of mass emergence (Baranov, 1939). Such flights take place even at high altitudes, and the direction taken is that of the wind. Creeping flights similar to those described for mosquitoes have been reported. Adults of one of the important Canadian species, S. *venustum*, rest between flights, particularly at night in the canopy of spruce and other trees.

Black flies are seldom host-specific but may become so because of limitations on availability of hosts. Some feed on large birds, some on large hairy mammals; others are domestic feeders that attack man, while those that remain near their larval sites feed on whatever animals are available. All species of both sexes feed on nectar of flowers, but only the females feed on blood. Peterson (1956) found S. *vittatum* apparently feeding on an ant. Pupae of butterflies were regarded as hosts by early observers according to Peterson. At times most species fly to a host with directness, and then strike with such force that they actually seem to have been shot at the host. This habit is particularly true of the buffalo gnat. Once on a body, the pests usually slither under the hair or feathers or into some crevice in clothing. Most gnats strike low on the body, particularly of domestic animals, and then work into the hair either on the belly or around the flanks. When they attack humans, they strike the lower legs, or parts near the ground of squatting or sitting persons. Sometimes they crawl under cuffs or inside socks and shoes to feed. Wolf and Peterson (1960) observed that the Canadian pests, S. *hirtipes* and *venustum*, usually feed on the back of the neck and scalp behind the ears of man. Biting rates increase during overcast periods. Rain, strong winds, and very high relative humidity inhibit feeding.

The feeding wound is of a ragged type. Gibbins (1938) says that feeding is a serial act involving an initial incision made by the mandibles. Cutaneous tissues are snipped as if by scissors. The recurved hooks on the maxillae actually abrade the puncture. Apices of mandibles are serrate and are locked together near the midpoint as blades of scissors. Tissue is so mangled that it may be pulled loose and ingested along with blood. The labrum is armed apically with two recurved teeth which serve as an anchor during the act of feeding. The labium with its labella forms a surface seal to confine the blood on its way to the mouth.

These flies may live as adults for three weeks or more during which time they may feed several times. Since all flies do not emerge at the same time and more than one generation is possible for the river forms, an outbreak could last throughout a summer in some localities. The extent of an outbreak may vary according to species and it may be determined by existing water levels, temperature, and humidity.

TABANIDAE

Tabanidae is a family of moderate to large Diptera (Figs. 48 and 49) commonly known as horse flies, deer flies, greenheads, gad flies, and bulldog flies. Regardless of name, the adults are pests of stock, wild animals, and even man. Their large size, buzzing sound during flight, and forthright attacks have caused harnessed horses to bolt, animals on the range to stampede, and herds of wild animals to move long distances. They were the bane of the pioneer and cavalry man when middle American prairie land was being opened to agriculture.

This family is evolving so rapidly that there are incipient genera in which speciation and subspeciation are active. More than 2,500 species are now known, about half of them in the genus *Tabanus*. Hays (1956) noted that there are 26 genera and about 500 species

Fig. 48. *Tabanus micans.* (After Edwards et al., 1939.)

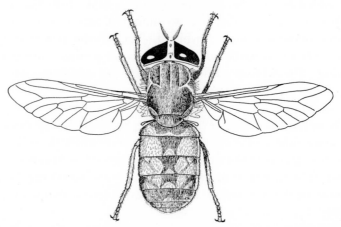

Fig. 49. *Tabanus distinguendus.* (After Colyer and Hammond, 1951.)

known from America north of Mexico. A great deal more taxonomic and bionomic information is needed for complete understanding of this important family. *Chrysops* (Pangoniinae), *Tabanus*, and *Haematopota* (Tabaniinae) are the better known genera of pests.

Significant characteristics of the family are as follows. Wings of the imago are bounded by the costa as an ambient vein (unique except for Acanthomeridae, a small family of large forest flies of

Neotropica). The flagellum of the antenna is short (compared with Nematocera) and is distinctly annulated apically. Sexes are dimorphic, males being holoptic (compound eyes contiguous) and females dichoptic (eyes separated). Genera with species of medical importance have females that feed on blood, while males are unable to do so. The larva is fusiform (rarely club-shaped) and is elongated with a caudal retractile air tube. The cuticula of a larva is a tough, elastic membrane that is whitish or clear with areas of microscopic, felted pubescence. The penultimate segment bears the pyriform, cystoid organ of Graber on the dorsal side. Pupae are elongate, cylindrical, and sclerous, and have numerous spines all over the body that are directed backward. A pair of subdorsal spiracles connects to tracheae anteriorly on the thorax. Eggs are deposited in shingle-like layers to form masses characteristic of genera and even species. They are fusiform and white, brown, or black in color.

Seasonal histories of tabanids vary widely in duration according to species, latitude, and weather. In general, *Chrysops* species require less time for development than do those of *Tabanus*. The former may have several generations each year in both the tropics and warm temperate regions where larval sites are continuous. Some *Tabanus* species have multiple generations each year, but most have one or fewer. *T. lineola* may have two or more generations in rice fields in central United States, while *T. sulcifrons, costalis, lasiophthalmus,* etc., require a year for development. *T. stygius* usually requires two years. *T. atratus* has been known to pass through two winters as an immature form before emergence.

Tabanids place their eggs on vegetation over suitable larval sites. This means eggs are generally found over water or waterlogged soil. Eggs are in masses attached to posts, leaves, sticks, or branches. Usually the anterior ends of the eggs are directed downward so that the young larvae may easily crawl toward their developmental sites or fall into them. *T. lineola,* for example, oviposits on leaves of grasses growing in water, but when other vegetation is dominant, leaves of other sorts may be selected. If living plants are absent, oviposition may take place on wood.

While tabanid larvae (Fig. 50) of many species have developmental sites on submerged or waterlogged soil, others live in relatively dry pasture soils having specific vegetative cover. Those species that develop in waterlogged and submerged soils usually enter drier soils for pupation. Some species are products of coastal salt marshes; others abound in rice fields; some live in bogs and marshes; while others live in seeps and banks of ponds; and more and more have been found in pasture sods. The greater number of economic forms are associated with a high water table.

The genus *Tabanus* contains several species that live in dry areas. *T. sulcifrons* in Oklahoma is almost always confined to well-drained, open woods that are never waterlogged, according to Schomberg (1952). Tashiro and Schwardt (1953) noted that *T. quinque-fasciatus* was a product of swampy areas in which larvae lived almost exclusively in the *Carex* zone where the soil was waterlogged early in the season and became relatively dry during the summer. Stray

Fig. 50. Larva of *Tabanus.* (After Oldroyd, 1954.)

larvae ranged in the wet zone below the *Carex,* and into the blue-grass zone on the other side. *T. nigrovittatus* lives in the drier parts of salt marshes among roots of *Spartina,* and marshes that have been ditched are more favorable to them than are unditched ones. Larvae were most abundant where the soil moisture was 70 per cent of the total weight of a soil sample (Gerry and Bailey, 1948). Lamborn (1930) found mature larvae of *T. biguttatus* in Nyasaland on mud flats after the soil had dried and cracked.

Chrysops larvae are more restricted to situations where soil is usually submerged. Davey and O'Rourke (1951) found larvae only in the soil and under the water along a horizon around the margin of very shallow pools. Rice fields of central United States are covered by shallow water, and they afford suitable sites for several species. *C. discalis,* an important western species, is associated with shallow water covering alkali flats in Oregon. Larvae in small alkali islands are concentrated near the margins around shallow lakes or in alkali strips on the shore. Sometimes they were found hundreds of yards from any possible oviposition sites. Roth and Lindquist (1948) found that larvae floated with the wind on the surface of the water during moonless nights. They can and often do swim by the jerky motion produced when the body bends rapidly first one way and then the other.

Larvae of all tabanids are both predacious and cannibalistic and seem to be indiscriminate in choice of food. They may be reared on crustaceans, larvae of other Diptera, earthworms, or bits of vertebrate flesh. Prey seems to be obtained at random while larvae are making their way through the soil. When an earthworm or an insect larva is encountered, the anterior parallel mandibles strike it by repeated downward thrusts until a hole is slashed through the cuticula that is large enough for inserting the anterior end. Mandibles continue to tear the tissue and comminuted particles are swallowed. Some species, at least, snap the mandibles with a clicking sound that is easily audible. Large species are well able to penetrate human skin with their powerful mandibles.

Adult tabanids are most often active diurnally in bright sun. Males may swarm at such times regardless of whether females are in the vicinity. Some swarm at dawn in the tops of trees while others use some prominent linear feature on the ground as a sidewalk or roadway for orientation. They course back and forth over the focal point from several minutes to an hour. Most species are active at temperatures of 22°–27° C when atmospheric turbulence and humidity are favorable.

Males feed solely on secretions and excretions found on and in plant parts. *T. striatus* feeds on a gummy exudate from "rain trees" especially in the early morning, according to Mitzmain (1913). Flowers of palmetto, bay, holly, and various composites provide nectar much sought by both males and females of species living in southern United States.

Females feed on blood found on the skin or they may obtain it by cutting through the skin to the capillary layer. Parts involved in the surface feeding on skin are the fleshy, pseudotracheate labella and labral gutter while all mouth parts are involved when the capillaries must be tapped. The flexible, fleshy labella is everted and spread over a site for piercing the skin. The crossed, blade-like mandibles slash the epidermis and dermis to make a wide opening into which maxillae, labrum, and hypopharynx enter. Slashes through the capillary layer cause hemorrhages from which blood may seep to the surface and form a pool. While the blood is oozing from the capillaries it is under positive pressure and readily flows into the labral gutter inserted in the wound. The cibarial pump draws the confined blood directly into the pharynx (Snodgrass, 1944, and Cragg, 1912). A feeding puncture is made when a fly literally stabs the surface as it lunges forward. The fascicle of stylets is projected into the wound by short jabs repeated in rapid succession while the fly weaves and lunges its body to widen and deepen the wound. When stylets are fully inserted, the theca of the labium is telescoped into a series of annular folds instead of being bent backward as it is in mosquitoes. Dickerson and Lavoipierre (1959) thought that labellar lobes played no part in feeding on subsurface blood. They may be used to collect surface liquids such as solutions of sugar. Gordon and Crewe (1948) have given a detailed account of the act of feeding in the various stages.

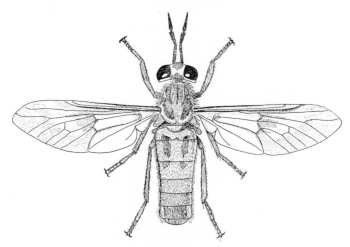

Fig. 51. *Chrysops centurionis.* (After Oldroyd, 1957.)

These flies provide a copious flow of saliva which contains a potent anti-coagulin that permits the blood to flow freely through a feeding puncture and labral gutter. The flow may continue freely even after the fly has vacated the feeding site. A coagulin secreted in the gut clots the ingested blood so that it may be retained for digestion. While in the mid-gut, the clotted blood is subjected to action of invertase, tryptase, peptidase, and other enzymes (Wigglesworth, 1931). Digestive fluids form in old epithelial cells, and as these are spent, new cells develop to provide a continuous supply of digestive fluids. These are spilled into the magma and digested quickly.

A considerable amount of blood is ingested by tabanids. The relatively small *Chrysops* (Fig. 51) may ingest 10–20 mg at each feeding and may take several blood meals during a life time. *Tabanus quinquevittatus* may take 85 mg of blood, and the large *T. sulcifrons* can take in four times as much at one feeding.

Tabanids exhibit characteristic behavior when attracted to a feeding site and one of the significant ones, that of *Chrysops silacea*, is outlined here. Duke (1955) found that flies bent on feeding would fly up a gradient provided by the smoke from a wood fire. Whatever the stimulus, the smoke provided the visual evidence of a gradient. Men who trapped flies in the Cameroons caught over 10 times as many flies at ground level near a wood fire as they caught away from a fire. There were no differences whether a fire was present or not when trappers worked high in the forest canopy. These flies feed largely on primates in the canopy; however, they come to the ground when cooking fires are made.

RHAGIONIDAE

The Rhagionidae (syn. Leptidae) are known as snipe flies (Fig. 52) and are regarded in almost all cases as predators on insects, but at least two genera have species that are hematophagous. Those that

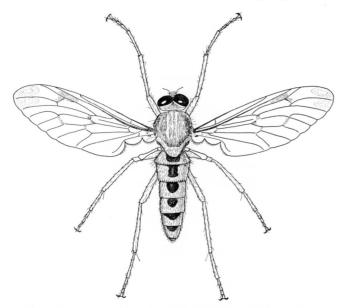

Fig. 52. *Rhagio* sp. (After Colyer and Hammond, 1951.)

take blood have a well-developed piercing fascicle similar to that of Tabanidae. These flies are smaller than tabanids and are more elongate. Squamae at bases of the wings are barely visible. The third segment of the antennae is not annulated but is reduced apically to a filiform style. Wings are not bounded by the costal vein. Larvae are predacious on insects and worms in the manner of tabanids. Eggs of several species are deposited in masses, and sometimes large numbers of the eggs cling together. Frohne (1959) said that two Alaskan species of *Symphoromyia* are the "biters *par excellence*" of the genus. They attack on warm, calm days in bright sunlight, and settle chiefly on the lower half of the body, but some will feed about the head and neck.

CHLOROPIDAE

This family of small flies largely has a reputation as plant feeders, particularly in Europe. However adults of the genus *Hippelates* are a great nuisance in the New World. These are tiny flies that may be seen on domestic animals about sores, scabs, eyes, and openings of the anus and genitals. They will swarm over purulent lesions as ulcers of yaws and infected wounds. The flies commonly feed on matter on eyelids of children, particularly those affected by conjunctivitis.

Like many of the cyclorrhaphous Diptera, the flies have sponging mouth parts, and feed by everting the soft, pseudotracheate labella over moist surfaces and then sucking in liquids. Burgess (1951) has quoted others to the effect that "tooth-like" processes on the labella may actually scarify edges of scabs and thus cause pus to exude. The flies feed rapidly and later regurgitate the food as a vomit drop that is held by the labella (see the discussion of the house fly). Kumm (1935a) noted that one fly regurgitated 10 times within less than an hour after feeding. The material would appear as a drop to be ingested and then another drop would appear. Often some of this material sticks to the surface on which the fly is perched, and it may contain viable pathogens from the lesion where the food is obtained.

Areas having the greatest abundance of these flies are the rolling sandy lands of southern United States from Florida to California. Well-drained soil devoted to the culture of truck crops is most productive of larvae. Desert and coastal alluvium deposited by spring freshets is a good source of larvae in western United States. Even uncultivated sandy areas associated with streams, dampness, and edges of forests may produce swarms of the gnats. Intensive cultivation of irrigated (not flooded) lands in western United States has greatly increased their abundance. *Hippelates collusor* of California may disperse over an area of four or more square miles during a 5- to 6-hour period of active flight (Mulla and March, 1959).

MUSCIDAE
General

The family Muscidae (including Anthomyiidae of some authors) includes such well-known insects as house flies, stable flies, horn flies, and tsetse flies. Unfortunately there is considerable confusion about phylogeny of these higher Diptera so that family limits are not uniformly accepted. The classification used by Hennig (1948, 1950, 1953) is followed herein because the forms of medical importance fall readily into satisfactory taxa. Hennig's subfamilies with genera of medical importance are as follows:

1. Muscinae
   Stomoxys
   Haematobia (syn. *Bdellolarynx, Lyperosia, Siphona*)
   Musca
2. Phaoniinae
   Muscina
   Passeromyia
   Mydaea
3. Coenosiinae
4. Fanniinae
   Fannia
5. Anthomyiinae
6. Glossiinae
   Glossina

Flies of this family are very common and are seen so frequently by the laymen that many think flies and insects are synonymous. So many of the family have taken to domestication or are attracted to domestic situations that they seem to be ubiquitous. One species, *Musca domestica,* is cosmopolitan wherever man has established himself permanently. All species are drab in appearance and are similar in size, which is considered "average" for insects. To comprehend other characteristics of the family requires specialized knowledge of morphology. For the purposes of this book, recognition of the species discussed is considered adequate.

Stomoxys

This genus is best known by its representative variously called the stable fly, straw fly, dog fly, or biting house fly (*S. calcitrans*) (adult: Fig. 53; larva: Fig. 54). Flies of this genus all resemble house flies except that the mouth parts form a rigid, shiny black proboscis protruding forward from the lower side of the head. Populations are largest where wet plant debris has accumulated in compact mounds. When piles of plant parts have repeated additions of new material, an excellent source of these flies is maintained. If frequent rains and high temperatures prevail, the climate is especially favorable. In the days before the advent of the combine harvester for grain, this fly reached fantastic proportions over the plains and prairies of central United States where straw piles were a

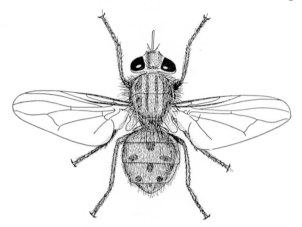

Fig. 53. *Stomoxys calcitrans.* (After Edwards *et al.,* 1939.)

Fig. 54. Larva of a muscid, *Stomoxys* (side view). (After Fox, 1925.)

familiar feature of the landscape. At one time during the early part of this century, Kansas alone was estimated to have over 200,000 acres of land covered by stacks of straw. Use of the harvester ended the accumulations of the straw in stacks since it is now scattered as the grain is threshed. This harvesting process has thereby eliminated the main source of the flies. Today populations of the stable fly in the Midwest come from piles of stable litter and stacks of upland hay exclusive of alfalfa, which, for some reason, does not support larvae. Elsewhere larvae live in packed lawn clippings, piles of vegetable wastes as those from celery packing operations, drifts of lagoon and sea vegetation stranded above high-tide levels, piles of peanut vines, and packed waste sometimes found under troughs in feed lots. Where these plant materials are allowed to accumulate, the flies are present in proportion to the number and volume of the piles. Simmons and Dove (1941) found that celery wastes supported larval densities up to 50,000 to a square foot, but few or no flies were produced wherever the depth of a mass was less than 6 inches.

Adult stable flies rest in the shade near their larval sites on all sorts of surfaces. Poles, posts, slatted fences, wire fences, trunks of trees, and sides of buildings are particularly favored perches. Few flies are found in enclosures except prior to and during summer electrical storms. They are very sluggish and are not readily dislodged from resting sites unless they are ready for feeding. Several observers have reported intense activity at dawn during warm weather with a second period of activity in late afternoon.

The flies feed on all sorts of mammals and the choice is in proportion to availability of feeding sites on the body. An active animal is more likely to be visited than a sedentary one, and the ears and lower legs of domestic animals are sites for feeding. Humans are often attacked about the ankles, but any exposed part of the body may become a feeding site. Both sexes of flies feed on blood, with little other food except succulent fruit or moisture on fresh manure. Total time for engorgement is about 2–5 minutes as a fly usually changes feeding sites at least once. An individual may engorge as many as 14 times in as many days. Feeding on man is most likely soon after the atmosphere has been cooled by a shower or at times when flies accumulate around dwellings.

Mitzmain (1913a) has recorded the act of feeding on human skin as follows: The fly punctures the epidermis and the capillary region of the dermis. It does so by the action of heavy, blade-like rows of denticles located along the inner face of the labella. The flexible labella at the end of a rigid labium (Fig. 55, left) is everted by hydrostatic pressure to expose the cutting teeth so they may be appressed to the skin. By rapid eversion and inversion of the labella, the teeth cut into the skin, and the labium is forced farther into the wound. A rapid twisting of the labella first one way then the other aids in the cutting. Within a short time the slender, anterior part of the labium is completely inserted. An undisturbed fly was seen to aspirate blood for over 12 minutes, though much of it passed on through the body and was immediately voided as a watery fluid.

Many flies make preliminary punctures in the skin on one or more animals in a herd before beginning to feed, and for this reason their mouth parts have potentiality as carriers of contaminants. After a feeding site is vacated, the puncture exudes blood for some time, and other muscids often feed on this surface blood.

Flies begin to oviposit after taking about three blood meals, and they continue to do so at intervals thereafter for 30–60 days. Gravid flies move to oviposition sites and then crawl into a pile of straw where odors of the wet, decaying materials are strong. Sometimes a female will go 2–3 inches below the surface, and several may use

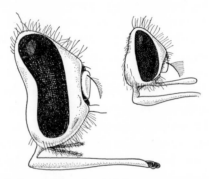

Fig. 55. Lateral views of heads of *(left) Stomoxys* and *(right) Haematobia* showing elbowed proboscises. (After Edwards *et al.*, 1939.)

the same tunnel into the fetid mass. Eggs may be deposited within nine days after the adult emerges. An entire generation can be completed within a month or less, and several can be completed during the warm part of a year. The generations overlap because females continue to oviposit for one or two months.

Haematobia

The horn fly (*H. irritans*) is one of the better-known representatives of the genus, at least in the United States. It is a cosmopolitan associate of bovines. These flies are commonly so abundant that thousands may be perched on one animal at the same time. The withers and top line, particularly of bulls, may be literally black with them. They are most severe on range animals as the adult flies live on them continuously, day and night, almost as if they were permanent parasites. This habit is the best means of recognition.

The only strong stimulus for flies to leave a host is the oviposition urge. Gravid females will fly to a dung pat immediately after it has been dropped. They swarm over the dropping and soon disappear under the sides where each fly deposits its eggs within 10 minutes. Fresh, warm, moist droppings are most desirable sites. Eggs hatch in about 20 hours at 25° C and in about 12 hours at 35° C. Humidity must be at or near saturation for incubation. A temperature of 40° C is lethal to eggs (McLintock and Depner, 1954).

Larvae live only in dung of bovines in natural conditions since only these droppings are used for oviposition sites. They feed on the fecal material near the surface. Their threshold for development is about 13° C and optimum is 32.3° C. When ready for pupation or hibernation, larvae move to the base of a dropping. They either transform at the base on the ground surface or burrow about one-half inch into the soil. Either the mature larvae or the pupal form goes into hibernation.

Adult flies rest on all parts of the animal's body and very commonly stay on parts less disturbed by tossing of the head or switching of the tail. Normally they live along the withers and about the poll; however, on cool nights they may move to cluster about the udder. For the most part they live where the air temperature is 34°–39° C. Bulls are more heavily infested than are cows or steers, and short-haired individuals are preferred to those with longer hair.

Both sexes feed exclusively on bovine blood at frequent intervals. Under field conditions each will consume over 1.5 mg of blood at a meal and will live for about three weeks. Cragg (1913) gives a good account of the structural features of the mouth parts of these flies. They resemble those of the stable fly (Fig. 55, right).

Musca

The genus *Musca* contains a number of notorious, domestic pests in the tropics, and at least one, *Musca domestica*, is cosmopolitan. By their numbers, they are annoying; by their origin and feeding, they become potential vectors of human pathogens, and by their predilection for domestic situations, some actually become vectors. The common house fly is also a vector-host for the larval stages of a spirurid worm, *Habronema*, a blood parasite of equines. The genus contains forms that feed on surface liquids including blood. Those with a penchant for blood obtain it from surface droplets that have oozed from punctures made by other hematophagous flies such as the stable fly. Some species can penetrate capillaries and cause surface hemorrhages.

Members of this genus have compact grayish bodies with the mesonotum (dorsum of thorax between the wings) longitudinally striped with black and gray lines. Wings have a conspicuous trapezoidal "cell" open only narrowly at the margin of the wing and immediately anterior to the apex of the wing. The wings are transparent and lie horizontally when the insect is perched.

The common house fly, *Musca domestica,* is the most publicized representative of the genus and has been long exploited in popular publications to illustrate all undesirable characteristics of insects. Unquestionably this fly deserves its historical reputation as a nuisance, and certainly in many parts of the world it is currently as common as ever. Its exact role in the epidemiology of human diseases may never be fully known and undoubtedly varies according to the relative incidence of the flies. Situations where enteric diseases are epidemic usually have sanitary conditions which also permit extensive development. Once the sanitation is good, incidence of both disease and flies declines. Because it is so well known, *M. domestica* will be used herein to illustrate the genus. For a more detailed account of this fly, the reader is referred to West (1951).

This house fly is a by-product of an economy and culture that motivates its transportation by energy obtained from grains. Wherever droppings from domestic horses are a familiar feature of the landscape, these flies are the familiar associates of man. One is struck with this evidence in certain rural communities of the United States where the horse is still the favored motive power for agricultural and transportation work. In such areas flies seem to be everywhere present, while in communities where tractors, trucks, and cars prevail, their distribution is spotted and the flies are no serious problem. Some have survived where the horse has gone into limbo, as flies also come from pit privies (in certain climates and soils); some come from piles of litter outside stables, barns, and chicken houses; and others arise from garbage disposal sites. Schoof *et al.* (1954) stated that "available evidence now indicates that in urban areas, household garbage forms the principal substrate . . . even in cities where horse excrement is available." Scattered garbage produces more house flies, while garbage in containers produces a greater number of blow flies. Urine-soaked mattresses have also been noted as sources of *M. domestica.* Rigid sanitation measures will decrease the incidence of this fly below the level of annoyance.

Genetical studies of this species (Milani, 1955) show a wide range of heterozygous traits. Polymorphism is commonly expressed. Even geographical populations exist, are recognizable, and may be hereditary subspecies. Milani's paper should be consulted for more information on hereditary variations within this species.

The house fly can live only in an environment which allows continuous generations. Any prolongation of conditions which arrest development will cause death of the population. In tropical climates and adjacent areas the development is continuous out of doors. In cooler climates where the soil is not frozen for any long period, outdoor development may be somewhat retarded but continuous. Adult flies tend to disappear seasonally. Wherever the ground is frozen during the winter, as it is above about 40° North, island populations survive only in places such as heated barns or buildings where warm garbage may accumulate. Any environmental factor, even a biological one, that causes compact masses of wastes to dry sufficiently will also stimulate production of these flies. Privies have been converted into significant sources of the house fly when certain chemical treatments caused the fly population to increase as much as 100-fold (Kilpatrick and Schoof, 1956 and 1959).

Since this fly produces continuous generations, limitations on its abundance are set by availability of developmental sites and suitability of the prevailing temperature. During the summer months only the site factor may impose limitations on numbers since a generation is completed in about two weeks in a favorable climate. While efforts of all sorts have been made to suppress populations of these flies, only those directed at reducing the availability of developmental sites have brought about dependable results.

Tolerance of flies toward insecticides is beyond the scope of this book, but it is of concern for reliable control, and it is constantly alluded to by the layman. The medical entomologist and medical man must be aware of this development. References to the general subject of resistance are multitudinous (Brown, 1958a), and the reader is urged to consult the extensive and current literature for details.

Eggs of *Musca domestica* have short periods of incubation, but since oviposition is continuous they are present all of the time. Gravid females crawl into cracks and interstices of the drier outer layer of wastes and oviposit clusters of 100–150 eggs on interfaces between dry and moist zones (Fay, 1939). Hatching follows deposition by 10–24 hours in summer, but incubation may be prolonged for several days for eggs in stables in winter.

The whitish maggots grow from about $\frac{3}{32}$ inch at the time of hatching to about $\frac{3}{4}$ inch in some eight days in summer or in 2–3 months under less favorable conditions. In a suitable medium, the most rapid embryonic development takes place at 34° C, however, it can continue in favorable media even at a temperature of 47° C, according to Fay. Larvae showing a high degree of tolerance toward DDT reputedly required a much longer time for development than did those of a susceptible strain (Pimentel et al., 1951). The larvae move about very little while feeding, but when ready to form puparia, they move to the drier part of the medium, which is usually near the surface.

In urban areas adult flies move according to availability of preferred resting surfaces and foods. Maier et al. (1952) noted that at night about 90 per cent of flies were perched in vegetation and about outbuildings, while diurnal perches were ground surfaces or garbage cans. Adults seeking food alight on all kinds of available sites, while those surfaces having odors of human food, feces, stale milk, and refuse are particularly attractive. Flies are most active when the temperature is high (about 30° C) and the humidity is relatively low (Dakshinamurty, 1948). When both temperature and humidity are high, their activity is reduced.

The feeding act of adult M. domestica and similar muscid flies is performed by means of a blunt, elbowed proboscis that protrudes from the venter of the head. Apically it bears two flexible lobes, the labella, on each of which are several transverse, ribbed grooves of complex structure called pseudotracheae. In reality each of the pseudotracheae is a trough that leads to a collecting canal on each lobe. The canals in turn open in the prostomial cavity, which contains several parts. In the feeding position the proboscis is straightened and the labella is expanded as a soft pad so that the openings of the pseudotracheae are in contact with the feeding surface. Saliva is extruded through the hypopharyngeal stylet to moisten the surface and to dissolve certain solids. The labella forms a covering for the area and also channels the dissolved matter of the prostomial aperture as the cibarial pump begins to function. From the prostomial opening, food flows along the labral gutter to the pharynx. Full details of the structure of the mouth parts are given by West (1951).

Materials capable of being ingested may consist of either solutions or suspensions of finely divided particles. Even large particles the size of helminth eggs may be ingested by passing directly into the prostomial opening. Prostomial teeth on the labella may be used to erode solid surfaces. The carrier fluid for suspended particles may come from the food materials, from regurgitated contents of the gut, or from saliva.

Flies may ingest food more rapidly than they digest it, so that after feeding they often perch on some nearby surface such as light cords, walls, or ceilings, and then regurgitate the contents of the gut, which form into a large droplet of liquid that is held by the cupped labella. This drop expands and contracts by alternate regurgitation and ingestion. Barber and Starnes (1949) noted that flies spend about a third of their time in this process of cycling ingested food from gut to vomit drop and back to the gut again. These droplets were visible from 15 seconds to three minutes each time. This same phenomenon has been noted for various cyclorrhaphous Diptera that do not have piercing mouth parts.

Adult house flies tend to remain in the vicinity of their larval sites, according to most observers. This resident tendency is pronounced when these sources are isolated premises, such as farm units. Hanec (1956) released some 10,000 tagged flies on a dairy farm in Canada and later recovered nearly four-fifths on the same farm. The remainder was trapped on eight farms within a radius less than two miles from the release point. Those produced at garbage dumps tend to range over the area nearby. Schoof and Siverly (1954) grant that the house fly is a wanderer and that a population may range 2–7 miles away from a larval site. Only the early records mention flights of 10 miles and more.

Oviposition of members of the genus is a more or less continuous process during the day when the weather is sufficiently warm. The preferred sites are piles of decaying plant products or feces containing plant products. When such matter has an ample moisture level and has fermented for less than five days, it is attractive to *M. domestica* (Fay, 1939). Little is known about the nature of the attractant, but moisture, temperature, and level of carbon dioxide and other volatile materials seem to exert some effect. Certainly the flies are selective, and species in the genus vary in their preferences. *M. vicina* seems to be attracted to latrines, pig pens, and piles of rotting refuse, while *M. cuthbertsoni* is attracted to cattle dung and rotting copra. The face fly (*M. autumnalis*), a rapidly spreading species in the United States, usually oviposits in cattle dung. The number of eggs placed in a pile of dung by a single fly may be in excess of 1,500 over an interval of 2–10 weeks.

At least three species (*M. vicina, sorbens,* and *autumnalis*) have the annoying habit of crawling on the skin of persons and animals. The first two species make life miserable for persons newly arrived in an infested area because these flies are very persistent in their habit of clinging to bare skin. The latter species is coming to be a domestic winter pest since the adults often hiberate in dwellings, and they become active and move to windows on warm and sunny days.

Glossina

This small genus of flies, called tsetse, when in league with a few species of mosquitoes, has contrived to make much of Africa south of the Sahara Desert an immense region of retarded cultural growth because they have provided the twin scourges of trypanosomiasis and malaria. In the past, vast areas were depopulated because of human trypanosomiasis. Even larger areas have been unable to advance toward a modern society, because nagana, an animal trypanosomiasis, prevented the use of domestic animals for the transport essential to the early development of inland trade routes. Instead, human porters provided all transport inland from the navigable rivers and coastal areas. Settlement was necessarily restricted to coastal or river sites, and urbanization was slow and poorly developed because the companion malady, malaria, sapped the vitality of the people. Development of equatorial Africa was entirely dependent on the value of exploitable raw materials and their power to entice outside capital. No integrated or stable social-economic development was possible under these unfavorable conditions.

Thanks to the untiring efforts of a few dedicated research persons and to the support given them by capital from the outside, the great mass of tropical Africa is at last approaching a period of vigorous social and economic development. While it is not the purpose of this book to treat the exploits of these great efforts, it is safe to say that no great land mass has ever before been so well prepared for cultural development by so few. To agencies in former British, Belgian, and French colonies and protectorates must go the credit for this unparalleled accomplishment.

The common name "tsetse" for flies of the genus comes from one of the African languages and carries in itself the meaning of the word fly. Buxton (1955) gives an excellent and extensive account of the morphology and bionomics of the genus.

Glossina is a genus of less than two dozen species that are so variable genetically that no suitable key exists. Species, however, do fall into three natural "groups." Group I, the *fusca* group (subgen. *Austenia*), contains the eleven large species, of which *fusca* is the one best known. Group II, the *palpalis* group (subgen. *Nemorhina*), includes five species, of which *palpalis* (and its subspecies) and *tachinoides* are the best known. Group III, the *morsitans* group (subgen. *Glossina*), includes five well-known species: *morsitans, longipalpis, pallidipes, swynnertoni,* and *austeni.* Hybrids occur between species within groups, and all degrees of sterility are known (Vanderplank, 1948).

Tsetse are robust, bristly flies ranging in color from near yellow through brown to near black. For the most part species that live in damp woods are darker and those in drier, more open situations are lighter in color. The size of these flies may vary from that of a house fly to that of a greenhead or horse fly. One characteristic feature is the proboscis that is ensheathed by the maxillary palpi; another is that the arista of the antenna has only one dorsal row of branched setae. The rigid labium with its flexible labella, while more slender, is very similar to that of *Stomoxys*.

Glossina is currently restricted to the Ethiopian region and to southern Arabia (Austen and Hegh, 1922) (fossil species have been found in central North America). The northern limit of distribution for all species is a line extending eastward from the Senegal River at about 15° North across Lake Chad to the Nile River at about 12°. The southern limit of any species is the southern boundary of coastal Angola on the west to the latitude of the mouth of the Zambezi River in Mozambique on the east. Specific distribution within this vast area is restricted to "belts" or "patches" of forest, bush, banana plantations, and even reeds. Basic sites for maintenance of the species of *Glossina* are shown in Table 10. Additional information follows for the more common species.

Glossina morsitans (Fig. 56) lives in scrub woodlands, or "miombo," which sometimes cover vast areas where the rainfall is seasonal and not abundant. Woody plants such as *Berlinia, Isoberlinia,* and *Brachystegia* characterize the flora of the typical habitat

Table 10. Distribution of Species of *Glossina*.

Area *	Species	Basic Habitat
West Africa (only)	*medicorum*	Evergreen forest; high rainfall
	caliginea	Mangrove, pandanus, and swamp forest
Central Africa (only)	*schwetzi*	Evergreen forest
	vanhoofi	Evergreen forest
	newsteadi	Evergreen forest
	severini	Evergreen forest
Central and West Africa	*haningtoni*	Evergreen forest; high rainfall
	tabaniformis	Evergreen forest; high rainfall
	longipalpis	Transition forest-savanna interface
	pallicera	Evergreen forest; high rainfall
East Africa	*longipennis*	Semidesert to thornbush savanna
	swynnertoni	Thornbush margins of transient swales subject to cracking when dry
	austeni	Dense canopy vegetation, particularly thickets
East and Central Africa	*brevipalpis*	Evergreen thickets and forest margins
	fuscipleuris	Evergreen forest
	pallidipes	Thicket-savanna (with thornbush) interface
West, Central, and East Africa	*fusca*	Primary forest and secondary forest
	nigrofusca	Evergreen forest; high rainfall
	palpalis	Linear distribution at water-side forest interface
	tachinoides	Savanna-woodland (including thicket) interface
	morsitans	*Brachystegia* woodland island over rocky slopes adjacent to *Combretum* or *Acacia* savanna

* Areas indicated are in accordance with those in use by the Brazzaville Conference in 1948.

of this fly in East Africa. Another type of woodland, locally called "mopani," in which *Copaifera* is dominant, provides suitable conditions for the fly in some areas. A miombo forest is open and has a grassy ground cover on ridges and slopes. During the dry season the trees shed their leaves and the ground is exposed to the sun. When the trees are in full leaf, the forest is shady and cool. The mopani woodland grows on clay soils above a hardpan in the valleys of large rivers. *Morsitans* is not confined to these two woodlands. In Nigeria, MacLennon and Kirkby (1958) found that this tsetse retreated into woodlands along with its chief host, the wart hog, as the temperature rose. Adult flies rest on trunks of trees within seven feet of the ground. Puparia were found in shaded, dry wallows made by wart hogs. During the season of rains, this tsetse ranged into savannas as did its hosts.

The characteristic site for *G. swynnertoni* is a dry area of hard-pan soils where thornbush, a low shrub, casts a scattered canopy shade. The grass covering the soil grows denser and taller than in the miombo woodlands. Occasional giant baobab trees are in the landscape.

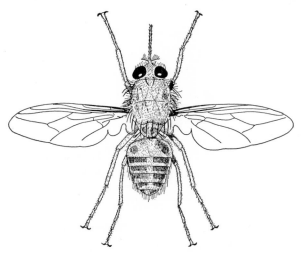

Fig. 56. *Glossina morsitans.* (After Austen, 1911.)

Glossina pallidipes is definitely restricted to thicket-savanna interfaces which are abundant in eastern and central Africa. Adults perch in margins of thickets and deposit their larvae there, but they feed in more open situations where bush pig and bushbuck range. Since the typical environment is so common, this fly often overlaps ranges of other flies.

Glossina palpalis always shows a linear distribution all over Africa along high shores of streams and lakes where upland forests abound. In West Africa it may live in small mangrove swamps near the high ground. These flies may move from any of these habitats to evergreen forests during dry seasons. Nash and Steiner (1957) noted that the form in West Africa needs good insulation from the sun provided by a high canopy, and also protection from wind offered by tangled creepers or steep banks of streams. In East Africa *palpalis* lives in dense, evergreen forests at edges of water. Shade and humidity, therefore, are regarded as the factors regulating this species more than any other.

   Glossina tachinoides is basically an inhabitant of savanna-wood-lands where it is confined to thickets near water. Specific sites tend to be linear and may be no more than a few yards wide. It survives in areas where the dry season lasts six or more months and the total annual rainfall is no more than 30 inches.

   Larvae of the tsetse live to maturity in the uterus of the parent fly (Fig. 57) before fending for themselves. Eggs hatch in the

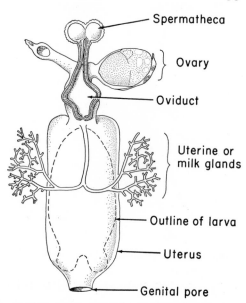

Fig. 57. Diagram of female reproductive system of *Glossina* contain-ing a mature larva. (After Buxton, 1955.)

uterus, and larvae remain there to feed and molt twice; however, only one larva occupies the uterus at a time. Presumably a larva in the first instar does not feed, but when in the second and third instars, it lives on "milk" secreted by glands in the hemocoel that empty their contents into the uterus at the head of the larva. A larva matures in nine or more days and is then deposited in a place suit-able for pupariation.

   Sites for pupariation vary somewhat according to species, as a few examples will show. Buxton (1955) noted that in most cases the sites are extremely localized and are definable but may vary according to the season. Puparia of *G. palpalis* are found under logs

or under trunks of fallen trees lying within two feet of the ground.
Elephants often create abundant sites by pushing down large
numbers of trees. Sandy or gravelly soils above a flood line are
usually chosen. Puparia are often widely scattered when the flies
are dispersed during the rainy season. Those of *G. morsitans* are
most often found under logs or in hollows of trees that are packed
with soil or debris; sometimes the dried wallows of wart hogs are
selected. Hard clay soil is unsatisfactory regardless of cover. During
seasons of excessive rainfall, larviposition may cease for a month or
so. However, much more detailed information is needed on this
aspect of bionomics.

The puparial period lasts about 20–25 days when soil temperatures are 27°–31° C, but the period may extend for at least three
times as long should the temperature drop about 10°. This stage is
sensitive to changes in soil temperature, a fact that has been important in campaigns against certain species.

Buxton (1955) has stated that adult tsetse live between 50 and
150 days according to species and season. Field observations on
G. morsitans show that adult flies may live about 70 days. High
temperatures and dry weather are inimical and, in any event, males
are less durable than females.

Tsetse are range parasites and as such seldom have specific hosts.
Certain kinds of animals are basic to their nutrition and have been
called dependable hosts, while other animals are considered as
casual hosts. Species of pigs (Suidae) supply about half the food
of *G. morsitans* and *swynnertoni* and nearly 90 per cent of the diet
of *austeni* (Weitz and Glasgow, 1956). Ruminants nourish about
two-thirds of *G. pallidipes*, and they also supply some food for the
remainder of these flies. Dung attracts flies to sites where animals
rest. Hippopotamus is the main host for *G. brevipalpis* in East
Africa. Neither *pallidipes* nor *brevipalpis* is attracted to man as is
morsitans. Man becomes a host to *Glossina* spp. when he is travel-
ing through their haunts. Large reptiles play host to *G. palpalis*, in
East Africa at least (Austen and Hegh, 1922).

Gordon *et al.* (1956) have observed the mechanics of feeding
of *Glossina* (Figs. 58 and 59). The proboscis while penetrating
shows a rapid vibratory motion coincident with alternate inversion
and eversion of the labella. Rasps and prostomial teeth on the surface of the flexible labella slash (rather than tear) the tissue above
the capillary layer. Saliva is intermittently injected from the hypo-

pharynx while a steady flow of blood races up the labral gutter from the dermal hemorrhage. When feeding stops, the hemorrhaged area may expand considerably.

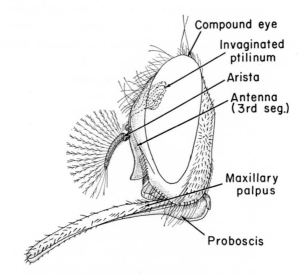

Fig. 58. Head of *Glossina*. (Modified from Jobling, 1933.)

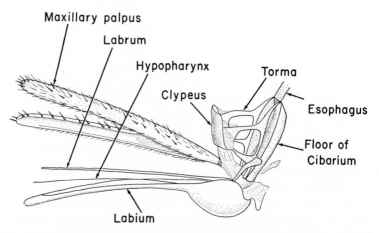

Fig. 59. Mouth parts of tsetse with proboscis exposed below trough-like maxillary palpi. (Modified from Jobling, 1933.)

CALLIPHORIDAE

This family of blow flies is one that greatly needs monographic treatment for better understanding of its limits. At present it overlaps the Larvaevoridae, on one side, and includes the genera formerly placed in Sarcophagidae, on the other (Hennig, 1952). It is not the purpose of this book, in lieu of a monograph, to attempt any proposal of arrangement; consequently placement of Hennig is followed. Genera of medical importance are placed in the sub-families Calliphorinae and Sarcophaginae of this family. Included in the former are *Chrysomyia, Callitroga, Calliphora, Lucilia, Cynomyia, Phormia* (Fig. 60), *Auchmeromyia, Cordylobia,* and *Pollenia.* The genus *Wohlfahrtia* of the latter subfamily is the only one of

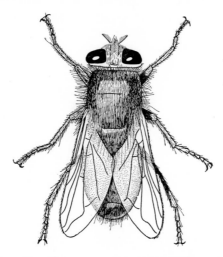

Fig. 60. *Phormia regina.* (After Hall, 1948.)

major medical significance. Larvae of these flies usually live in wounds or in carrion. A few become nuisances as adults by their presence in domestic situations.

Larvae of the genus *Wohlfahrtia* live in open wounds in humans and other mammals. Imagoes deposit active larvae either in wounds or on the skin, and they either enter the skin after it is broken (*magnifica* and *nuba*), or they may actually penetrate tender skin (*vigil* and *opaca*). The latter two species are nearctic and will attack babies sleeping out of doors and various wounded domestic animals (James, 1947). Usual areas of infestation are neck, chest, shoulders, and anus; but sometimes eyelids, cheeks, palms, and navel are sites for entry. As many as 40 larvae have been taken from a single wound. Mature larvae leave the wound to pupariate in the soil. Generations are repetitive as long as the weather is warm enough for imagoes to be active.

Callitroga (syn. *Cochliomyia*) spp. are the American screw-worm flies (Fig. 61). Two of them cause primary myiasis, while the others are secondary invaders. The best-known one is *C. hominivorax*, that ranges over southern Nearctica but with rare exceptions is capable of surviving the winter only in Florida and southern Texas. The infestation in Florida is believed to have been eradicated. In the past the pest has been transported widely over the United States in infested livestock. It is a primary parasite in wounds of all sorts of animals including humans, especially those who handle livestock. No wound in the skin, however small, is without danger of attack by

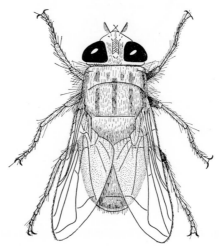

Fig. 61. Screw-worm fly, *Callitroga hominivorax*. (After Hall, 1948.)

these flies in season; even tick bites have become entry sites for larvae. Parman (1945) reported that over 90 per cent of winter infestations began in avoidable man-made wounds in livestock. When larvae are mature, they drop to the ground, burrow a few inches into the soil surface, and pupariate. Generations are continuous.

The genus *Cordylobia* contains only the one species *anthropophaga*, the tumbu fly, or verdu cayor, of tropical Africa (Blacklock and Thompson, 1923). This is a pest of both domestic mammals and man when their habitations are on ground fouled by urine and excrement. Rats are presumably the normal hosts, but dogs and man are infested as well. Eggs are deposited on fouled areas of a hut floor. Newly hatched larvae invade the skin of persons or animals while they are lying on the floor. A tumor or boil forms about each larva. About 8 or 9 days after invasion, the larva vacates the host, burrows into the dirt floor of the hut, and pupariates. Elementary hygiene will avoid infestation.

Auchmeromyia luteola, the Congo floor maggot, is a domiciliary parasite of man and hogs in domestic situations of tropical Africa (Roubaud and Holstein, 1950). Adult flies live in dense shade as inside huts, where they feed in the manner of a common house fly. Oviposition is in dust or loose sand in corners of huts, and newly hatched larvae secrete themselves in the sand or in cracks under sleeping mats. A questing larva reaches out of the soil and punctures the skin of its host while the latter is lying on the floor or a

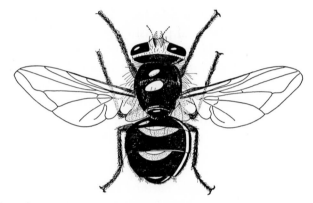

Fig. 62. *Lucilia caesar.* (After Colyer and Hammond, 1951.)

sleeping mat. After the skin is punctured, it sucks up the exuding blood. Larvae will not leave the floor, and the elevation of a sleeping mat only a few inches is sufficient to prevent any feeding on persons.

Members of the genus *Lucilia* (Fig. 62) live as larvae in decaying animal matter as a rule. However, at least two may become serious invaders of wounds in sheep and even man. *L. sericata* is cosmopolitan and lives in manure, garbage, and especially the foul sores of sheep (Cragg and Hobart, 1955). However, *Phormia regina* may be the more common maggot in wool of sheep. When larvae invade wounds they seldom penetrate beyond superficial layers. Incidentally, sterile larvae of these flies were once widely used in the treatment of deep, pus-discharging wounds on humans. For details see Brumpt (1949). Carcasses of sheep, rabbits, and other animals support vast numbers of the flies.

The genus *Pollenia* is mentioned because it is a household pest of annoying proportions during warm days in winter and in spring. *P. rudis* is known as the cluster fly. It invades houses in the fall, where it remains in walls, ceilings, and attics all winter. At intervals flies emerge to the warm interior of the houses. The fly is only an annoyance, particularly during the winter, though housekeepers often confuse this fly with *Musca domestica* and *M. autumnalis*. Larvae are parasitic in earthworms of the genus *Allolobophora* (Keilin, 1944).

OESTRIDAE

General

This family is here enlarged to include all groups, the larvae of which live as obligate, internal parasites of mammals in accordance with the grouping by Hennig (1953). The genera have been grouped into four categories which are given status of families by different observers. In the absence of an adequate monograph, and because family limits are so difficult to establish for genera of higher Diptera, all are considered as belonging to one family. Relatively little is known about the group except for a few economic forms, some of which will be discussed briefly. A summary for the family appears in Table 11.

Adults of all species have certain habits characteristic of the family. They are active about animals only during oviposition. Adults have no functional mouth or oral appendages and therefore take no nourishment. Since only larvae feed, they must store reserves necessary for pupation, flight, and development of eggs. Eggs are glued to hairs on specific parts of the host except for those rare phoretic forms whose eggs are placed on an arthropod for incubation. In general the flies are about the size of bumble bees.

Gasterophilus

Members of the genus *Gasterophilus* are called horse bots and live as larvae in the food tubes of horses and other equids. At least three species, *G. haemorrhoidalis, intestinalis,* and *nasalis,* are common in the horse, and eggs are placed so that larvae may enter the mouth of the host soon after hatching. Those of *intestinalis* are glued to hairs on the shoulders and forelegs. After embryogeny the eggs hatch at the moment they are in contact with the horse's tongue as it licks the part of the body bearing them. The warm, moist tongue provides the ultimate stimulus to hatching. Eggs may remain latent for a few months. A sponge wet with water at 40°–45° C will cause nearly all eggs to hatch when it is rubbed over an area bearing hatchable eggs (Wells and Knipling, 1938). *G. nasalis* oviposits on the intermaxillary hairs, where the eggs hatch without the licking stimulus. *G. haemorrhoidalis* oviposits on the hairs about the lips.

Table 11. Genera of the Family Oestridae.

Group	Genus	Distribution	Larval Host and Feeding Site
Gasterophilus	*Gasterophilus*	Cosmopolitan	Equidae: oral, subcutaneous, stomach, rectum
	Gyrostigma	Sumatra, Africa	Rhinoceros: gut
	Cobboldia	Asia, Africa	Elephant: gut
Cephenemyia	*Cephenemyia*	Europe, N. America	Cervidae: sinuses and throat
	Pharyngomyia	Europe	Cervidae: throat
Oestrus	*Oestrus*	Cosmopolitan	Sheep, goat, antelope: sinuses
	Pharyngobolus	Africa	Elephant: esophagus
	Neocuterebra	Africa	Elephant: sole of foot
	Kirkioestrus	Africa	Hartebeest: sinuses
	Rhinoestrus	Europe, Africa	Horse, hippopotamus, pig: sinuses
	Tracheomyia	Australia	Kangaroo
	Gedoelstia	Africa	Hartebeest
	Cephalopina	Palaearctica	Camel
Hypoderma	*Hypoderma*	Cosmopolitan	Ungulates: subcutaneous
	Oedemagena	Holarctica	Reindeer: subcutaneous
	Oestromyia	Africa, Europe	Rodent: subcutaneous
	Dermatoestrus	Africa	Antelopes: subcutaneous
	Cuterebra	Holarctica	Rodents: subcutaneous and genital region
	Alouattamyia	Neotropica	Primates: subcutaneous
	Dermatobia	Neotropica	Canines, human: subcutaneous

Little-known genera include *Bogeria, Pseudobogeria, Rogenhofera, Ruttenia, Platycobboldia,* and *Rodhainomyia.*
Arranged according to Hennig, 1953.

Larvae of these three common bots are subsurface parasites in the buccal cavity throughout the first larval instar, and later they live in the lumen of the gastrointestinal tract. Some invade tissues around the teeth where pockets of pus may form, some burrow into the tongue, and others invade the mucosa inside the lips. Older larvae live in the stomach or near the anal opening. Keilin (1944) noted that some live in the stomach in a medium deficient in oxygen, and these larvae are peculiarly modified to use oxygen swallowed by the horse. The spiracles open caudally in a cavity that can be opened or closed by the insect. When a bubble of air is in contact with the insect body, the cavity opens and oxygen enters the large tracheal trunks which lead to masses of cells containing hemoglobin. Excess oxygen is bound to the hemoglobin in the storage cells to be used as needed.

Larvae leave the anus of the host animal during warmer parts of the year to pupariate in the soil about the pasture. Some three weeks or more later, adults emerge to mate and oviposit.

Oestrus

Representatives of the genus *Oestrus* live as larvae in sinuses in the heads of sheep, goats, antelopes, and other hoofed animals. Of these *O. ovis*, a parasite of sheep, is best known. Embryos mature inside the female fly, and larvae are deposited on or near the nostrils of the hosts as the flies dart past. Larvae are in the sinuses by the time they reach the second instar, and the time they spend there varies widely according to season. Mature larvae are ejected when the sheep sneezes. Like the other bots the larvae burrow into soil to pupariate.

Hypoderma

Larvae of the genus *Hypoderma* are called cattle grubs or ox warbles, and the adults are known as heel flies or bomb flies. As an economic group they attack cattle, and as a medical problem they sometimes invade persons who tend cattle. Larvae live a peripatetic early life in connective tissues of cattle and a sedentary later life in subcutaneous boils on the back. The genus is cosmopolitan, but it is erratically distributed over its range. Bruce (1938) has shown that species in the United States may be entirely absent from areas where soil moisture is high either because of inadequate drainage or texture. One such area is in the valley of the Red River between Minnesota and North Dakota, through the extinct glacial Lake Agassiz between the first and inner banks. This soil is Fargo clay, a greasy gumbo impervious to water.

Eggs are deposited low on the body, either on the legs of standing animals or on the underside of a cow while it is lying down. Larvae invade the skin near the site of the egg attachment and burrow through the skin to the subcutaneous connective tissue.

They move along the tissues to the belly line, thence forward to the neck region. Those of *H. lineatum* congregate in the submucosa of the esophagus. After a time the larvae move backward in the esophageal tissue to the diaphragm; then they spread outward along the diaphragm to the pleural connective tissue. Finally they lodge in the tissue just under the skin along the loin region of the back. In its wanderings, a larva of *H. bovis* tends to enter the neural canal before it lodges in the back. The last larval instar cuts a hole in the skin of its host and finally completes its growth in a pocket beneath the skin. The larva spends some 8 or 9 months in this extensive moving through the bovine body.

Cuterebra

Little is known about warbles of the genus *Cuterebra*, or rodent grubs. Larvae of the genus usually live subcutaneously in rodents, lagomorphs, and some small domestic animals in the Western Hemisphere. Domestic cats may harbor larvae of a species (*C. horripilum*) that normally infests cottontail rabbits. Field mice (*Peromyscus* spp.) are very commonly affected by *C. peromysci* (Dalmat, 1943) in the fall of the year. Bennett (1955) has reported on *C. emasculator* in chipmunk (*Tamias*) in Canada where about half of the collection was infested. Apparently this species is host-specific since larvae live in the groin region of male chipmunks and on the belly line of females. Sometimes several large larvae are to be found in one animal; Ryckman (1953) took four of *C. latifrons* from a *neotoma* rat in California. Penner and Pocius (1956), while working with one species that infests rats, found that those larvae entered through the nostrils and finally lodged in the groin.

Haas and Dicke (1958) reported in a bionomic study of *C. horripilum*, a parasite of cottontail rabbits in Wisconsin. The incidence of infestation near Madison was about 20 per cent, based on capture of wild rabbits. Adults oviposit on objects away from potential hosts, and larvae must board a host. Newly hatched larvae anchor themselves by a caudal attachment organ and sway back and forth when questing. They cling to hairs of a passing host, burrow into the skin, and develop as do other subcutaneous species. This species has been reported from a kitten.

Beachley and Bishopp (1942) reported that a case of nasal myiasis had been caused in humans by a larva of *Cuterebra* sp.

Dermatobia

The genus *Dermatobia* is the best known of the Cuterebra group. Larvae often attack man in sylvatic situations in Neotropica. Its wild hosts are canines and doubtless other mammals, while domestic hosts include horse, cow, and donkey. Members of this genus ovi-

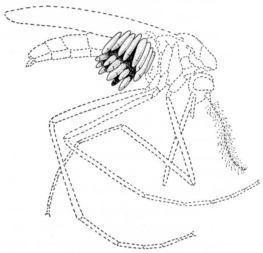

Fig. 63. Cluster of eggs of *Dermatobia* sp. on abdomen of a mosquito. (After Séguy, 1950.)

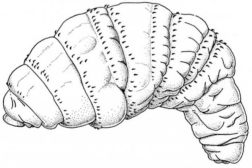

Fig. 64. A larva of *Dermatobia* sp. (side view). (After Pierce, 1921.)

posit on some hematophagous arthropod or even a house fly if in the vicinity of a potential mammalian host (Fig. 63). A dozen or more eggs may be placed on a fly, mosquito, or tick, and this phoretic host carries the eggs about for several days while they incubate. Larvae (Fig. 64) escape from the eggs when the phoretic host alights on the skin of a mammal and soon afterward they burrow through the intact skin. After a period of wandering, they form a pocket beneath the skin (Floch and Fauran, 1954).

PUPIPARA

Calyptrate Diptera are represented by three families of vertebrate parasites, Hippoboscidae, Nycteribiidae, and Streblidae, that are often grouped together as Pupipara. Adults of all live as ectoparasites, while larvae live as endoparasites in the female that produces them. For the most part the adults are flightless, permanent, personal parasites as are lice. Some species are able to fly from host to host, but they seldom spend a long period away from the host.

Contrary to the usual condition among higher Diptera, limits of the family Hippoboscidae, or louse flies, are sharply defined. Representatives are characterized as follows: The body of the adult is dorsoventrally flattened to give the family the common name of flat flies. The head is said to be directed forward so that the mouth parts are anterior instead of ventral. Antennae usually arise in pits and are very short and flattened. Characteristically, the first segment of the antenna is often fused with the head while the second segment is large and bears the third segment embedded in an apical cavity. The eyes are large and compound. Wings may be functional or variously atrophied. The abdomen is leathery and without visible external segmentation; however, it expands on engorgement in the manner of a tick.

Louse flies are essentially tropical parasites of birds, but a few species attack mammals (Table 12). Characteristically they live on or very near the host and leave it only to deposit larvae. With very few exceptions (*Melophagus*) larvae pupariate away from the host. Some species, especially those lacking functional wings, larviposit in the nests or about rookeries or even in the vesture of the host. Fully winged species may larviposit without regard to hosts; then later the adults must fly in their search for a host.

Larvae of these flies live parasitically on products elaborated by the female and possibly on seminal secretions of the male in much the same manner as species of *Glossina*. Only one larva develops in the uterus at a time. When a larva is mature, it is expelled and then replaced by a new egg that comes into the uterus. A male copulates with the female almost as soon as a larva is extruded.

Table 12. Genera of Hippoboscidae.

Genus	Distribution	Host Range
Ornithoica	Tropicopolitan	Birds; not specific
Ornithomyia	Cosmopolitan	Birds; rarely specific
Crataerina	Tropical and Old World	Swallows, swifts
Myiophthiria	Circumpacific	Swallows, swifts
Stenepteryx	Orient	Swallows, swifts
Ornithoctona	Tropicopolitan	Birds; not specific
Ornitheza	Orient	Owl
Stilbometopa	Neotropical	Quail, pigeons
Lynchia	Cosmopolitan	Birds; not specific usually
Microlynchia	New World	Birds; wide range
Pseudolynchia	Tropicopolitan	Pigeons, predators
Olfersia	Tropicopolitan	Birds; by taxonomic or ecologic groups
Ortholfersia	Australia	Marsupials
Neolipoptena	Western N. America	Mountain deer
Lipoptena	Cosmopolitan except Australia	Cervidae, and stray onto birds
Echestypus	Cosmopolitan	Cervidae
Melophagus	Cosmopolitan	Domestic sheep, and stray to deer, etc.
Hippobosca	Palaearctica	Ungulates, carnivores, ostrich (1 sp.)
Allobosca	Madagascar	Lemur

From Bequaert, 1954 and 1957.

Incidence of parasitism by these flies varies widely. Species that are bound to nesting sites and rookeries may be very numerous, while those that fly with their hosts are seldom numerous. *Lipoptena* sometimes number thousands on one deer. One reason the parasites are so numerous is that larvae drop from the hair in the haunts where the deer congregate, and later vast numbers of adult flies emerge in a site most favorable for their attachment. In the case of *Hippobosca equina*, a parasite of equines, incidence is highest in England, where bracken is abundant in horse pasturage.

Melophagus ovinus, the ked of sheep (Fig. 65), is probably the best known economic representative of the family. It has only the most rudimentary wings and spends its entire life span in the wool of its host. The larvae are coated with a liquid cement and are then deposited on the wool, where they adhere. Details of this species are well outlined in Bequaert (1942).

This parasite is adapted to life on sheep where flocks are maintained all year. Since the sheep are sheared after lambing, the young lambs become infested, and they carry the keds through the summer. By September the wool has grown long on the sheep, and reinfestation is established from lambs.

A peculiar phoretic relation exists between some species of hippoboscids and the lice of birds. Sometimes bird lice cling to the louse flies and may be transported from host to host.

Nycteribiidae and Streblidae, which are parasites on bats only, live in the manner of the hippoboscid flies. Their lack of medical import causes them to be omitted from this account. Kessell (1925) gives a synopsis of the Streblidae, and bionomics of the family is contained in Jobling (1949). Hase (1930) contains a summary of the literature of Nycteribiidae.

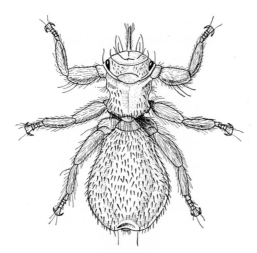

Fig. 65. Sheep ked, *Melophagus ovinus*. (After Edwards *et al.*, 1939.)

ADDITIONAL READINGS

General

Hennig's series of books (1948, 1950, 1953) provides a taxonomic background for this order. Also, consult Imms (1957) and Borror and Delong (1954) mentioned at the end of the preceding chapter.

Smart (1956) has given an account of the classification of insects of medical importance. Diptera are very well treated.

Psychodidae

Hertig (1942) is a series of papers on biting flies of the genus *Phlebotomus* and their relation to disease in the Western Hemisphere.

Lewis and Kirk (1954) discuss the bionomics of an array of species found in arid lands. Where and how these flies live is covered well.

Culicidae

Horsfall (1955) is a compendium on the bionomics of the species of the world. Arrangement is alphabetical by genera and by species within genera. An extensive bibliography to the literature is given.

For taxonomic treatises consult the Appendix to the present volume.

MEDICAL ENTOMOLOGY

Ceratopogonidae

See references cited in the text. No extensive treatment of the family as a whole exists.

Simuliidae

SMART (1945) is a classification and discussion of these midges. This, together with references cited in the text for species in different areas, should be consulted for details.

Tabanidae

No monographic treatment of the family has been made. Consult general references and taxonomic ones listed in the Appendix.

Rhagionidae, Chloropidae

See references under General, above.

Muscidae

WEST (1951) is a book about house flies as problem insects. Most bionomic details are covered.

BROWN (1958a) should be consulted for information about the whole problem of resistance to toxicants, a subject of great interest to the layman.

BUXTON (1955) is an excellent summary of all aspects of knowledge of tsetse. The current interest in Africa makes this book essential reading.

Calliphoridae

JAMES (1947) is a readable treatise on this group of flies. It gives names and effect of the flies.

Oestridae

The literature is mostly scattered. Reference to citations in the text must be made.

Pupipara

BEQUAERT (1942, 1954, 1957) has written in detail about the Hippoboscidae, and his papers should be consulted for taxonomy and bionomics of the group.

CHAPTER 6

Diseases Caused by Arthropods

GENERAL

Arthropodiasis is a generic term used in describing the direct effects of arthropods on vertebrates. It includes (1) both local and systemic reactions to bites and stings; (2) allergenic, constitutional effects resulting from vertebrate contact with a part or parts of the bodies of arthropods, as scales, hairs, exuviae, and fragments; (3) psychological reactions, as discomfort or fear with induced avoidance; (4) measurable constitutional effects such as loss of body weight; and (5) the factor of "absenteeism." Arthropodiasis is so commonly experienced today that it may be considered an occupational hazard of major proportion in numerous activities, just as it has always been a cause of concern for the farmer, gardener, camper, and traveler. Even now in some parts of the world, stings and bites from arthropods cause more deaths than the total of deaths resulting from all other venomous animals in the areas (Stahnke, 1953).

One may mistakenly believe that our highly organized and well-ordered way of life has taken us away from insects. Let us examine this concept in light of fact. More than half of the peoples of the world still live intimately with insects and have never accepted the fact that noxious forms are not necessary burdens. Enlightened people contend with far more discomfort from arthropods than they realize. Each of us can remember being stung or bitten and many may recall severe reactions to bites or stings. We read every year about persons being stung by a bee or wasp and suffering violent reactions or even dying as a result. Even more insidious are the many constitutional allergies from protein sensitivity which are caused by arthropods, but the association is often unrecognized. When we include the widespread and directly harmful effects of arthropods on livestock, pets, and wild life with those on man we have added cause to seek more information about arthropodiasis.

The medical and veterinary practitioner has more and more need for specific knowledge about arthropods as etiological agents because the human tolerance-level is decreasing. At the same time there is a growing passion for outdoor activities in the summer which takes hordes of people into the haunts of biting and stinging pests. Even when we spend an evening on a porch or on a patio, some flying and crawling creatures are after us. At times our well-lighted urban areas beckon insects from remote areas and thereby encourage concentration of some forms. This tendency presently looms so large in the case of certain mosquitoes that specialized abatement operations are maintained to reduce the menace. Some businesses have come to recognize arthropods as occupational hazards, and certainly arthropod-human problems have extended the legal field. All of these examples require specific knowledge about the pests concerned if we are to protect and treat the human population.

Entomological knowledge is necessary for the proper medical appraisal of the causative arthropod in cases of arthropodiasis. A physician who is to assign a cause must first know enough about these animals to suspect them. Secondly, he must have a familiarity with the bionomics of the local fauna of likely medical importance.

Clinical histories show that arthropods representing all classes and orders are actual or potential agents for the cause of human diseases and distress. Most species cause disturbance because they either puncture the skin or release toxins on the skin or in tissues. The results of human contact with arthropods may cause reactions such as wheals, blisters, rhinitis, and asthma that may be difficult to identify without a known specific cause (Table 13). Only the alert diagnostician will suspect insects in a case of generalized allergy unless an insect outbreak in the immediate geographic area is common knowledge. Actually wind-blown fragments of insect bodies may become a major cause of respiratory allergy (Feinberg et al., 1956). Proving that insects are the causative agents of such allergies is unfortunately more difficult than proving that pollens are involved since insect allergens may be no more than amorphous dust. Table 13 gives some idea of the range of such allergens.

Arthropodiases may be caused by insects in any of the following ways. The mere presence of an insect may cause any of the fear reactions. Toxicants may be given off from the bodies of insects in contact with the human skin, and these are designated *contact toxins*. Allergens, called *inhalant allergens*, are tiny fragments of the

Table 13. Arthropods Known to Cause Local and Generalized Allergic Reactions of Humans.

Name	Order	Allergenic Part	Allergic Reaction
Waterflea	Crustacea	Dried bodies	Bronchial asthma
Booklouse	Psocoptera	Crushed bodies	Dermatosis
Cockroach	Cursoria	Secretions	Linear dermatoses and edema of eyelids
Bed bug	Hemiptera	Fragments	Asthma
Mayfly	Ephemeroptera	Fragments	Asthma
Aphid	Hemiptera	Fragments	Asthma
House fly	Diptera	Fragments	Sneezing and asthma
Mushroom fly	Diptera	Fragments	Asthma
Honey bee	Hymenoptera	Hairs	Bronchial asthma
Mexican bean weevil	Coleoptera	Scales	Rhinitis and asthma
Dermestid	Coleoptera	Larval hairs	Asthma
Webbing clothes moth	Lepidoptera	Fragments	Asthma and rhinitis
Ochrogaster	Lepidoptera	Larval hairs	Urticarial erythema
Range moth	Lepidoptera	Larval hairs	Asthma
Euproctis	Lepidoptera	Adult hairs	Urticarial erythema
Flannel moth	Lepidoptera	Larval hairs	Urticarial erythema
Tussock moth	Lepidoptera	Larval hairs	Urticarial erythema
"Slug"	Lepidoptera	Larval hairs	Urticarial erythema
Cnethocampa	Lepidoptera	Larval hairs	Contact toxic dermatitis
Yellow-tail moth	Lepidoptera	Adult hairs	"Caripito itch"
Processionary caterpillar	Lepidoptera	Larval hairs	Contact dermatitis
Caddisfly	Trichoptera	Adult setae	Asthma and rhinitis

bodies of either live or dead insects that may enter the respiratory organs. Venoms are injected into a body through bites or stings and are known as *injected allergens*. Sometimes the insect actually invades the body of a host and remains there as a parasite, and this phenomenon is herein called *invasion*.

PSYCHOLOGICAL REACTIONS

The most common, generalized human reaction to insects is possibly an individual's emotional responses. It is certainly the reaction that entomologists hear the most about. The buzzing of mosquitoes keeps some persons awake even though these people may sleep well only a few feet distant from a noise level of many decibels. Various gnats and small beetles cause annoyance or even extreme distress as they fly about the face or crawl over exposed parts of the body. The presence of larger flies and beetles as well as ants may completely spoil picnics and other outdoor activities. Certain flies and cockroaches are so repulsive as to produce nausea to sensitive individuals. The odors of many insects or their products are offensive; for example, the volatile, oily liquid secreted from "stink" glands on the thorax of bed bugs offends some persons. Secretions from cockroaches cause a disagreeable residual odor in kitchens and basements that are overrun by them. Stink bugs leave a pungent, distasteful liquid on fruits and berries which may persist even after the fruits have been washed.

Domestic animals likewise may be annoyed by the mere presence of flies and gnats as well as other insects. When an infestation is mild, the animals react by repeatedly tossing their heads, switching their tails, or twitching the skin. More numerous pests will cause animals to move either indoors, into water, into shade, or to another pasturage. A few heel flies will cause nervousness among placid cows, while the more excitable animals on the range will actually stampede.

INHALANT ALLERGENS

Inhalant allergens may come from any kind of arthropod at any time, and they may be suspected when isolated or atypical cases of allergy occur (Pruzansky *et al.*, 1959). Unfortunately proof of such allergens is sometimes difficult to obtain since the evidence is either amorphous or so minute as to be unrecognizable. Any part of these animals may be allergenic for sensitized persons. Air-borne fragments of insect bodies may be encountered in the attics and basements of any house, hence the household could actually harbor the cause of some asthmatic conditions. Body fragments such as hairs and scales may be dislodged from beetles, caterpillars, moths, or flies, and be blown about. Sensitized laboratory workers sometimes show asthmatic symptoms after contact with dried feces of grasshoppers and cockroaches. Wind-blown body fragments certainly may be a possible cause of hay fever during times of grasshopper outbreaks. Massive populations of mayflies, caddisflies, mushroom flies, sewage gnats, and other insects may produce enormous quantities of friable exuviae that finally dry, break up, and become wind-blown. We must be aware that even though the large populations of arthropods about us are not always recognized, hundreds of pounds of these animals are produced annually on every acre of field and forest. When they die, their bodies become fragmented and often become wind-blown. Figley (1940) noted that over 7 per cent of his allergy patients in an area near Lake Erie were sensitive to exuviae of mayflies. Tons of these insects disperse inland from this lake alone. Lewis (1956) reported that midges (Tendipedidae) are generally believed to be responsible for much asthma and other allergic conditions in Khartoum and vicinity since the establishment of a large lake nearby. Elsewhere in Sudan and Egypt the impounding of lakes has been followed by a rise in respiratory ailments. In some years cast skins from large outbreaks of aphids are cause of common allergens. Hairs from larvae of the carpet beetle can be a domestic as well as an occupational hazard. The older a house becomes, the more likely it is to harbor these beetles (Wiseman et al., 1959). One museum worker had a severe asthma caused by these beetles. Dock workmen on one occasion were reported suffering from "severe, pruritic, erythematous and vesiculating eruption" on the skin, accompanied by a dry, hacking cough which had been caused by carpet beetle hairs encountered while the men were unloading a heavily infested cargo of bones. Scales from the adult Mexican bean weevil have caused general asthma among many handlers of beans. Asthma has been caused also by an allergen left by bees in a car robe after its use as a wrapping for a hive of bees. A housewife in Alberta, Canada, was said to be sensitive to an allergen left by buzzing flies in the house. These widely varying sources of allergens make insects suspect when (1) isolated, unseasonal cases occur and (2) outbreaks of insects are known to be in a specific area.

CONTACT TOXINS

A bullous dermatitis commonly follows contact with certain beetles. Blister beetles (Meloidae) contain cantharidin, a lactone of cantharidic acid. When a beetle is relieved of this toxin either by secretion or by being accidentally crushed on the skin, the cantharidin first causes a tingling sensation at the site of contact. Shortly afterward a mild local erythema develops, and a vesicle or bulla appears within 2 or 3 hours and then continues to enlarge for several hours. The blister is slightly flaccid and elongated, and lacks inflammation at the base. The symptoms usually are definite and present no difficulty in diagnosis.

In many tropical countries beetles of the genus *Paederus* (Staphylinidae) cause a bullous reaction. Persons affected are usually ranging outside inhabited areas; for example, well-drillers in the hinterland of Ecuador have been seriously afflicted. The toxicant is a body fluid as found in blister beetles, but possibly it is other than cantharidin. The fluid is usually released when a beetle is crushed on the skin, and if this is done by a brushing motion, the toxin is streaked across the skin, producing a bullous area some 2 to 3 inches long and ½ inch wide. At first the site is purplish-red; then it becomes covered with tiny blisters surrounded by an area of hyperemia. The blisters are purulent and very painful by the second day. Conjunctivitis will result should the toxin enter an eye, as may easily happen to a child.

The glandular secretions of some arthropods create medical problems. Injuries from this source are far less frequent than those from inhalant allergens; however, the consequences may be severe. Millipedes (Diplopoda) of the subclass Chilognatha have glands in each trunk section which open by means of one pore on each side of the section. While most species of this group secrete toxic fluids, those presently known to have medical significance belong to the order Juliformia. These animals curl up tightly to resemble a watch spring. Their lateral pores exude a fluid that is irritating to the skin on contact. When the body is curled and shortened, pressure is applied on the glands and the irritant either oozes or is jetted out of the pores. Some species may discharge irritants so forcefully that droplets are dispersed over ranges up to three feet. The secretion is a volatile oil that is slightly soluble in water, is more soluble in alcohol, and may withstand distillation. The color may vary from colorless, through yellow, to brown and red. Burtt (1947) has stated that effects on the skin vary as follows: (1) a tingling sensation throughout an extremity resulted when a mild secretion was rubbed into a scratch; (2) the skin is stained yellow, brown, or black over an area of three or more square inches; (3) semilunar vesicular areas bordered by diffused erythema may appear; (4) the surface of the skin may harden and become scaly; (5) the skin may even slough away leaving a large raw patch that sometimes heals by scarring; (6) severe conjunctivitis occurs when the irritant from *Rhinocrichus* sp., for example, has been squirted onto the face, or into the eyes.

Blinding of chickens has been caused when millipedes jetted poisons into their eyes.

Centipedes, at least those of the order Geophilomorpha, may likewise cause a dermatosis by secretions from their glands. *Otostigmus* extrudes a luminous irritant from unicellular ventral glands through pore canals. Records from Indochina show that these animals sometimes crawl over sleeping persons, and if the venter slides over the skin, painful blisters will result.

Insects may eject irritating secretions from glands that open on various parts of the body. Roth and Willis (1957) quote observations of others to the effect that cockroaches have glands that produce allergenic secretions. When these substances come in contact with sensitized skin, a linear dermatosis or generalized hives results. If fluids from crushed roaches are rubbed on eyelids, edema of the lids will often result. Laboratory workers who clean cockroach cages have experienced vertigo, watering of the eyes, and nausea from contact with excreta and fragments of the roaches. One species, *Eurycotis floridana*, ejects a liquid that is a dermal irritant when in contact with skin or eyes. Some beetles have tarsal, cuticular, rectal, or genital glands that yield mildly toxic substances. A very different insect, the bombardier beetle, ejects an acrid liquid as fine droplets from its rectal glands, and when this material gets into an eye, there is immediate and sharp pain. Hemiptera, too, produce oily, pungent liquids that may cause mild skin reactions. Certain mantids discharge colored, fetid fluids from the anterior dorsum of the prothorax, and some of these insects are said to be able to spray the secretions for distances up to several feet. These fluids cause intense burning when they come in contact with the eye; the cornea becomes scarlet, and vision may actually be temporarily impaired (Stewart, 1937).

Human reactions to contact with Lepidoptera are similar to those caused by other arthropods. Early and delayed reactions are produced by contact with fragments of all stages, but reactions to caterpillars are best known (Goldman *et al.*, 1960). Kemper (1958) stated that when hairs from a wide variety of caterpillars were rubbed into skin, symptoms were as follows: erythema, papules, urticaria, pigmentation, and desquamation. Intensity and duration of responses varied with the persons affected. Skin on different parts of the body showed varying degrees of sensitivity. There are differences in reaction according to the form, coarseness, and dryness of the hairs applied to the skin. Some hairs had effects very like those of stings; others caused reactions similar to those from sterile glasswool fibers.

INJECTED ALLERGENS: BITES

The arthropodan act of biting is one of puncturing the skin incident to feeding and results in characteristic lesions. Insects and arachnids most often involved are ticks, mites, spiders, fleas, gnats, lice, flies, mosquitoes, and bugs. However, insects of other groups may bite man occasionally. Normal reactions to bites are localized and involve only tissues at the sites of puncture. Itching is a common reaction, and secondary effects from scratching may be serious. In some instances local cutaneous reactions persist for weeks and even years. Sometimes there are constitutional symptoms characterized by fever, malaise and even shock. Table 14 compares reactions to arthropodan bites.

Table 14. Usual Cutaneous Responses of Sensitized Humans to Salivary Injections of Arthropods.

Arthropod	Cutaneous Histopathology							Symptomatology							
	Hemorrhage	Edema	Vasodilation	Polymorphonuclear Infiltration	Lymphocytic Infiltration	Histiocytic Infiltration	Necrosis	Wheal	Papule	Erythema	Bulla	Lymphadenitis	Local Fever	General Fever	Anaphylaxis
Aedes aegypti		+	+	+				+	+	+			+	±	±
Aedes vexans	±	+	+					+	+	+	±				
Aedes sticticus	±	+	+					+	+	+	±		±		
Anopheles maculipennis	±	+						+	+	+	?				
Culiseta incidens	±	+	+					+	+	+	±		±		
Culicoides sp.	+	+	+	+	+	+		+	+	+					
Phlebotomus sp.	+	+	+		+?			+	+	+	±	+	±		
Simuliid fly	+	+	+	+	+			+	+	+					
Tabanid fly	+	?	?					?	+	+	±				
Melophagus sp.	+	?	?					+	+						
Glossina spp.	±°	+	+			+		+	?	±					
Pulex irritans		+	+	+				+	+	+	±		+	±	±
Cimex lectularius	+	+	?					+	+	+	±		+	±	±
Pediculus humanus		+	+	±	+			+	+	+	+			±	±
Trombiculid mite	0	+	+				+	+	+	+	±	+	+	±	
Dermanyssid mite	+	+						+	+	+	±				
Ornithodoros moubata	+	0				+	0	+	+	+	±				
Ornithodoros erraticus	+	+				+	+								
Ixodid tick	+	+	+	+	+	+	±								

+ Present.
± Variably present.
0 Absent.
? Uncertain.
Blank Presumably absent.
° Also intramuscular.

Medical literature contains a great many clinical reports of reactions of humans and other animals to bites by arthropods, but there is a dearth of information on the histopathology of such lesions. Vitzthum (1929) has depicted that for chiggers. Gordon and Crewe (1948) observed biopsies of bites of mosquitoes, bed bugs, and biting flies. Both clinical and histological symptoms of a few are detailed herein as an aid to the diagnostician.

Goldman (1952) stated that, as a rule, most clinical reactions to arthropodan bites are characterized by an immediate wheal followed by a papular or tuberculin-type inflammatory response. Specifically, there is (1) a puncture canal in the epidermis and (2) a local edema of the superficial dermis. Edema may or may not extend into the epidermis. There is a marked vasodilation and perivascular infiltration of leucocytes, especially near the puncture canal. Areán and Fox (1955) noted that local sensitivity reactions may be severe and accompanied by intense itching. Sometimes the sites are maculopapules; at times they are bullous lesions with diffusing edema and regional lymphadenopathy. The extent and intensity of a reaction seems directly dependent on the degree of sensitivity of the individual.

Allington and Allington (1954) reported that (1) the location of a bite and (2) the age of the person bitten may influence the degree and character of an eruption. Bites on the ankle or leg are often more severe than those elsewhere because of the relative circulatory stasis in the legs. In these areas the tendency is toward greater vesiculation, hemorrhage, infiltration, ulceration, and eczematization. The association of bites with the clinical manifestation of papular urticaria or lichen urticatus is much more common among children than it is among adults. These lesions tend to heal slowly, and some develop a pigment that persists for weeks or months. Comparative histopathologies and symptomatologies of bites from representative arthropods are shown in Table 14. Edema and vasodilation are the common reactions in the tissue. External evidence is a wheal, a papule, and erythema. From this table it is apparent that classification of bites is possible when details are known.

The degree of response to arthropodan bites is proportional to the distribution and amount of antibodies in the host. If antibodies are absent, reactions may be extensive. Delayed papular symptoms result from the effect of residual antigen and newly formed antibody. A wheal is formed immediately after a bite when cells in the vicinity have sufficient antibody to react with the antigen, however, blood serum is lacking antibody. When antibody is present in both cells and blood serum, an immediate wheal is formed, only to disappear very soon. The person having abundant and free antibodies experiences no disturbing response to bites.

Perhaps mosquitoes are the insects most universally encountered by persons who later seek medical help. They tend to bite exposed parts of the body near the ground; otherwise they bite at random through the clothing in close contact with the body as on arms, shoulders, and buttocks. In the United States those who work or play out of doors are most often bitten. Domestic animals are usually attacked on parts of the body nearest the ground as legs, udders, flanks, and dewlap.

Clinical reactions of sensitized persons are as follows. A localized erythematous region about a puncture wound is accompanied by heat, pruritus, and possibly some degree of pain. The primary wheal appears within a few minutes and usually disappears in about two hours; however, a delayed reaction occurs within a few hours to a day. This may be accompanied by pruritus and stinging, especially on application of pressure. A dermal hemorrhage accompanies the wound of pool-feeding species, and the pain accompanying the delayed reaction is related to the degree of hemorrhaging. These responses are proportional to the number of pool feeders puncturing the same general area. Constitutional symptoms of hay fever, asthma, and more violent anaphylaxis have been reported (Hecht, 1930).

Saliva of mosquitoes contains at least four active fractions about which very little is known. Most of the antigenic components are in secretions from the lateral acini of the salivary glands (Buck, 1937). Agglutinins and anticoagulants are produced by some species (Anopheles maculipennis) while others (Culex pipiens, Culiseta annulata, and Aedes aegypti) produce neither. Chromatographic fractionation of whole extracts has revealed that the antigenic principle contains at least four components, and eluates of each have caused positive reactions in sensitized persons (Hudson et al., 1958). McKiel and Clunie (1960) recalled that the immediate reactions by persons are the result of previously acquired sensitivity to the toxin and are not caused by histamine in the injection. The amount of active material necessary to produce manifestations similar to those resulting from a mosquito bite in a sensitive person was estimated to be of the order of 10^{-3} μg. The saliva will inhibit growth of chick embryos and may cause the death of guinea pigs if large doses are injected intraperitoneally. (Allington and Allington, 1954). Extracts of dried salivary glands are said to retain the active principle (Manalang, 1931).

Tissue reaction to the mechanical aspects of the penetration of the fascicle of a mosquito will vary. Actual insertion of the fascicle causes no sensation. The puncture may penetrate several capillaries, and slow or retard the flow of blood because of blockage as the tip of the fascicle passes through. A mosquito may repeatedly puncture the same capillaries while probing for a single meal. Blood oozes from the capillaries, and thus tiny hemorrhages form in surrounding tissue. Feeding of several hundred mosquitoes over an area of a few square inches will cause an extensive hemorrhage as the tiny ones coalesce. This gives a slightly bruised appearance to the damaged area.

A number of higher Diptera such as the tsetse, stable fly, horn fly and sheep ked have similar mouth parts, and all inflict wounds that are very much alike in the superficial appearance of the punctures. Each is made by cutting both the epidermis and the dermis with the mass of stout teeth on the flexible labella of the proboscis. Capillaries are slashed apart as the tip of the proboscis penetrates the capillary layer. Specific details of penetration are known for tsetse (Gordon and Crewe, 1948, and Fairbairn and Williamson, 1956).

Clinical reactions to bites of tsetse vary in degree according to sensitivity of individuals, but regardless of sensitivity the histological effects are similar. The proboscis penetrates to the subcutaneous muscular layer, and in this process the probed capillaries are mutilated and a local hemorrhage results. Some of the uncoagulated blood may seep between muscle fibers below, and within 24 hours the hemorrhage may be extensive. No degenerative changes take place until absorption of the hemorrhage begins after some 48 hours; then histiocytes may invade cells. Inflammation is not apparent in non-sensitized persons, while those sensitized show some dilation of the blood vessels and extensive separation of the collagen fibers. A wheal as much as 3 cm across is formed presumably as a result of leakage from mutilated capillaries; the adjacent area may swell and remain painful for several days. The delayed manifestation is far more severe than the actual damage caused by a mosquito bite. The intensity of the reaction of sensitized persons increases with the length of time a fly is allowed to feed.

Saliva of the tsetse contains the substance responsible for sensitivity reactions. This was demonstrated by the surgical removal of the salivary glands of the flies and the subsequent negative responses to their feeding. The saliva contains a powerful anticoagulant which has properties of an enzyme. It is not dialyzable, and is soluble in both water and dilute ethanol with no loss in potency. The saliva is insoluble in ether, absolute ethanol, and solutions of ammonium sulfate. Unlike enzymes, the anticoagulant is little affected by heat below 90° C.

Some flies, like the sheep ked and the stable fly, inflict puncture wounds in much the same manner as the tsetse. Shepherds, wool shearers, and handlers have all reported painful swellings caused by bites of the ked. A reddish wheal with a serum exudate from the puncture, accompanied by pain and swelling in the region surrounding the wheal, is characteristic of the effect on a sensitized person. The wound heals slowly. Infested sheep bite and scratch themselves at the site of a puncture until the wool becomes taggy. Stable flies usually bite persons around the ankles, and this biting causes a sharp stinging sensation. Massive attacks on cattle will cause loss of weight (Cutkomp and Harvey, 1958) and losses in milk production (Bruce and Decker, 1958). Herds of cattle plagued by the flies have been known to crowd together in darkened barns so tightly that injury and death resulted for some.

Tabanid flies, commonly known as horse flies and deer flies, when biting make a thin incision with the narrow blade-like mandibles. The cut may extend through the capillary layer even to the subcutaneous muscles. The hemorrhage at the incision site may extend into the muscular layer as well as outward through the puncture canal to the surface. A large population of horse flies has a pronounced effect on the behavior of unprotected animals. Game animals in Africa and others on open ranges will migrate long distances in response to attack (Lewis, 1953). Caribou in Canada move to summer grazing areas relatively free of tabanids. It is thought that the bison of central United States once traveled east and south out of the prairies to escape biting flies. Red deer in Scotland move to higher altitudes at times of abundance of flies in the lowlands. Dairies in the Pacific Northwest have reported declines in milk production of as much as 50 per cent during a season of maximum activity of *Chrysops discalis* (Roth and Lindquist, 1948). Losses of 300 ml of blood per animal per day have been reported in northern United States during periods of tabanid abundance (Philip, 1931).

The bites of sand flies (*Phlebotomus* spp.) cause reactions in humans similar to those of *Anopheles* mosquitoes. The actual wound is similar to those made by tabanids and is a tiny, painless, knife-like incision through which capillaries are cut rather than punctured. A dermal hemorrhage results from the injured capillaries and excess blood may exude from the wound. Sensitized persons often produce a wheal up to about 7 mm in diameter within a few minutes after being bitten (Theodor, 1935). Within four days after the bite there is a delayed reaction appearing as a hard, reddish papule in the skin. The site may itch intensely, especially at night. In extreme cases bites on the forearm have been known to cause swelling and edema of the arm and inflammation of lymph nodes of the elbow. A residual brown pigment sometimes remains for months at the site of each papule.

Tiny gnats of the genus *Culicoides* (Ceratopogonidae) may become serious pests in areas of extensive marshes, and are particularly pestiferous near coastal salt marshes. These insects may become such a nuisance as to interfere seriously with seasonal tourist trade. An Alaskan species has been known to interfere with handling of cargoes on docks.

Areán and Fox (1955) have explicitly characterized reactions of a sensitized person to bites of a Puerto Rican species of *Culicoides* as follows: The site of the puncture is sealed by clotted blood. A wheal forms quickly with focal fragmentation of the collagen fibers. An interstitial edema of the dermis develops, and monocytes, lymphocytes, and occasional polymorphonuclear leucocytes invade the area. Cellular infiltration is more pronounced around blood vessels, sweat glands, and sebaceous glands. Vesicular papules form after about 24 hours. The dermis shows marked edema in the outer portions with bullous formation. Degeneration of collagen fibers is pronounced. Capillaries are dilated and congested. Older papules may have a larger bulla in the epidermis. Smaller intraepithelial vesicles form near the main bulla. Lesions 18 days old may be described as "shotty nodules" and scars.

All over the world black flies (Simuliidae) are annoying pests in mountainous areas and in the flood plains of the great rivers. Usually they strike the skin as a pellet might with no preliminary circling or hovering about the victim. When persons are fully clothed, the flies attack the cheeks, ocular regions, or the back of the head especially along the hair line and behind the ears; however, any exposed part of the body may be struck. These aggressive pests will crawl into openings in trousers and shirts and even into the hair and nostrils.

Lesions caused by bites of black flies may become confluent, vesicular, excoriated, weeping, and crusted. Evolution and involution are slow and may take three or more weeks. The puncture is of itself painless. Gudgel and Grauer (1954) give the following details about the bite of a black fly in Japan. The puncture exudes blood that trickles for some time. Non-sensitized persons react with a small ecchymosis surmounted with a blood crust that is followed in a few hours by a small pruritic papule that may persist for a few days. Occasionally there is some tenderness and a bruise appears at the site. Sensitized persons react first with a pronounced wheal and erythema. Pruritic papules form with central vesicles and even satellite vesicles. Pruritus is often intense and excoriations keep lesions raw. Weeping patches form crusts. Lesions may persist as long as 11 months. Two distinct delayed reactions occur, however. The more common one is that of corymbiform, nodular, vesicular patches with associated lesions indistinguishable from nummular eczema. Other reactions show hard, pigmented, rough, pruritic nodules that remain quiescent unless scratched. Histopathology is one of vascular dilation, edema, and early infiltration of the perivascular region with polymorphonuclear leucocytes. The epidermis shows edema with vesicles and pseudovesicles. Biopsies of older lesions (6 weeks to 7 months) showed hyperkeratosis, parakeratosis, serous crust, edema, and vesicular formation. Healing finally occurs with scarring and pigmentation.

Constitutional reactions may result in death of both domestic and wild animals during outbreaks of the buffalo gnat, the Golubatz fly, or the arctic black fly. The enormous loss of blood presumably results in anemia, and as the animal becomes weaker, the flies invade the nostrils and bronchi. Death finally ensues (Ciurea and Dinulescu, 1924). The loss in milk flow in dairy herds during outbreaks of the arctic black fly is very serious in Canada (Rempel and Arnason, 1947).

From Japan come reports (Otsuru and Ogawa, 1959) of bites of larvae of horse flies (Tabanidae) on workers in rice fields. Both

Tabanus and *Chrysops* species are involved. Persons are bitten while wading barefoot in flooded fields. A severe pain at the site of a bite is experienced for intervals up to three hours. A pale flat wheal about 3–10 mm in diameter forms around the puncture. Itching persists up to 15 hours.

Bites from motile fleas that climb onto man tend to be multiple and are concentrated on parts of the body where clothing fits snugly, as around the waist and over the shoulders. Children having pets often show patterns of bites easily identified as areas of close contact between child and pet. Each lesion is characterized by a central puncture surrounded by a wheal or papule. Confusion between a generalized papular urticaria and a serious case of flea bites may be avoided by noting that, in case of the latter, each papule has a center puncture and the lesions are distributed as indicated above (Allington and Allington, 1954). Goldman *et al.* (1952) reported that flea bites were very similar in appearance to those of mosquitoes and body lice.

The chigoe flea (*Tunga penetrans*) produces reactions that are somewhat different from those caused by more motile fleas. Fertilized females attach themselves by means of a spur to parts of the body where the skin is thick (Costa, 1945), as on the feet and toes. They tend to become embedded in the thick skin. The bite provokes intense itching and pain, and a swelling resembling an abscess appears. The body of the parasite enlarges so that it may be a half centimeter or more in diameter. Usually after a few days the parasite spontaneously detaches; however, it sometimes dies *in situ* and causes ulceration.

Sucking lice have surely lived on heads and bodies of humans from time beyond records. Today primitive man is normally infested at all times with one or more species although civilized man is seldom afflicted. Men living under conditions imposed by warfare are very likely to become parasitized. Buxton (1947) noted that in 1917 one of the British armies had over 10,000 hospital admissions for inflammatory skin troubles most of which were caused by lice. Non-sensitized individuals show only a puncture wound and a slight delayed reaction while sensitized individuals respond as they might to other biting insects: the usual wheal and even extensive edema forms about the bite, then after about four hours a local, delayed, papular reaction begins and persists for a week or more. Vesicles may be associated with papules. Pruritus is often intense, especially at night, and the consequent scratching causes excoriation which offers a favorable situation for impetigo.

It has been stated (Moore, 1918) that when large numbers of lice are deliberately fed on a person, vague, general symptoms occur. The victim usually experiences dull headache, drowsiness, pains in the joints, rash, and a slight, persistent rise in temperature. Prolonged infection by pubic lice is usually signalized by the presence of bluish spots on the skin. These are called "taches ombrées" by the French. A general thickening and pigmentation of the skin characteristically results from a prolonged infestation of body lice. Such a condition is known as "vagabond's disease."

Sucking lice cause economic losses of major proportions, particularly in range cattle during the winter. Peterson *et al.* (1953) have noted that *Haematopinus eurysternus* causes anemia in cattle which may be identified by the pale mucous membrane of the muzzle and the lack of color on the udder.

Bed bugs have a long history as domiciliary parasites and as constant companions of man. They often cause severe local skin reactions in sensitized persons. The most common injury is lacerated capillaries from which small dermal hemorrhages spread into dermal tissues for some 24 hours. Occasionally blood may ooze from the opening to the puncture. The initial wheal gives way to an irregular bulla bound by an erythematous zone. Several bites are usually found close together and they are often arranged in an irregularly linear pattern. The bites tend to be more numerous on the legs, buttocks, shoulders, and neck. The appearance, grouping, and location of wheals and subsequent bullous papules, together with flecks of blood on bed linen, are essential diagnostic features.

Giant bed bugs (*Triatoma* spp.) cause characteristic reactions in sensitized persons. Large wheals that are erythematous and edematous are at the site of the puncture. Papular lesions appear and then become vesiculated and in a few cases lesions become nodular or bullous, especially on the legs. These lesions are clinically identical with the so-called "signal de romana" often associated with Chagas' disease (Lumbreras *et al.*, 1959).

Ticks that bite man either are transient feeders, as are bugs, and require an hour or less to engorge, or they attach themselves to the skin for a period of several days to a week or more. The leather or soft ticks (Argasidae) and most males of the scutate ticks (Ixodidae) are transients. Larvae, nymphs, and females of the latter family require a relatively longer time of attachment. Ticks of the first group feed often and ingest relatively little blood at each feeding, while those of the latter group feed once in each instar and take in such a large volume of blood as to cause a great increase in the size of the individual.

Ticks of the family Ixodidae make puncture wounds by slashing the epidermis and dermis with the digits of the tubular chelicerae. Often the wound is widened at the deepest point of penetration, and the chelicerae tend to be spread apart apically. In this cavity a hemorrhage develops which is in direct contact with the mouth. Shortly after insertion the hypostome and chelicerae come to be encased in multiple layers of amorphous material (Arthur, 1953). This wall penetrates between the host tissues as root-like extensions into the dermis in all directions for about a millimeter. There is a tube in the center through which blood moves into the mouth of the tick. Ultimately this wall hardens to anchor the mouth parts and to form a food tube. A half day or more is usually required for the penetration and cementing of the mouth parts of female ticks.

Cutaneous responses to the bite of a female ixodid tick are characteristic (Cowdry and Danks, 1933). The capillary endothelium swells and becomes infiltrated with polymorphonuclear leucocytes, and a marked cytolysis of fibroblasts occurs. A localized hemorrhage is maintained between the chelicerae. Necrosis may result from the feeding of any of several species. *Dermacentor sinicus* causes local necrosis (Hoeppli and Feng, 1931) and *Hyalomma asiaticum* may produce lamellate or columnar necrosis of muscles. Some ticks cause infiltrated papular or nodular reactions that may persist for years. Ross and Friede (1955) reported the occurrence of scaling followed by scarring of the scalp, with attendant loss of hair at the site of tick attachment. Foggie (1959) shows drawings of tissue reactions at the site of attachment of an ixodid tick.

Constitutional symptoms of four types can be caused by the bites of ixodid ticks. Those severe enough to end in death are tick paralysis, anemia, and water-belly, while one of lesser proportions is tick-bite fever. The paralytic expression is well known in sheep and cattle, but it is rarely seen in man. It has been responsible for anemia in cattle, sheep, moose, and rabbits. Peterson *et al.* (1953) have shown that an infestation of 60–80 engorging females of *Dermacentor andersoni* may cause a rabbit to die of anemia from loss of blood in about five days. Horses that are heavily infested by the winter horse tick (*Dermacentor nigrolineatus*) may develop water-belly. Tick-bite fever has been characterized by Feder (1944) as follows: fever without chills accompanied by anorexia, malaise, headache, and sometimes abdominal pain and vomiting. It occurs in early summer, and the symptoms may be caused by one female ixodid tick that is less than fully engorged. Improvement is rapid and recovery is known within 12 to 36 hours after removal of the tick.

Tick paralysis is a disease caused by secretions of a gravid, ixodid tick which has attached near the brain or spinal cord. It is an acute, ascending, flaccid paralysis that has been produced by all of the common ixodid ticks the world around. While occasional cases have been known among children, the usual cases are among livestock on ranges, particularly in North America and Australia. One tick attached at the base of the skull is sufficient to cause paralysis of a child, with death following in 24–48 hours. Cattle may require 10–50 ticks attached along the back to cause the same result (Gregson, 1952), but a 1000-pound bull was reported to be paralyzed by one tick. Wild ungulates and porcupines seem to be resistant. Weight for weight, man is said to be the animal most susceptible to the toxin. The poison is said to be present in all stages including the egg, but the quantity is sufficient to produce symptoms only when the salivary glands of an attached gravid female begin to atrophy (Miller, 1947). It is a protein that can be salted out at 51° C, but it is resistant to drying and to treatment with 70 per cent solution of ethanol.

Murnaghan (1958) observed the effect of the toxin on dogs, the following results being noted: paralysis is caused by a failure in transmission of impulses at the neuromuscular junctions; hence paralyzed muscles behave as if denervated. Increasing paralysis causes accelerated sensitivity to acetylcholine. The blockage seems to be unlike that produced by competitive and depolarizing blocking agents or anticholinesterases.

The argasid or soft ticks feed in the manner of bed bugs and at a time when persons or animals are resting or sleeping. Lavoipierre and Riek (1955) have found that reactions to these ticks vary to the degree that the tick reactions form four groups. Ticks of Group I as represented by *Ornithodoros moubata* cause only a moderate reaction. A small hemorrhage some 3 mm in diameter occurs at the feeding site within an hour after attachment, though the surface of the skin is not raised. Sometimes the puncture oozes blood for a short time after detachment of the tick. All macroscopic effects disappear within a few days.

Ticks of Group II as represented by *O. erraticus* rapidly feed to repletion. Shortly after feeding the hemorrhage extends 6–12 mm in diameter and below the dermis to the muscles. The resulting lesion is elevated above the general level of the skin. About 12–24 hours after detachment of the tick there is a dark red central zone surrounded by a narrow and lighter-colored ring. Both areas are encircled by a broad, dark region. Some 14 to 21 days later the wound begins ulceration which is sometimes extensive. A representative of the group (*O. coriaceus*) is said to be feared as much as a snake in arid mountainous areas of southwestern United States. Herms (1916) noted the cumulative effects of two bites within two weeks. The first caused a painful arm for 2 or 3 days. The second bite produced the red spot and ringed effect followed within 30 minutes by swelling of the appendage, which became severe within 3 hours. At this time even the site of the first bite became symptomatic. Pain was intense and necrosis was severe.

Bites of ticks from Groups III and IV cause only mild effects. Group III is represented by the large form of *O. savignyi*. These ticks cause an extensive hemorrhage as do those of Group II, but there is no elevation of the skin, and no necrosis ensues. Group IV, the so-called *Argas* group, causes insignificant reactions, at least on mammals. Results reported by Hoogstraal and Kaiser (1957) show that *Argas brumpti* belongs in another group, as its bite is painful, and large subcutaneous nodules may be left on the victim for years.

Ticks of the genus *Otobius* are called ear ticks because they attach inside the ears of various animals. *O. megnini* infests ungulates. They cause calves to shake their heads vigorously and to race wildly about at times. Excessive wax flows from the ears and deafness may follow.

Mites that puncture the skin are either facultative or accidental pests of man. Some of them come from quarters of associated domestic animals; others climb on humans who have invaded the haunts of the wild hosts. Medical aid is most often sought when some species become facultative parasites. Other mites that invade the skin are considered later in this chapter as tissue parasites.

Medical accounts of diseases caused by mites that are facultative parasites are numerous and have been reported from around the world. In the lay person's mind, the diseases generally have been associated with some stored products rather than with the arthropod. As a consequence we have copra itch, grain itch, grocer's itch, baker's itch, barley itch, and so on. The mites are present in such large numbers in the associated products that handlers of a particular material come to be infested. While details of the various mite associations are only partially known, they may be considered to be similar to the grain-itch pattern.

Booth and Jones (1954) have stated that straw (grain) itch or acarodermatitis urticarioides is an eruption found on millers, bakers, granary workers, dock workers, tobacco handlers, and some others. It is even becoming a hazard in industries which use straw in fabrication of building materials. The disease is so common in Europe that it has legal status as an occupational hazard. It is an annually recurrent problem at exhibition sites for farm animals because the grooms stay near the animals at all times. Once, over 1,000 farm youths were affected at a big state fair in central United States. Straw or grain itch is caused by the mite *Pyemotes ventricosus*. It is current in the warmer months of the year and virtually absent during the winter. An eruption is caused by the mites puncturing the skin, and is generalized, with forearms, neck, and trunk usually being involved. A wheal with a central pinpoint vesicle is characteristic, and vesicles may become pustules. Vulvitis and cystitis have also been reported. Any atypical, chronic eczema may be suspected by a diagnostician as having a mite for its cause. Born (1956) observed symptoms on the hands of a lumberman that were caused by mites of this group that had not previously been known to attack man. Therefore, all mites of the group must be suspected as possible causes of acarodermatitis of man. Since the mites are only temporary in their association, symptoms are prolonged only when a repeated infestation is possible.

Mites normally parasitic on rodents and birds may become accidental parasites of man. Pigeons or sparrows, nesting on the ledge of a building, or canaries, chickens, and other birds could be a source. De Oreo (1958) cites a case of pruritic dermatitis of nine years' duration that had been caused by the mites from a caged canary. Mynah birds in cages have provided foci for mites of this sort. The chicken mite, tropical fowl mite, and tropical rat mite are the usual offenders. However, six or more species may cause this form of acarodermatitis.

Bites may be typified by those of either chicken or rat mites. De Oreo (1958) characterizes them as follows: clusters of 3–6 erythematous papules each up to 1 cm in diameter; a tiny hemorrhagic punctum in each; vesicles sometimes present. When vesicles are unilateral, they may be confused with herpes zoster, while vesicular lesions on children may be confused with chickenpox. One must remember that the rat mite, particularly, is very likely to attack singly and feed at several places, so that only a few papules or vesicles, spaced at irregular intervals, may occur on a victim each time. Occasionally the fur mite of cats, *Cheyletiella parasitivorax*, may cause a pruritic papular dermatitis. Infants in a hospital nursery were once afflicted by plant-feeding mites which overran the building. The lesions consisted of erythematous papules 2–10 cm across (Mandoul *et al.*, 1956).

Chiggers or scrub-itch mites are nearly microscopic larvae that attack persons while out of doors. The pests climb from stems, leaves, or branches near the ground onto any accessible part of the body. They crawl upward very rapidly until they lodge at a point where both tight-fitting clothes and high body humidity retard crawling. Legs and genitals are most often attacked. The mite becomes attached to the skin and remains so for several hours, but seldom is present by the time a physician is consulted.

Trombiculosis, the disease caused by chiggers, seems to always be caused by species normally parasitic on birds and reptiles (Wharton, 1952). It may be confined to a few lesions that cause local pruritus, or it may be general with fever and malaise. A specific lesion on a sensitized person is first a wheal that is erythematous; later it becomes a papule that may be bullous. Intense pruritus causes scratching, which in turn removes the attached mite, but this has no effect on reducing the lesion.

The reason for symptoms continuing after removal of a mite is to be found in the histology (Vitzthum, 1929). A chigger attaches to the skin by means of the pointed chelicerae which are driven through the epidermis to the outer layer of the dermis. In the first injection the saliva digests the proximal cells and this causes a slight cavity. Further secretion extends the zone of necrotic cells, and a peg-like area, called a stylostome, becomes walled off by growth of the *stratum germinativum* of the dermis. Peripheral necrosis continues while the center becomes a canal extending inward from the mouth of the mite. Alternate ingestion and secretion by the mite keeps the central canal open and causes extension into the dermis. Finally the area of necrotic cells is walled off at its inner extremity and the stylostome is complete. The chigger ingests the digested cells within the stylostome until replete. Contrary to popular notion, no blood is ingested; neither is the chigger killed by a mammalian diet, as was unfortunately first stated about a century ago and has been quoted endlessly. The stylostome may persist for weeks to cause intense itching.

One of the chigger mites, *Schöngastia ulcerofaciens,* causes an acute inflammation or even ulceration in the ears of field mice in central Europe (Daniel and Slais, 1957). Scars form as the ulcers heal.

Spiders are commonly known as venomous arthropods by lay persons, but those most likely to bite are seldom recognized. Unfortunately for the diagnostician, the spider responsible for an attack is almost never caught and preserved for identification. Equally unfortunate for diagnostic purposes is the "treatment" often used before proper medical aid has been sought. An undisturbed lesion reveals a double puncture caused by insertion of the two chelicerae. Some spiders have opposable chelicerae, which cause two punctures pointing toward each other, while others have parallel chelicerae, which make dual, parallel punctures. In the absence of the offender, the clinician relies on (1) an oral description given by the patient, which in many cases must be reconstructed from knowledge of likely species, (2) the locality and surroundings where the victim was bitten, which should be compared with known habits of harmful spiders, and (3) the characteristics of the lesion.

Most spiders bite humans as defensive reflexes to a vibration. Normally an insect is the cause of the vibration, and the spider strikes to impale it. If the vibration is caused by a human disturbing the web, the spider usually strikes and then quickly retreats. For this reason the culprit seldom is seen and almost never captured. Situations in which bites are most often received are (1) seats of outdoor privies, where the male genitals are frequently attacked; (2) little-used clothing hanging in an outbuilding, where an appendage is usually bitten; and (3) piled objects that have been undisturbed for a time, where hands are attacked. Piles of wood, bunches of bananas, piles of crates, and greenhouse accessories are common sites for spiders.

The venom of spiders is secreted through the thorn-like chelicerae by way of an opening near the tip. Toxic digestive fluids may enter the wound. Both fluids are injected into the prey for incapacitating it and also for digestion of the body. When the toxic fluids are injected subcutaneously into vertebrates, they cause one or more of several possible reactions according to Vellard (1936): (1) The toxin may act on (a) the nervous system to cause stupefaction, convulsions, or paralysis, (b) the secretory glands to stimulate salivary, lachrymal, and gastric secretions, or (c) the blood vessels in the kidney and liver to produce hemorrhages. (2) As a necrotic agent the toxic fluids may cause (a) a superficial eschar, (b) an extensive local cutaneous lesion, or (c) general necrosis with hemorrhage. (3) Some species produce a hemolytic agent in addition to one or both of those above. (4) Some fluids injected cause coagulation of the blood. (5) Some spider bites produce an apparent proteolytic agent.

Maretic and Stanic (1954) described the sequence of gross symptoms following an injection from the widow spiders, *Latrodectus* spp. The general condition of the victim becomes poor soon after he is bitten. A sense of pressure is first felt in the chest; then pains develop in the abdomen, lumbar region, and lower extremities. Rigidity develops in the abdominal muscles, abdominal reflexes disappear, but tendon reflexes increase. Alarm reactions, vomiting, and conjunctivitis are pronounced. Urinary and cardiovascular changes are variable. A dangerous illness is usual and death may ensue. Attacks by this group of spiders are more common in the drier parts of the temperate regions and in the tropics.

Species of the genus *Loxosceles* of the Americas are the principal causes of spider bites in domestic situations. *Loxosceles laeta* of the west coastal region of South America is a domestic spider that produces a venom which causes severe local pain and numbness. Bullae form at the site. A dry, necrotic gangrene sets in after a few days. The venom is strongly hemolytic. Atkins (1957) has proposed that the "brown spider," *Loxosceles reclusus,* is at least one species responsible for necrotic spider bite in central United States.

A psychological anomaly caused by real or imaginary bites from lycosid spiders has been recognized and given the name of tarantism. This nervous disorder was common in Italy and reached its acme in the seventeenth century. Sufferers were presumably sensitive to particular musical variations, and at times they reputedly danced in a frenzied manner until completely exhausted. Certain music is alleged to have therapeutic value (Thorp and Woodson, 1945).

Centipedes cause dual puncture wounds that may be confused with spider bites. The single pair of opposable, chelate front legs of centipedes is capable in some cases of penetrating skin. A toxin is secreted and enters the punctures. Some of the giant species (six or more inches in length) may inflict painful bites. A wheal develops at the site and erythema extends around it. Local symptoms abate after a few hours, and systemic symptoms are rare.

INJECTED ALLERGENS: STINGS

Stings of arthropods are herein defined or interpreted as puncture wounds of the skin with attendant sequellae, that are always made by caudal appendages, in contrast to bites, which are made by mouth parts. This distinction between stings and bites is one of etiological convenience rather than pathological significance. Arthropods that sting humans are hymenopterous insects and scorpions. Females of the former group, which includes wasps, bees, and ants, are all capable of stinging. The stinging organ of bees and wasps is the ovipositor, a complex structure which may be extruded at the tip of the abdomen and jabbed into the skin. In the case of worker honey bees, the whole organ is detached from the bee during the stinging act. The released stinger literally works its way into the skin as the attached gland gives up its venom along a trough between the needle-like parts. The stinger of a wasp may be used repeatedly instead of only once. Scorpions have a dorsally recurved, sclerous, caudal spine at the end of a supple postabdomen. All species have a pair of poison glands in the bulbous base of the stinger.

Literature on the composition of venoms of stinging arthropods is extensive, but apparently much remains unknown about the specific nature of the toxins present. Marshall (1957) summarized the current knowledge of the venom of honey bees, on which there is much information. It seems that only the gross composition of the venom is known, even though analysis has been made repeatedly. It is a colorless liquid secreted by glands in the abdomen. The effect of the venom is somewhat between that of a sapotoxin and cantharidin. Venom of viperine snakes is similar in that it is hemolytic, hemorrhagic, neurotoxic, and histaminic. It raises the coagulation time of blood and may cause uterine bleeding.

Reactions to bee stings may be local or constitutional, according to Marshall. The sharp prick gives a variable degree of pain then immediately a small, reddish area forms at the site. This area is surrounded by a whitish zone which in turn is surrounded by a reddish "flare." A wheal quickly forms, then subsides within a few hours. This reaction can be accounted for by (1) histamine in the toxin and (2) histamine released by the tissues of the victim. Stings on the mouth or throat may cause edema of such severity as to choke a victim. Large numbers of stings inflicted at one time may cause diarrhea, vomiting, faintness, and even unconsciousness. The volume of venom injected by stings of about 500 bees is sufficient to cause death of an adult. Venom injected by only one sting may cause a hypersensitized person to react within 20 minutes with peripheral circulatory shock, followed by edema of the face and pharynx, with fatal results in some cases. A summer hardly passes but one reads of a death from bee stings.

Some ants produce venoms that may cause severe reactions in humans. Caro et al. (1957) outlined the reactions to stings from the fire ant (Solenopsis saevissima), a recent importation into the southern United States. The ant pinches up the skin with its mandibles and then repeatedly inserts its stinger. First a flare appears about the puncture, then the area becomes a wheal. The wheal subsides within about an hour, and the site becomes vesiculated. After 24 hours the lesion is an umbilicated pustule surrounded by an erythematous halo or painful edema. Within 3 to 10 days the pustule ruptures, and a crust develops. A scar forms, which may be associated with either fibrotic nodules or an eczematoid dermatitis. The chief diagnostic feature of the sting by this ant is the consistent formation of a pustule. The pustules are normally free of microbes, which may be explained by the antibiotic activity of the venom (Blum et al., 1958). Several cases of anaphylaxis have been reported. Total body edema with cyanosis about the mouth is evident in such cases.

Stings of wasps have received little attention from workers interested in venoms. Kershaw et al. (1949) have the following to say about the reactions of a guinea pig stung by the wasp, Vespa vulgaris. A scanty cellular infiltration was noted in the dermis. No edema or other changes occurred in the muscles during the first hour; however, necrosis was observed after 24 hours. Fatal anaphylaxis in humans has been reported several times.

Scorpions of many species sting man and have been known to cause reactions varying in severity from painful pricks to death. When pressed against a surface as one's skin or when disturbed, the scorpion flicks the flexible postabdomen forward and upward with sufficient force to stab the skin with the thorn-like stinger. The stinger may cause either a single puncture wound or a series if the victim is struck several times in rapid succession. The poison is secreted by a pair of glands situated in the enlarged basal part of the caudal segment and is ejected through a canal.

Present knowledge about the venom of scorpions indicates that a neurotoxin is present and a hemolytic one may or may not be a component. Coagulants are usually lacking but are known to be in the venom of *Androctonus* from South America. An anticoagulant is present in *Scorpio* but is absent in species of Buthidae. The hemolytic action of the venom of *Buthacus* of northern Africa is said to exceed that of poisonous snakes, and that of *Scorpio* causes some hemolysis. Species of Buthidae of South America lack hemolytic agents. Peripheral nerve endings are injured and autonomic centers may be stimulated. In such genera as *Tityus, Prionurus, Centruroides,* and *Buthus,* the neurotoxin is similar to that in cobra venom.

Scorpions are much more dangerous than is commonly realized. Stahnke (1953) stated that during a 20-year period *Centruroides* scorpions killed more than twice as many people in Arizona as were killed by all other venomous animals. Similarly Balozet (1956) said that in North Africa the danger from scorpions is greater than that from venomous snakes. Most deaths have been among children. The lethality of scorpion venom varies greatly according to species; thus, venom of *Prionurus australis* is said to be 140 times as toxic to mice as is that of *Scorpio maurus* (Sergent, 1949).

Patterson (1960) reported that a sting of the scorpion (*Centruroides sculpturatus*) of southwestern United States produces the following symptoms in man: convulsions of skeletal muscles, respiratory arrest, excessive salivation, visceral hyperemia, and gastric hyperdistension. Respiratory difficulties develop in a sequence. First there is an increased rate, then follows a stasis, and finally gasping develops. Skeletal muscles, too, go through a similar sequence of degrees of activity. Initial action is seemingly direct on muscle tissue. The spasmodic activity results from effect of the toxin on the central motor centers.

INVASION BY ARTHROPODS

Human bodies and those of most mammals may be invaded by arthropods either naturally or accidentally. The physician usually sees results of the casual or accidental invasion while the veterinarian may frequently see specimens of obligatory parasites. Services of the medical man may be required when an eye has been invaded by a gnat, a small beetle, or an aphid. Other casual intruders include maggots, millipedes, beetles, and other forms that may enter the alimentary canal. Rarely are maggots encountered in oral and nasal regions or in necrotic surface lesions, but a medical practitioner in the tropics may be called to treat lesions caused by them.

The eyes and ears are vulnerable sites for injury by flying insects and occasionally by ovipositing flies. Gnats, midges, aphids, small bugs, and small beetles often strike the eyes of children at play and persons riding in open vehicles. Children who are running, riding bicycles, tumbling in grass, or leaning out of automobile windows may be struck by these flying insects. When an eye or ear is involved, the experience is painful and often requires the services of a physician. Not infrequently, larvae of filth flies invade the eyes of man and various animals, since eyes infected by microbes are especially attractive as oviposition sites. Maggots indigenous to the nares of sheep occasionally invade the eyes of shepherds. Krümmel and Brauns (1956) prepared an exhaustive paper and a long bibliography on this aspect of ocular myiasis. The ears are often invaded while persons are lying on the ground or in straw or leaves. Many people have had great pain as a result of small beetles entering an ear and then crawling over the ear drum. Mites have been known to crawl into the ears and then cause an annoying humming sound. Ears fouled by infection with microbes may be invaded by larvae of filth flies, which cause aural myiasis.

The nostrils of sheep and goats are sites for development of larvae of an obligatory parasite, *Oestrus ovis*, the sheep bot fly. Infested animals continually sneeze and rub their noses and mucus is discharged in stringy masses. Infested animals are retarded in growth.

The skin of man and domestic mammals is commonly invaded by sarcoptic mites, with scabies resulting. Scabies is known as itch

on humans and as mange or scab on livestock. The mites make hair-
line, whitish or yellowish burrows in circumscribed areas in and
beneath the outer layer of human skin. Burrows usually extend into
the dermis. Sometimes their presence is asymptomatic, especially
in non-sensitized persons or animals. The skin of sensitized ones
becomes inflamed, swollen, and pruritic near the lesions. Pruritus is
apt to be particularly severe at night after the victim has gone to
bed. Papules, vesicles, small nodules, and even pigmentation may
follow. Serum discharged from vesicles often forms crusts or scabs.
Mites remain active at the margins of the scaled areas. Scabies is
prevalent among people who live crowded together in unhygienic
surroundings. A particularly severe form, called Norwegian itch,
may result in scaling of the entire body, with the finger and toe nails
becoming involved. Lepers are said to show this form of the disease
when infected. Various sarcoptic parasites of domestic animals may
invade skin of persons closely associated with the infected animals;
hence occupational hazards may be of concern. Details of these
diseases are well described in medical and veterinary clinical guides
and will not be characterized further.

Members of the family Demodicidae likewise invade the skin
and may burrow deep into the lymphatic nodes. These mites are
almost universally present in the skin of man, and in both non-sensitized humans and domestic animals they are normally innocuous
(Hirst, 1919). Presumably this condition obtains in animals that are
hosts of related species. Unsworth (1946) reported that about 10
per cent of clinically normal dogs may support populations of 50 or
fewer of the mites on 0.1 gm of skin, but instances are known in
which populations 20 times as great caused no apparent abnormality.
Sensitized persons may show evidence of rosacea (Brodie, 1952), a
dermatosis affecting the nose, cheeks, chin, and forehead. The
chronic congestion and dilation of capillaries in the skin of these
regions produces the flush that suggests the name. Multiple papular
lesions may accompany an advanced phase of the disease.

Larvae of one group of flies, the calliphorid, *Auchmeromyia*, are
called Congo floor maggots, since they usually crawl from debris on
the dirt floor of huts to puncture the skin of persons lying on the
floor. They feed in a transient manner by cutting through the skin.
A hemorrhage is caused, and the larvae suck up the blood on and
below the skin surface. The size and nature of the wound is the

reason for including this type as an invader rather than as a strictly biting insect.

All sorts of living arthropods may pass through the food tube of man, and some lead a kind of parasitic life while doing so. Usually they are accidentally or unwittingly ingested. Centipedes, beetles, maggots, and caterpillars are among these accidental invaders. Clinical manifestations seldom develop, but symptoms of vomiting, cramping, and diarrhea are characteristic. Not all invasions are accidental because chickens have been known to feast on ants, only to die a day or so later. Other arthropods normally develop in the digestive tract of some domestic animals as horses. Rat-tailed maggots occasionally invade the intestinal tract in numbers. See James (1947) for more detail about species of flies that invade tissue.

Obligatory invaders of the gut usually attack equines. They belong to the subfamily Gasterophilinae of the Oestridae. Larvae of the early instars move into the buccal mucosa and the tongue, and some cause lesions to form between the teeth, where purulent matter accumulates. Animals so afflicted often rub lips or tongue over any rough surface, or chew on wooden posts or rails. After molting the first time, larvae leave the buccal region and become established along the intestinal tract, where most of them cling to the lining of the stomach, and then create ulcers at sites of attachment. Certain species, especially when almost mature, line the walls of the rectum and may even cause rectal prolapses.

Subcutaneous penetration of tissue is largely restricted to larvae of dipterous insects, particularly those of the higher taxonomic categories. Their bullet-shaped bodies and burrowing abilities make them suited to enter tissues. Their secretory process and adaptable respiratory organs permit survival once they are inside the tissues. Consequently several families of flies have become obligate invaders of tissue, and species in other families are frequent facultative invaders. All of the larvae pierce the skin and force their way through the tissues.

Relatively few species of larvae enter uninjured tissues of man, and those that normally do so are tropical forms. Larvae of *Dermatobia* in Central and South America and those of *Cordylobia* in Africa are best known. The former are parasites in the jungle, and the latter are parasites in domestic situations. Larvae of *Dermatobia* cause a furuncular myiasis as they form pustular nodules in subcutaneous muscles near sites of their entrance into the skin. Each pustule contains a bottle-shaped larva that may be as large as the last joint of one's little finger. The nodule has an opening through the skin. An unusual site for attack by *Dermatobia* was reported by an insect collector whose tongue became infested. While using an aspirator he had sucked some insect bearing the eggs into his mouth. One case of fatal invasion of the brain has been reported. Larvae of *Cordylobia* cause painful, itching pustules in subcutaneous regions. Each pustule has a larva in the center.

Myiasis, particularly of necrotic wounds, is well known in medical history. Larvae of several calliphorid and muscid flies invade these sites. Some will enter a new wound, while others are secondary invaders since they require that bacteria be first established in the wound. Sometimes both primary and secondary invaders occur together. The color of these maggots is near white with a pink cast. The primary invaders will enter margins of a wound and attack live tissue as do the screw-worms (*Callitroga* spp.), while the secondary invaders attack only large purulent wounds. *Lucilia* spp. and *Phormia* are calliphorids that readily attack necrotic wounds though some strains will attack marginal healthy tissues as well (Stewart, 1934). Species of certain calliphorids were once used by clinicians to clean persistent wounds and thereby hasten healing.

Cattle are particularly susceptible to attack by tissue-invaders such as larvae of the family Oestridae, genus *Hypoderma*. Common clinical evidence of their presence is the formation of pustules in the loin region. Pustules the size of marbles occur on each side of the backbone and hundreds may occur at a time. Inside each pustule is a single larva ranging in size up to that of the last joint of the thumb. Each pustule opens through the skin even though it is covered with a serous scab. Hides from infested cows were said to be "elf-shot" in medieval England. For details of entry of these invaders into the back, see the discussion of the species.

Anaphylaxis following attack by myiasis-producing larvae is well known. Apparently any tissue-invader can cause this constitutional effect. Certainly the larvae of bot flies in the alimentary system of horses may induce anaphylaxis. The so-called rose fever of cattle is a sensitivity reaction to the crushed larvae of *Hypoderma* spp.

The literature records a number of cases of the *Hypoderma* species invading humans, especially persons who have close contact with cattle. The painful boils which result when these pests enter tissues are very much like those produced by the *Dermatobia* larvae. In at least one instance meningitis was caused when *Hypoderma bovis* entered the brain of a child.

The urogenital tract has been known to become infested with arthropods since various forms have been removed from the vaginal regions of both children and aged persons. The cheese skipper has caused a urinary myiasis in North Africa. Mites have been known to penetrate the urinary system and to pass out with the urine.

Mites in particular invade the respiratory system of humans, while some species normally inhabit the bronchi of snakes, birds, and some mammals. They have caused a pseudo-tuberculous condition in both humans and monkeys. Mites of the genus *Pneumonyssus* have been obtained from the lesions in lungs. Diseases that have been given the general names of pseudo-tuberculosis, eosinophil lung, and tropical eosinophilia are caused to some degree by such mites. Even facultative invaders are common in some situations (Carter *et al.*, 1944). *Tarsonemus, Acarus, Carpoglyphus,* and *Cheyletus* mites cause general respiratory disorders with occasional asthmatic symptoms. Infection is presumed to be by inhalation.

ADDITIONAL READINGS

Contact Toxins

BURTT (1947) is an account of the action of certain types of contact toxins. Otherwise the reader should consult papers cited in the text.
KEMPER (1958) discusses toxins from caterpillars.

Bites

GORDON and CREWE (1948) and FAIRBAIRN and WILLIAMSON (1956) are accounts of the histology of bites.
ALLINGTON and ALLINGTON (1954) discuss various clinical aspects of bites. It is an excellent reference.
MURNAGHAN (1958) discusses paralysis attendant on feeding of ticks. The clinician is advised to study this reference.
VELLARD (1936) is an extensive account of the composition and effects of the venom of spiders.

Stings

MARSHALL (1957) discusses the venom and effects of stings of bees on persons. The relation of histamine to clinical features is also discussed. There is a series of papers on venoms in *Publ. Amer. Assoc. Adv. Sci.*, vol. 44. This series had best be consulted for details of venoms, their composition, and effects.

Invasion

KRÜMMEL and BRAUNS (1956) is an excellent study of ocular myiasis and should be consulted in the original.

CHAPTER 7

Agents of Disease Carried by Arthropods

GENERAL

Having seen how arthropods cause disease, we shall now examine their relations to other organisms that cause disease. In this latter relationship they have an important medical significance because they provide the means for moving many disease-producing organisms from one vertebrate to another. In the capacity of middlemen, arthropods serve in every conceivable way to pass along the organisms. Some are mere carriers; others provide developmental sites; and still others serve as hold-over sites where an organism bides its time between vertebrate infections. The purpose of the remaining chapters is to discuss these relationships.

CLASSIFICATION

Vertebrate pathogens having arthropodan associations represent a wide range of forms from microbes to worms and even arthropods. The category most often involved is that of the viruses, but many protozoa and some tapeworms and round worms spend a part of their lives in arthropods. Less numerous, but no less important, are associations between arthropods and such organisms as rickettsiae, acanthocephalid worms, and insects. The following categories of organisms contain forms that spend part of their lives in or on arthropods and part in vertebrates:

A. Protophyta
    1. Microtatobiotes
        a. Virales: viruses

    b. Rickettsiales: rickettsiae, haemobartonellae, and ana-
      plasms
  2. Schizomycetes: bacteria, spirochetes, and bartonellae
B. Animals
  1. Protozoa
    a. Flagellata: *Leishmania, Trypanosoma*
    b. Sporozoa
      1) Coccidia: *Haemogregarina*, etc.
      2) Haemosporidia: *Plasmodium*, etc.
    c. Piroplasmorida: *Babesia, Theileria*, etc.
  2. Platyhelminthes
    a. Cestoda
    b. Trematoda
  3. Aschelminthes: Nematoda
  4. Acanthocephala
  5. Arthropoda: phoretic Diptera and lice

ECOLOGY

With few exceptions, arthropod-borne parasites of the above categories only periodically or erratically trespass in humans. Instead they revolve usually in feral and domestic orbits. They do so because environments providing most frequent contacts between susceptible arthropods and susceptible vertebrates are those where both components range freely. All wild animals, most domestic ones, and primitive people live in intimate association with many arthropods. Some arthropods, particularly certain insects, have become domesticated, and carelessness may produce significant populations of these carriers. Man, therefore, may acquire certain arthropod-borne pathogens by ranging into haunts of carriers, or he may encourage the carriers to enter domestic situations and thereby set the stage for epidemics. In the former capacity arthropods pass a pathogen around in animals other than man, normally, while in the latter situation man more frequently is both donor and receiver of the agent of disease. There are possibilities of elaborate ecological bonds that must be understood before we can control diseases borne by arthropods.

Definite centers or *foci* seem to account for both the remarkable local occurrence and the recurrence of diseases tied to arthropods (Pavlovsky, 1946), and the foci may survive without regard to the presence or absence of humans. They may exist as chronic infec-

tions in populations of wild or even domestic animals without manifestation of malignant symptoms. Basic to such foci are (1) causative
agents: *pathogens,* (2) hospitable vertebrates: *hosts,* (3) potential vertebrate hosts: *suscepts,* and (4) animate or inanimate carriers: *vectors.* Many of such diseases involve one or several arthropods either as simple vectors or as *vector-hosts* of the pathogens. A
hospitable arthropod has capacity as a vector-host largely in proportion to the time it spends in contact with the vertebrate host of the
pathogen. However, the presence of pathogen, vector, and suscept
accounts for only part of the necessary environment.

Foci may be isolated, but more often they are interlocked by
carriers. In the presence of adequate vectors, survival of a pathogen
depends on kind and abundance of suscepts. Survival is most dependable where some of the hosts are tolerant and develop parasitemia to a level infectious to vectors. However, most hosts vary
in response to a parasite so that a combination of susceptible species
provides the most stable environment. Interconnected foci permit
a pathogen to expand its horizon as carriers move it to new combinations of hosts. Parasites circulating in such complexes may do
so even though no tolerant host occurs, provided the foci are sufficiently numerous and are isolated part of the time. Man is particularly involved in the latter situation when epidemics strike. He also
becomes an incidental host when he invades a zoonotic focus. Examples of these will be developed in the following chapters.

Contacts between agents of disease in these categories and
arthropods show varying degrees of dependence on the part of the
agents. A number of bacteria that are contaminants in food and
water and are also found on or in bodies of insects (enteric bacteria)
are incidental associates. In these instances the pathogens merely
have short rides between hosts and suscepts. Others are more dependent on some arthropod in which the pathogen is *propagative* (*Pasteurella*) or even *cyclopropagative* (Protozoa and worms) (Meyer,
1948). In any event relatively few hosts, known as *effective hosts,*
are responsible in any one environment for maintaining a center of
infection. Effective hosts offer hospitable tissues, but they also provide the proper exposure of the pathogen to a susceptible host.
Pathogens in all categories may have sequences of vertebrate hosts
that vary according to season, locality, or complexity of the ecological relationships. In each instance a definite combination of
hosts is basic to the maintenance of the parasite. Some hosts permit

the parasite to expand its horizon, and still others provide the chain that results in epidemic explosions. Actually there are few agents that cause arthropod-borne diseases of man that do not also have extra-human hosts. Even though the final link in the transmission chain may involve some other means, one or more arthropods are always in the chain.

Any parasitic association that perpetuates itself must have a component (host or combination of hosts) that is susceptible to infection, and it must have a parasite favorable to some part of the host population. A good host allows a dependable proportion of parasites to be propagated. At the same time a "good" parasite must permit adequate survival of its host or some part of the host complex. Agents that cause these diseases very often find man a poor host since he dies, becomes immune, or leaves a sphere of transmission while infective. A good host not only must be hospitable to a parasite, but it must dispose the parasite for ready transfer to a vector. As an example, after a parasite infects the blood of a vertebrate, the host in turn must circulate the infective stage near the body surface so that it is easily available to some hematophagous arthropod. Further, the good arthropodan vector-host must have a feeding habit that will enable it to puncture the infected tissue. This may mean a clipping action of mouth parts as in the case of black flies and *Onchocerca* worms. It may mean capillary feeding instead of pool feeding as in the case of mosquitoes and blood-vascular filariids. Lastly, a good vector must have recurrent contacts with the mutual host of the parasite.

ZOONOSIS

Diseases, the agents of which periodically trespass human spheres, in general belong to an ecological class called *zoonoses*. The word "zoonosis" was introduced into parasitological literature some time ago by Virchow. It has now been adopted by the World Health Organization and other responsible agencies to mean those infections the agents of which are naturally transmitted between vertebrate animals and man. In accordance with ideas of Heisch (1956), the word "infection" instead of disease has been used in stating the general concept of zoonosis because an agent does not always show clinical manifestations even in some of its vertebrate hosts and yet may do so when inoculated into man or some other vertebrate. As of 1957, the World Health Organization listed only

87 diseases of vertebrates (zoonoses), the agents of which are transmissible to man by one means or another. Many new ones of viral
origin have been added since (Casals, 1961) (see also Chapter 8).
Medical entomology is particularly concerned with those infections
having arthropods appearing somewhere in the chain of transmission.

Usual transmission routes for zoonotic agents are from wild or
domestic animals to man. This orientation of thought should not be
held rigidly as some organisms may pass from humans to domestic
or wild animals as well (see *Pasteurella pestis*). The usual zoonosis
involves man as an accidental or terminal host for the pathogen, and
the resulting disease is a kind of *parazoonosis* (Garnham, 1958).
When man is an essential host of a pathogen, the category of disease
is that of *euzoonosis*.

RESERVOIR

A zoonotic agent lives part of its life in an arthropod and has it
as a host just as it has a vertebrate. While it may cause no malignant
effects, it is a parasite. It also lives serially in the two kinds of hosts.
In some instances it may be more durable in the arthropod than it is
in the vertebrate component of its host complex. A term is needed
that encompasses the gamut of hosts as an ecological complex. Such
a term does exist in the one word *reservoir,* a term that occurs commonly in the works of European and other writers. Unfortunately
the word reservoir has been used by some writers in a variety of
restricted senses, but in the absence of a better word, it will be used
in this book in its wider scope. The complex of organisms hospitable
to a pathogen may be said to be its reservoir, and no distinction is
made between vertebrate and arthropod. Some tissues are more
suitable to a parasite, and certain tissues harbor a pathogen for
longer or shorter intervals than do others, but these conditions affect
only the degree of significance of a particular host in a reservoir.
Ecologically, and therefore epidemiologically, the grouping of all
hosts hospitable to a parasite as one entity, the reservoir, will permit
fuller comprehension of the whole environment of a parasite.

Arthropod-borne zoonotic agents may have combinations of six
possible transmission chains in their progress toward humans. Current usage now sanctions the following terms: (1) intersylvatic,
(2) sylvatic-domestic, (3) sylvatic-human, (4) interdomestic, (5)
domestic-human, and (6) interhuman. An *intersylvatic* chain of an

infectious agent is one involving arthropods, vertebrates, and any other organism outside a domestic orbit. A *sylvatic-domestic* chain includes both wild and domesticated hosts either vertebrate or arthropod. A *sylvatic-human* chain exists when man ranges into haunts of the wild hosts of a potential human parasite. An *inter-domestic* chain involves domestic vertebrates and their associated arthropods. A *domestic-human* chain includes man and a domestic host, while an *interhuman* one involves humans as the only verte-brate hosts and one or more arthropods.

TRANSMISSION

Maintenance of any aspect of a reservoir of an infectious agent requires transport of the agent by either an arthropod or a verte-brate. The arthropodan carrier of a pathogen is usually called a *vector,* but no name is commonly used for a vertebrate carrier. Brumpt (1937) designated the latter a *porter.* A specific name is needed because common acceptance restricts usage of the word vector to non-vertebrate carriers. Very often a vertebrate provides the means for transport of a pathogen to new orbits, therefore some name should be given. Porter might just be the word.

Another useful ecological gambit is a series of terms for routes of transmission of an infectious agent. A discussion in Horton-Smith (1957, p. 177) calls attention to *vertical, horizontal,* and *zigzag* or *circuitous* routes. Any pathogen that goes directly from one animal to another within a species without intervention of another species is said to be transmitted vertically. Examples are (1) serial passage from generation to generation (rickettsiae and spirochetes from parents to offspring of ticks and mites) and (2) direct, intraspecific transmission (as bacteria from man to man). The horizontal trans-mission pattern requires one species each of vertebrate and arthro-pod in the manner of plasmodia that move between humans by way of some *Anopheles* mosquito. A *circuitous* or *zigzag* route involves an interrelated combination of vertebrates and arthropods, as does the agent causing jungle or sylvatic yellow fever and most arthro-pod-borne infectious agents.

One of the more significant aspects of the transmission of these agents in the sylvatic phase of the reservoir is that which occurs at interfaces or zones of transition. The environments at margins of deserts and flood plains of rivers are subject to recurrent and violent changes in response to variable rainfall. Both vectors and porters of pathogens are activated by the changes and contact between arthropodan vectors and vertebrate hosts is increased. Savanna-forest and prairie-forest interfaces provide sites for exchanges of vectors and porters that may extend the reservoir of an infectious agent. Changes at such interfaces have much to do with fostering outbreaks of otherwise latent zoonoses.

The following chapters of this book are devoted to relating the components of reservoirs of numerous pathogens to their total environment. By gaining insight into interactions of the components, the student may see more clearly some ways to lessen the distress caused by arthropod-borne diseases. The great strides made in the direction of control have employed such knowledge. Much more remains to be done.

ADDITIONAL READINGS

AUDY (1958a) and GARNHAM (1958) must be read thoroughly in connection with the reservoir concept. Zoonoses require greater knowledge of ecological predisposing factors. These references highlight the field.

The Russians, notably PAVLOVSKY (1927, 1946, 1955) and his co-workers (1945, 1951, 1955), have contributed much toward the significance of focal centers for arthropod-borne pathogens. Nearly all of this work is in Russian. For those with knowledge of the language, works by these authors should be seen.

CHAPTER 8

Protophyta I: Virales

GENERAL

Protophyta has come to be the taxon sometimes used to include biota lacking nuclear organization and thought to be primitively acellular (Breed, 1956). It includes such diverse forms as viruses, phages, bacteria, spirochetes, rickettsiae, and blue-green algae. While doubt exists about details of phylogeny of this entity, it is a convenient category for placement of organisms so different from those with elaborate organization. Three of the components of this taxon, spirochetes, viruses, and rickettsiae, are categories whose vertebrate zoopaths, with few exceptions, are dependent on arthropods for their maintenance and propagation. Several species of pathogenic bacteria also are dependent on arthropods.

The phylogeny of the order Virales is a subject of disagreement among microbiologists. Breed (1956) has placed here the phages, viral phytopaths, and viral zoopaths as suborders within Virales. He then groups them with Rickettsiales to form a class in the Protophyta. Philip (1956) gave the name Microtatobiotes to this class. At all levels below suborder, attempts at classification of Virales have failed because phylogeny is wholly unknown, and no acceptable system for a binomial nomenclature has been proposed. Nomenclature within the order is now in a chaotic state reminiscent of that of the naming of pets. Some agents have been given geographical designations (Rift Valley fever); others have been named for some prominent symptom with which they are identified (yellow fever); still others have been named for an associated arthropod (Anopheles A); lastly, names may combine geography and symptomatology

(St. Louis encephalitis). Whatever the deficiencies of the current system of nomenclature, chaos bids fair to be perpetuated for some time. In the following discussion each pathogen is designated by the word *Virus* followed by the trivial name in italics (example: *Virus yellow fever*).

Viruses are microbial midgets characterized by Rivers (1948) as a "heterogeneous group of infectious agents that are smaller than ordinary bacteria and require susceptible host cells for multiplication and activity." Cells respond to invasion by viral agents by becoming hyperplastic or by becoming necrotic or by both, according to Rivers. Viruses change or "mutate," and the changed form is capable of propagation. They may be either a complex of chemicals or disarmingly simple in form; therefore it is difficult for some to accept them as monophyletic.

Viruses of medical importance either have man as the sole host species or have him and some arthropod as hosts, or they move from other animals, sometimes through arthropods, to humans. Mites, ticks, lice, flies, and fleas provide the means for inter-vertebrate passage for those borne by arthropods. Those having arthropods in the chains of transmission are called arthropod-borne animal viruses and are usually zoonotic in origin, and man is often a terminal host. The closer man lives with the zoonotic hosts, the more frequently he becomes infected. In some instances he may be removed from basic foci of a pathogen and yet become infected by way of intermediate chains.

Viruses that have been associated with arthropods include scores of forms, and new ones are constantly being added to the list. Over 100 of these currently known are distinctly arthropod-borne. Casals (1961) has placed these in four large groups and nine minor ones. They have an obligatory trophic association with arthropods and furthermore depend on them for transmission between vertebrates. A number of the viruses are known only from the arthropodan components of their reservoirs. Undoubtedly some of these agents cause diseases that are now grouped in such categories as "fevers of undetermined origin." Casals (1957) began systematizing the order into groups on a physiological basis. Those borne by arthropods will be discussed according to the known groups.

The fate of zoopathic viruses in arthropods is known only superficially. Either they are contaminants, especially on surfaces of the mouth parts, or they become benign parasites of tissue (Dick, 1957).

The following viruses are contaminants: *equine infectious anemia, rabbit myxoma, Shope fibroma, vesicular stomatitis, swine pox,* and *fowl pox.* Shope and myxoma viruses may multiply in mosquitoes, but they have been found only in the head. Viruses that develop in arthropods become distributed throughout their bodies. For a time they may be non-infective, only to increase later and then continue infective for the life of the host. Those that are systemic in ticks may invade the gonads and be transmitted to the F_1 generation. The case for biological association with an arthropod is considered established when at least one of the following relationships exists: (1) virus requires an insect in its reservoir, (2) a non-infective interval follows ingestion, (3) virus survives vertical transmission, and (4) virus ultimately increases in titer.

Transmission of viruses between arthropod and vertebrate occurs normally at the time of feeding of the arthropod. If the agent is merely a surface contaminant, it first becomes detached from that part of the arthropod in contact with vertebrate tissue; then later it enters a proper infection court. If the agent has a propagative phase in an arthropod, it is introduced with saliva into a feeding puncture after a generative phase in tissues of the arthropod.

In spite of deficiencies in knowledge of true phylogeny within the group, physiological affinities beyond the scope of this book permit grouping of viruses into categories, however unnatural. The groups currently in use are (1) Group A, (2) Group B, (3) the Bunyamwera group, (4) Group C, and (5) ungrouped. Viruses are considered here according to these categories.

VIRUSES OF GROUP A

Of the twelve viruses shown in Table 15, those best known are the ones causing eastern and western equine encephalitis. We know that few of the group are narrowly restricted in range, but the extent of none is known. All have avian-culicine reservoirs, and domestic animals and man often become terminal hosts.

Chamberlain *et al.* (1954) have noted that "between the time of ingestion of virus-infected blood by an arthropod and the ultimate transmission (of the agent) to a susceptible animal, there must be an infection of invertebrate tissue, multiplication of virus and distribution of virus in infectious amounts to the feeding organs. The interval during which this occurs has been termed the extrinsic incubation period." The titer of eastern equine encephalitis virus does increase in mosquitoes. Sudia *et al.* (1956) found an over-all increase up to 500 times in *Aedes sollicitans* in the laboratory. Optimal transmission occurs after 13–17 days at 26.6° C in *Aedes aegypti*, according to Chamberlain *et al.* First the level declines along the line of the normal death curve; then it follows the normal growth curve. Chamberlain and his coworkers considered that a concurrent growth and decay of virus is the likely reality. Viruses of eastern and western equine encephalitis behave similarly.

Table 15. Viruses of Group A.

Name of Virus	Distribution
Aura (Be Ar 10315)	Brazil
Chikungunya	Eastern and South Africa
Eastern equine encephalitis (EEE)	U. S. and Caribbean Islands
Mayaro	South America
Middleburg	South Africa
O'nyong nyong	Uganda
Semliki Forest (SF)	Uganda, Philippines
Sindbis	Northern Africa, Australia
Una (Be Ar 13136)	Brazil
Uruma	Bolivia
Venezuelan equine encephalitis (VEE)	Northern South America
Western equine encephalitis (WEE)	North America, Europe

Virus Chikungunya causes a dengue-like disease, in which severe joint pains are characteristic. This virus is similar to, but distinct from, *Virus Semliki Forest* (Mason and Haddow, 1957). There appear to be two forms of the virus now called A and B which need to be clearly separated. Some part of the complex has caused outbreaks in man in southern Tanganyika, in Transvaal, and in Uganda. The disease is familial, involving all persons in the same hut and often all in the same village. It strikes Africans, Asians, and Europeans indiscriminately during an outbreak. Only the interhuman phase of the reservoir in a domestic orbit is currently known, but a sylvatic one is postulated since *Aedes africanus*, a sylvan mosquito, has been found naturally infected. The domestic *Aedes aegypti* has been found infected also. Bed bugs harbor the virus when they occupy residences where patients live. Salivary transmission is the probable means of movement of virus from host to host.

Virus eastern equine encephalitis causes inflammation of cells found in the central nervous system of horses, primates, and numerous birds. Permanent damage may be done to areas of the central nervous system, and death is common. Isolated outbreaks have been reported among humans in the United States from Kansas eastward to the Atlantic Coast. Its range now includes the southern Caribbean Islands, and it may be much more extensive. Daubney and Mahlav (1957) have reported a form in the Middle East and Asia that is indistinguishable from this virus. Birds are particularly prone to harbor the virus, and pheasant and redwing blackbirds sometimes suffer severe decimation because of it. Between 1951 and 1958 some 15 outbreaks were reported among captive pheasants in Connecticut alone (Luginbuhl et al., 1958). Wallis (1959) reported that the virus is significant as a cause of disease only in horses and pheasants in Connecticut, since human cases have not been confirmed.

The basic focus is woodland in character and involves several species of birds and possibly several species of "swamp" mosquitoes. Woods having a high water table where boggy conditions grade into drier soil provides the ideal environment (Fig. 66). Mosquitoes most apt to be vector-hosts in the basic reservoir in eastern United States are *Culiseta melanura* and possibly *Anopheles crucians* as they are wholly or largely avian feeders. Vertebrate components over the same area include over 20 species of wild birds that may roost or nest in the basic environment; among these birds are several migrants. The grackle, egret, black-crowned night heron, and ibis circulate the virus at subclinical levels. While viremias attained in some birds are no doubt below the level required for inoculating mosquitoes, the ibis and black-crowned night heron do tolerate viremias well above minimal. The redwing blackbird, English sparrow, cedar waxwing, and pheasant are highly susceptible to the virus, and many die from attacks. Crows, jays, and catbirds may show pronounced viremias while domestic fowls and pigeons seem to be tolerant. The migrants become porters for the virus up and down their flyways when their ranges overlap those of resident species and when local vectors such as *Culex salinarius* are present.

The virus escapes its sylvatic orbit and invades a domestic one where suitable mosquitoes provide escape routes. Horses, domestic fowl, captive pheasants, English sparrows, and man may become inoculated with the virus. *Culex salinarius*, a species that invades domestic sites, is a possible vector. This mosquito is found in places frequented by migrant water birds during their flights. Species of *Mansonia, Psorophora, Aedes,* and even *Anopheles* may play some parts as vector-hosts. Downs et al. (1959) found the virus in *Culex*

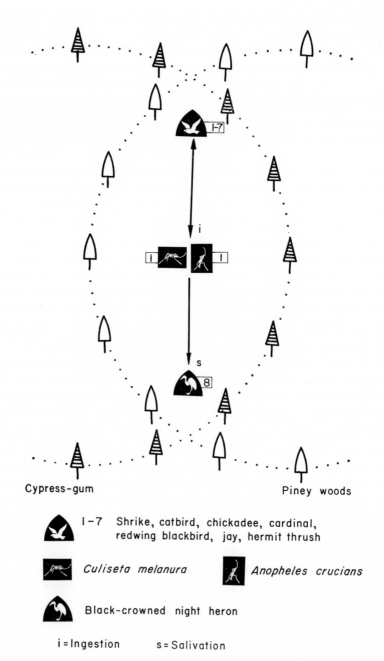

Cypress-gum   Piney woods

1-7   Shrike, catbird, chickadee, cardinal,
       redwing blackbird, jay, hermit thrush

       Culiseta melanura   *Anopheles crucians*

       Black-crowned night heron

    i = Ingestion   s = Salivation

Fig. 66.   Reservoir for *Virus eastern equine encephalitis* in southern
United States in the spring.

nigripalpus and *C. taeniopus* in Trinidad during migration seasons of birds.

Karstad *et al.* (1960) found by neutralization tests that numerous wild birds and rodents had been inoculated in Wisconsin. Pheasant, ruffed grouse, starling, fox squirrel, and three-lined ground squirrel showed a high incidence of prior infection. Apparently the virus can survive in dried blood for two or more weeks and may be transmitted directly from bird to bird (pheasant) through "peck wounds."

Virus Mayaro (syn. *Tr.* 4675) causes a mild febrile disease of humans in South America. As now named, it has been determined from Trinidad and Brazil. Its name is of geographical origin as the site of its discovery was Mayaro County, Trinidad. The reservoir includes man, but the phases and routes of transmission remain to be discovered. The original isolation was from a pool of the mosquito, *Mansonia venezuelensis.* Symptoms of headache, nausea, aches and pains, and mild jaundice may persist from 2 to 6 days. This virus is closely related to *Virus Semliki Forest* and its specific identity has been questioned (Casals and Whiting, 1957). The two agents do differ consistently in complement fixation and in inhibition of hemagglutination. Possibly they are parts of a complex of viruses representing extremes of a sort which more study will clarify.

Virus Semliki Forest (syn. Kumba) is a neurotropic one in monkeys which was isolated from wild mosquitoes of *Aedes* (*Aedimorphus*) *abnormalis* complex of eastern Africa in 1942. The area is a relict strip of primary forest which was in contact with the main Semliki Forest in western Uganda. Immunological evidence indicates that the virus seems to have been active in both humans and at least 12 species of wild primates over a large area of Uganda (Smithburn, 1948). No actual human cases have been reported. Range of this virus may be considerably greater than restrictions here indicate.

Virus Sindbis was first recognized in 1952 in the Sindbis area of Egypt. It is probably widely spread over Africa and India. Limited surveys in the Nile Valley indicate the presence of an extensive reservoir, including wild and domestic birds and domestic mammals together with the common mosquito, *Culex univittatus.* Isolation of the virus has been made from wild hooded crows in Egypt. Laboratory efforts have incriminated monkeys, chickens, heron, crow, and dove, in which the virus circulates in the peripheral blood. Mosquitoes of the subgenus *Culex* provide an adequate arthropodan component of the reservoir because of their predilection for blood of both birds and mammals. Dermanyssid mites and argasid ticks may harbor the virus.

Virus Venezuelan encephalitis causes a mild disease of man and is encephalitic in horses in the coastal region around the southern Caribbean and across Colombia to Ecuador. Encephalitis caused by the virus is significant to public health in several endemic sites, especially around the coastal plain of Ecuador. The vertebrate reservoir involved horses and man in nature, and no doubt birds enter the picture since several species can maintain the agent in the laboratory. Levi-Castillo (1952) listed the following mosquitoes as part of the reservoir in Ecuador: *Aedes taeniorhynchus, A. serratus, Mansonia titillans,* and *Culex pipiens fatigans.* Later he suggested that a *Culicoides* sp. was possibly a part of the reservoir. In the laboratory the several species, after ingesting an infecting dose of virus, become capable of transmitting the virus within 1 or 2 weeks.

Virus western equine encephalitis (syn. epizootic equine encephalitis), like its eastern counterpart, causes epidemic neurotropic disease in horses and a dengue-like disease in man. It, too, causes a variably severe zoonosis in birds. The disease is of most concern for humans in the irrigated areas like those in the central valley of California. It has been epidemic among horses and humans at least on the northern Great Plains. In 1941 an epidemic struck man in an area of North Dakota, Minnesota, and neighboring parts of Canada, and over 3,000 cases were reported, with a mortality of 8–15 per cent. It was said that an outbreak in central United States in 1937 resulted in the death of many thousands of horses. Bardos (1957) recovered this virus from the brain of a rodent, *Apodemus* sp., in Czechoslovakia.

Two axes of distribution for the disease occur from south to north across contiguous United States into Canada. The better-defined one is in the West wherever irrigated farming is practiced; it extends from southern California to British Columbia. Along this axis the pathogen is uniformly present. The eastern axis is somewhat spotty though it ranges from the Caribbean littoral to southern Canada. It is related to flood plains of rivers as well as the vicinity of lakes of the Great Plains. Some outbreaks have occurred east of the Mississippi River.

The reservoir for this pathogen basically includes mosquitoes and birds, as does its eastern counterpart (see Fig. 67). Foci con-

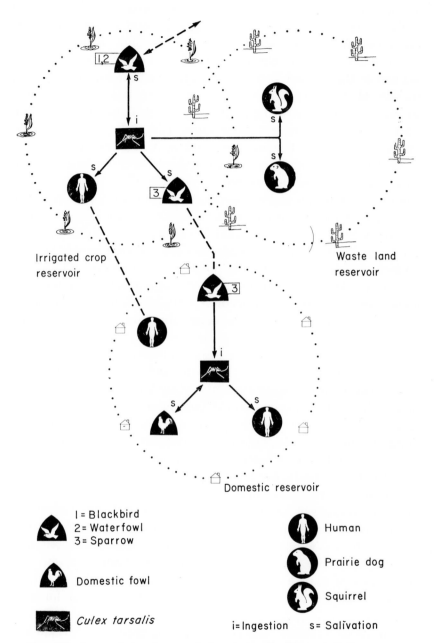

Fig. 67. Reservoirs and transmission chains for *Virus western equine encephalitis* in western United States.

taining reservoirs are in woodland sites, irrigated arid areas, and the northern plains. Kissling *et al.* (1955) described a reservoir in central Louisiana at the interface of a cypress-gum swamp and pine woods. Shrike, catbird, chickadee, cardinal, redwing blackbird, jay, and hermit thrush have been found to harbor the virus in that locality. By March, *Culiseta melanura* and *Anopheles crucians* may become infected. *Aedes infirmatus, A. mitchellae,* and *Culex* spp. enter the reservoir during the summer, and *Culex* mosquitoes are especially significant because they feed on both birds and man.

Migratory wading and swimming birds may become infected before they move north, and any or possibly all of them could distribute the pathogen to local mosquitoes along the route of migration. Since some migratory forms fly directly to the lake regions of the Great Plains, inoculum could be carried great distances. The significant vector-host of the plains is *Culex tarsalis,* as it is in western foci; and *Aedes nigromaculis* has been incriminated in Colorado. *A. vexans,* a known vector-host, may be significant where rookeries of the black-crowned heron occur. Ground birds such as pheasants and prairie chickens are highly susceptible and could provide the explosive force for an epidemic on the northern plains.

The importance of domestic reservoirs must not be overlooked. These include chicken, duck, pig, horse, and English sparrow. The latter could take the agent from a sylvatic focus to a domestic one because it ranges between them. Chickens sometimes show an incidence of infection of over 50 per cent. Domestic *Culex* are hospitable to the virus, and variants that cross-feed between birds and man are suitable vector-hosts. Dermanyssid mites may acquire the virus from their hosts, but whether they are incidental or basic to a domestic reservoir is in doubt.

Two reservoirs of interest are as follows. Foci on the West Coast of the United States involve irrigated areas adjacent to waste land (see Fig. 67). Various migratory waterfowl, blackbirds, and sparrows together with *Culex tarsalis* comprise the basic reservoir. The significance of squirrels (*Sciurus griseus*) and prairie dogs (*Citellus beecheyi*) in the reservoir is possibly important in California at least.

This virus survives well in susceptible species of mosquitoes. Immediately after ingestion, and for some four days, the virus declines even in favorable host species, but after the fifth day it increases. The preliminary decline is possibly caused by the loss of virus that fails to invade hospitable tissue. The subsequent increase is a result of new virus generated in the tissue. Incubation at about 21° C results in a decline in the transmission rate for about nine days. Between the thirteenth and the fortieth days, transmissibility rises. It is surmised that the decline in rate of transmission for the first nine days is due to decrease in mechanical transmission of ingested virus. Subsequent transmission is by salivary injection of new virus. High temperatures (32° C) had the effect of compressing the required times, so that a high rate of transmission was attained within 13 days.

Culex tarsalis is a good host for this virus, as has been shown by the work of Barnett (1956). The mosquito may become an effective vector within four days after its infective meal, and in one instance a single mosquito was able to inoculate 107 birds. A significant feature of this species is its capacity to retain the virus for some months even in cold weather. Females collected in abandoned mines in Colorado at elevations between 5000 and 8000 feet yielded virus as late as December 30. This ability to carry virus for long periods may be significant in inaugurating an active focus among vertebrates the following year.

VIRUSES OF GROUP B

Only four of the viruses listed in Table 16 are widely enough known to be discussed. These cause dengue, Japanese B encephalitis,

Table 16.   Viruses of Group B Other than Tick-borne Ones.

Virus	Region
Bat (salivary gland)	North America
Bussuquara	Brazil
Dengue	Tropicopolitan
Ilhéus	South and Central America
Japanese B encephalitis (JBE)	Orient
Modoc	California
Murray Valley encephalitis (MVE)	Philippines, southern Australia
Ntaya	Africa, Philippines, Malaya
Powassan	Canada
Spondweni	South Africa
St. Louis encephalitis (SLE)	U. S., Caribbean Islands, Philippines
Turkey meningoencephalitis	Israel
Uganda S	Southern Asia, eastern Africa
Wesselsbron	South Africa
West Nile (WN)	Asia, Africa
Yellow fever (YF)	Ethiopian, neotropical
Zika	Eastern Africa, Philippines

St. Louis encephalitis, and yellow fever. The last of these is best known historically and is the one most feared. The Bunyamwera and tick-borne subgroups have been placed together for convenience.

Virus dengue (syn. breakbone fever, etc.) is a complex of immunologically distinct but antigenically related viruses that cause a febrile disease of short duration in humans. Symptoms of intense muscular pains accompanied by fever are followed by a rash. Within 5 to 9 days the symptoms subside. Strains of the virus are antigenically related to those causing yellow fever, West Nile fever, and Japanese B encephalitis.

Dengue is caused by a complex of four currently known strains designated I, II, III, and IV. The first of these is known from Hawaii, New Guinea, Japan, India, and Malaya. Strain II has been isolated in New Guinea, India, Thailand, and Trinidad. Strains III and IV are known from the Philippines. While the disease is widely known, the composition of strains elsewhere is unknown at present. From foci in the wet tropics, the inoculum has been exported to all of Pacific Oceania, parts of Australia, and littorals of the Indian Ocean, the Mediterranean, and the Caribbean. Coincidence of this disease and the coastal environment has long been a subject for speculation, and the work to determine the reservoir was done quite recently. Heretofore, man and aedine mosquitoes of the subgenus *Stegomyia* have been presumed to be the essential reservoir in spite of the fact that no part of the human component is tolerant toward the agent.

It is true that continuous coastal distribution of the virus is possible in a culicine-human reservoir (Fig. 68). Undoubtedly this was so in the days when coastal transport was by means of sailing vessels. Transient man infected the domestic *Aedes aegypti* living aboard the vessels and transmission was effected in a closed *aegypti*-human reservoir while in transit. Vector-mosquitoes as well as human porters transmitted the agent to resident humans and local mosquitoes at ports of call. Epidemics resulted wherever unlimited contact was provided between man and *Aedes aegypti*. Prior to establishment of quarantine stations, transmission was uncontrolled. It is conceivable that at one time the culicine-human reservoir was of itself enough to maintain the virus in an intricate tropical trading community even though man is not a tolerant host. Isolation of the ports for a period that would permit return of massive susceptibility but not long enough to allow all ports to be freed of virus is all that

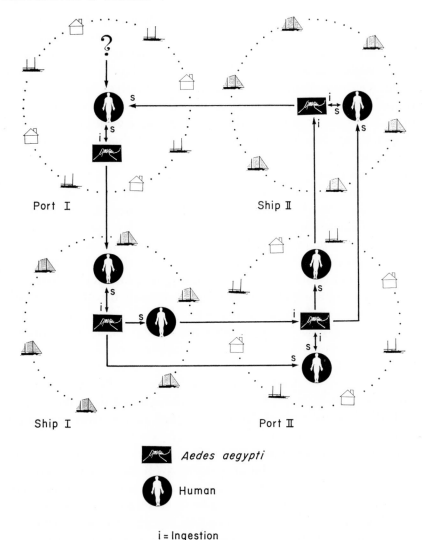

Port I

Ship II

Ship I

Port II

Aedes aegypti

Human

i = Ingestion
s = Salivation

Fig. 68. Transmission routes for coastal foci of *Virus dengue* as they probably existed during the age of commercial sailing.

would be required for maintenance. Modern means of ocean-transport and port inspections have eliminated this chain, as neither porters nor vectors move from port to port. Dengue still persists as a localized urban problem in Panama for reasons not clear.

Mosquitoes that may act as hosts for this virus all belong to the subgenus *Stegomyia* of the *Aedes*. This group is South Asian, Australasian, and African in distribution except for the tropicopolitan, domestic *Aedes* (S.) *aegypti*. Outbreaks of dengue in the New World and temperate regions everywhere have been altogether associated with this mosquito, while those in Malaya, Australia, and Pacific Oceania seem to have other representatives in the reservoir as well. Smith (1956) considers that dengue is a zoonosis among animals of forest canopy in Malaya (Fig. 69) and must have sylvan *Stegomyia* species in the reservoir. In Pacific Oceania, *Aedes* (S.) *albopictus* and those in the *scutellaris* complex are vectors of the virus to rural man.

The status of animals other than man as components of the reservoir for this virus is unclear. Rosen (1958) stated that all evidence now available indicates that only man is involved, at least in Panama, where local urban outbreaks occur. Observations in Queensland (Rowan and O'Connor, 1957) extended earlier observations that an association exists between occurrence of epidemics of dengue in Australia and subsequent ones in a northwesterly direction to coastal Asia. They examined several species of wading and aquatic birds and found evidence of prior infection by the virus. That animals other than man are hospitable to the virus is shown by the fact that the cave bat (*Myotis lucifugus*) is an excellent laboratory host (Reagan and Brueckner, 1952). The flying fox (*Pteropus* sp.) was shown by Rowan and O'Connor to be infected in the wild.

Little is known about the development of the virus in mosquitoes. It may become infective to a mosquito when ingested from a donor during the 18-hour period prior to onset of symptoms and up to three days after the initial symptoms (Rodenwaldt, 1952). An infected mosquito may transmit the pathogen not less than two days after an infective meal, and usually after seven days. Mosquitoes have been known to remain infective for six months (Blanc and Caminopetros, 1930). This agent cannot be maintained in mosquitoes at temperatures below 18° C.

Virus Japanese B encephalitis (syn. Russian autumnal encephalitis) is a neurotropic species that in its severe form causes fever, vomiting, rigidity, and mental confusion in man. Degeneration and necrosis of neurones in the cortex, together with edema, are pathological effects. A mortality as high as 60 per cent has been reported. Characteristically the disease is mild or inapparent, with the ratio of inapparent to clinical cases estimated at about 1,000:1 (Rivers and Horsfall, 1959). Symptoms are also manifest in pig and domes-

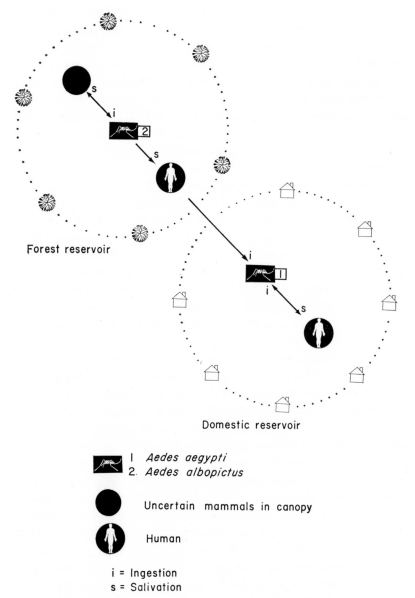

Forest reservoir

Domestic reservoir

1 *Aedes aegypti*
2. *Aedes albopictus*

Uncertain mammals in canopy

Human

i = Ingestion
s = Salivation

Fig. 69. A possible reservoir for *Virus dengue* in Malaya.

tic fowl. The virus is widespread over the Orient from Borneo to
India and northward to Japan and eastern Siberia.

The reservoir for this pathogen seems to be an avian-culicine one
of both wild and domestic birds (Gresser *et al.*, 1958). Scherer and

Smith (1960) established the fact that herons and egrets are the important feral hosts of the virus. They have inapparent infections and develop antibodies. Domestic swine may be significant in domestic reservoirs. Both birds and swine become viremic for as long as four days, and in the presence of abundant vector-hosts provide a potential source for human outbreaks. A number of observers have incriminated *Culex* mosquitoes of the subgenus *Culex* as vector-hosts. In Japan and Singapore *C. tritaeniorhynchus* is the usual one, while *Culex gelidus* is the vector-host in Malaya and the *C. vishnui* group is involved in Southern Asia. The virus has been obtained from wild *C. pipiens pallens* in China. Savanna mosquitoes belonging to the genera *Aedes* and *Culiseta* are also hospitable to the virus and must be regarded as potential feral hosts. A mosquito-bat chain may account for survival of this parasite in some instances.

The fate of the virus in mosquitoes has been demonstrated by Hale *et al.* (1957) and LaMotte (1960). *Culex tritaeniorhynchus* ingests the virus along with the blood, and some ten days later the virus has increased in amount so that transmission by salivation is possible. After ingestion the usual decline in virus (eclipse phase) has been noted for 48 hours. The initial site of multiplication of the virus appears to be in the epithelial lining of the mid-intestine. Particles of the agent are released into the hemolymph and are carried to secondary tissues, including the salivary glands, where multiplication continues. High concentrations of it occur in tissues of the nervous system, but no damage to the cells has been observed. There is great latitude in amount of virus that constitutes as infective dose for this mosquito, and regardless of amount, some individuals would not become infective. This may mean that genetic or individual differences explain non-susceptibility within species.

Virus Murray Valley encephalitis causes a disease (sometimes called Australian X disease) in birds, mammals, and man in southern Australia. Characteristic symptoms are vomiting, trembling, convulsions, coma, and even death. Hemorrhages of capillaries in the meninges and other parts are characteristic histological conditions. Most domestic mammals and fowls may be components of the reservoir in one way or another. Numerous species of water, shore, and land birds in endemic centers have antibodies for the virus, and a high proportion of domestic chickens sometimes show antibodies. At least four species of culicine mosquitoes enter the reservoir, and seven others are known to be hospitable to the virus. Species of the genus *Anopheles* seem to be inhospitable to the extent that transmission is blocked. McLean (1955) reported that when the virus is ingested by a hospitable mosquito it first multiplies in the cells of the gut and then becomes translocated to the hemocoel, where some hundredfold increase takes place. The ability of a mosquito to transmit the virus appears to be related in some way to the reproductivity of the virus in the gut of the mosquito. At 26° C the virus requires about 13 days for incubation (Rozeboom and McLean 1956). The salivary system becomes infected and serves as means of transfer of this pathogen.

Virus St. Louis encephalitis causes a neurotropic disease that usually follows a benign course manifested by a headache and slight fever with complete recovery within a few days. Inapparent infections may be experienced by over half of a population in an infected area. Severe symptoms are convulsions followed by a prolonged recovery period. The virus was thought to be confined to central and western continental United States until Downs *et al.* (1957) isolated it from Trinidad and Galindo *et al.* (1959) found it in Panama.

The basic reservoir is thought to be an avian-culicine one. The exact nature of the environment in which the virus maintains itself is not known though it is thought to be upland woods. All species of blackbirds are probably important porters. Downs *et al.* incriminated nestling rusty doves. The flicker and at least 10 other species of upland birds may play some part in maintaining this agent. Over much of the range the culicine component involves species of *Culex* (particularly subgen. *Culex*) such as *C. pipiens fatigans, C. coronator,* and *C. caudelli. Psorophora* spp. and members of the sabethine genus *Sabethes* are possible vector-hosts in the tropics. All of the *Culex* mentioned feed readily on birds, and *C. pipiens fatigans* does so in domestic situations. The virus is transmitted by salivation, and it will persist in tissues of mosquitoes for several weeks.

Existence of acarine components of the reservoir is considered likely, but the significance needs further study. In 1941 Blattner and Heys reported that the tick (*Dermacentor variabilis*) could ingest the virus and impart it while feeding during any subsequent stage even to the F_1 larvae. Virus persisted in these ticks for 10 months at 12.5° C, and then it was transmitted in a viable state by feeding. Controversy continues over the significance of mites in the reservoir, but evidence credits mites with frequent infection during times of severe outbreaks.

Virus yellow fever causes an acute, febrile disease of man and other primates in Africa, South America, and Central America. Death or immunity is the reward for an attack. Diagnosis requires detailed knowledge beyond the scope of this account. The disease is known to the French as *fièvre jaune,* and to the Spanish as *negro vómito* and *fiebre amarilla;* at the time of the Spanish conquest, Indians in Mexico knew it as *matzlazahuatl.* Whatever the name, this disease has caused panic equaled by few others. Its appearance was always sudden, and the mortality occurring within a few weeks of the onset of an epidemic was often high. As a direct effect, trade and even communication was virtually stopped in an afflicted city, and many persons left for the hinterland or for areas far removed.

Symptoms of yellow fever vary from a mild infection to death. Between these extremes are fever, jaundice, and hemorrhagic tendencies in mucosa and food tube. Lifelong immunity is the reward for survivors. The incubation period in humans is roughly 3–6 days when the agent is transmitted by normal means. Details of symptomatology are to be seen in Strode (1951) and Rivers and Horsfall (1959).

Yellow fever came to prominence as a disease of the trade territory of the Caribbean Sea and the Gulf of Mexico during the eighteenth and nineteenth centuries (Fig. 70). Port cities of North America and even some in Europe having commercial contact with the area experienced outbreaks. As interisland and interport trade flourished, epidemics became progressively more frequent. Boston, New York, and Philadelphia felt the heavy hand of yellow fever. In 1793 the death rate in Philadelphia attributable to this one cause was reported as one in ten. New Orleans, Mobile, and the Texas ports suffered heavy casualties. During the last century New Orleans alone had eight epidemics, each of which killed over 2,000 residents, and in one outbreak some 13,000 deaths were reported. The disease often spread from port cities of the Gulf Coast to the hinterland along navigable rivers. St. Louis, Missouri, and other riverine ports of the Mississippi Valley experienced outbreaks following those in New Orleans.

The virus of yellow fever exists in a primate-mosquito reservoir. Man is the primate component in urban areas, while monkeys are needed in tropical forests. The culicine element ingests the agent

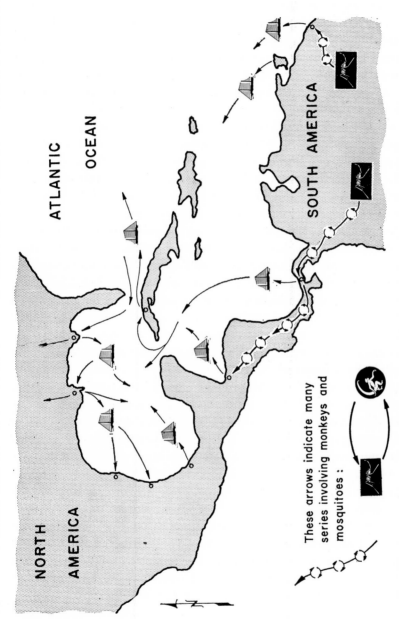

Fig. 70. Routes of movement of the virus of yellow fever overland and by way of sailing ships around the coasts of the Caribbean Sea and the Gulf of Mexico.

These arrows indicate many series involving monkeys and mosquitoes :

while feeding on a febrile primate soon after the onset of symptoms. A parasitized mosquito itself becomes infective after a period of several days. Inoculation is by salivation. The agent first invades the lymph nodes where it multiplies; later it re-enters the blood and is carried to the spleen, liver, kidneys, other lymph nodes, and even the bone marrow. Either death or immunity of the primate comes after an inoculation. Chronic yellow fever is unknown, in man at least.

The port or urban phase of the transmission, shown in Fig. 70 as it appeared until a century ago, required only man and the tropico-politan, domestic mosquito *Aedes aegypti.* This mosquito is adapted to all domestic situations where the water level fluctuates in open water tanks, barrels, and small containers, and to sailing ships having water casks and innumerable small collections of water above and below decks. Thus a sailing ship at sea could carry a closed reservoir for the propagation of the virus of yellow fever when either an active case of the disease or infected mosquitoes came aboard at some port of call. On arrival of a seagoing reservoir at a port, the pathogen was taken ashore in either a sick person or an infected mosquito. If the transfer to shore was effected by a mosquito, initial cases in the port were quick to appear. If the pathogen went ashore via a diseased person, resident cases were delayed until local *Aedes aegypti* became infected.

An urban or port reservoir could and did exist only as long as maritime transients, both human and culicine, were available for dispersal of the virus (Carter, 1919). Each isolated port reservoir was a self-limiting one because the pathogen either immunized or killed the human component before a new generation of susceptibles was born. As a result, an epidemic in a port would die out automatically irrespective of the population of *Aedes.* While an epidemic was in progress, a transient human or a local mosquito might become infected and board any ship in the harbor. Then the seagoing reservoir would maintain the agent in transit. By this means the virus could reach a new port, where a new epidemic would begin if a non-immune population was available. In time, the port of origin would be freed of the pathogen as a result of either immunization or death of the inhabitants. Years later an epidemic might repeat itself in such a city because a generation of non-immunes had come into being. For example, New Orleans had only eight epidemics within the span of a century.

Late in the nineteenth century the United States Public Health Service instituted off-shore inspections of all inbound ships, and those having cases of yellow fever aboard were quarantined or refused entry. As a result of these regulations, the disease began to disappear from ports along the Gulf Coast. Final eradication of the disease from the shores of this country came during the first decade of this century when sailing ships disappeared. Soon afterward yellow fever was eliminated as a port disease in the Western Hemisphere.

The work of a commission sent by the United States Army to Cuba at the close of the Spanish-American War hastened the progress of eradication of yellow fever from port cities. This commission proved the Finlay hypothesis that, in ports, *Aedes aegypti* was the vector of the virus. Gorgas and others directed campaigns first to free Havana, then other port cities in the islands and around the coasts of the Caribbean Sea, by rigid elimination of larval sites. Permanent eradication came with elimination of vectors and porters aboard vessels at sea. With no new cases coming into ports, a local epidemic died of its own inertia.

Although yellow fever disappeared from urban populations, the virus continued to thrive in vast tropical forests. The medical world became aware of this in 1933 when a small outbreak of the disease struck the interior of Espirito Santo, Brazil, where no port reservoir existed. All of the cases were widely scattered in unrelated rural areas, and rarely was more than one person (always an adult) affected in a family. Furthermore there was no known domestic vector. Absence of a vector and presence of disease in only one class of the society suggested transmission along paths other than those of urban yellow fever. Some reservoir other than an interhuman one was indicated.

For a long time a sylvatic reservoir had been thought by the layman to exist. Folk tales often called attention to the fact that the jungle became quiet immediately preceding outbreaks. Balfour (1914) reported that residents of Trinidad foretold epidemics in man when they saw dead and dying howler monkeys in the "high woods." Records of the chief medical officer of that island reported one outbreak prior to 1914 that had no possible connection with ports. The first cases were among oil drillers working in the forest near the site of a newly cut right-of-way. Balfour said that cases often occurred among oil drillers in remote sections of Venezuela.

At present the disease is confined to the wild reservoir in the forested areas of South America, Central America (see Fig. 71), and central Africa (Fig. 72). In the main, each of these reservoirs is a complex of wild primates and their diurnal mosquitoes found in the

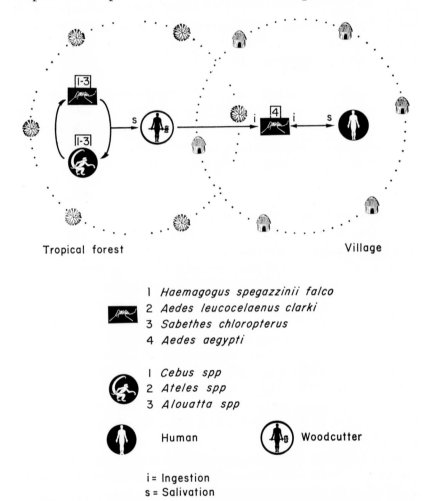

Tropical forest   Village

```
    1 Haemagogus spegazzinii falco
    2 Aedes leucocelaenus clarki
    3 Sabethes chloropterus
    4 Aedes aegypti
```

```
    1 Cebus spp
    2 Ateles spp
    3 Alouatta spp
```

Human   Woodcutter

i = Ingestion
s = Salivation

Fig. 71. Reservoir for *Virus yellow fever* in northern South America.

high canopy of forests. In the Americas at least three kinds of monkeys and as many canopy mosquitoes are important. The most highly susceptible is the howler (*Alouatta*); spider monkeys (*Ateles*) are somewhat tolerant, while the white-faced ones (*Cebus*) are more tolerant. Davis and Shannon (1929) noted that *Cebus macrocephalus* harbors the virus without clinical symptoms. The night monkey (*Aotus*) and the marmosets (*Marikina*) are susceptible, but probably are not normal components of the reservoir, since neither their habits nor their ranges bring them into contact with

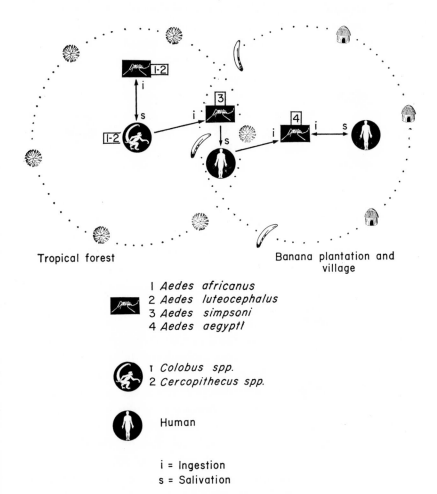

Tropical forest   Banana plantation and village

1 *Aedes africanus*
2 *Aedes luteocephalus*
3 *Aedes simpsoni*
4 *Aedes aegypti*

1 *Colobus spp.*
2 *Cercopithecus spp.*

Human

i = Ingestion
s = Salivation

Fig. 72. Reservoir for *Virus yellow fever* in gallery forests and adjacent banana plantings in central Africa.

the proper mosquitoes. Other mammals suspected of being a part of the reservoir are opossums (*Metachirus*), kinkajou (*Potos*), olingo (*Bassaricyon*), agouti (*Dasyprocta*), and pygmy anteater (*Myrmecophaga*). Unless some other mammal is found that is sufficiently tolerant of the virus and permits its circulation for a long time, we must consider primates as the only efficient vertebrate components. We also assume that colonies of monkeys must make and break contact as they (or some of them) move about in large forests. Colonies of monkeys in the sylvatic reservoir must be sufficiently detached from each other to permit the production of a new generation of non-immunes after each outbreak and before a new one strikes. This situation parallels the case of man in a port reservoir.

Forest mosquitoes that have been implicated in the South American reservoir are *Haemagogus spegazzinii falco, Aedes leucocelaenus clarki,* and *Sabethes chloropterus.* These mosquitoes are most abundant in the canopy of rain forests and their numbers decrease in a northerly direction across Central America. Some species of *Haemagogus* cover the entire range of monkeys to the northward, and one species, *H. equinus,* has a range beyond that of monkeys to the southern tip of Texas.

The stable phase of yellow fever in the Western Hemisphere occurs in forested areas of South America especially where riverine and hill forests meet. The populations of any one species of monkey are low and the number of species is greatest in this area where the populations of the canopy vector-hosts are relatively high. This results in a high rate of transmission even when a substantial portion of the mammal hosts is immune. In Central America culicine components are present in reduced numbers while the population of non-immune monkeys is relatively large so yellow fever exists in an apparently unstable state. The few mosquitoes that become infected have maximum possibility for disseminating the virus because nearly all hosts of the mosquitoes are suscepts. *Haemagogus mesodentatus* ssp., *H. equinus,* and *Sabethes chloropterus,* together with *Ateles* and *Alouatta* monkeys, comprise the reservoir in Guatemala (Rodaniche and Galindo, 1957, and Boshell and Bevier, 1958). *Sabethes chloropterus* is a vector only when a primate is attacked by several infected mosquitoes because each harbors little virus (Rodaniche *et al.,* 1959). Its potential as a vector lies more in its great longevity especially during dry seasons. These observers propose that this trait may be the answer to the question of survival of the virus when new mosquitoes are not being added to the population.

Yellow fever is currently recognized in two endemic areas of Africa. The large one is encompassed between 15° North and 10° South. The smaller one is in Northern Rhodesia. The larger area extends from the savanna country south of the Sahara across the rain forests to their southern fringe, and from the Atlantic on the west to Ethiopia and Uganda on the east. Urban epidemics are known in West Africa, but usually the virus is in its sylvatic reservoir. The extensive wild reservoir occurs largely in the gallery forests along the great rivers. In addition, two other kinds of reservoirs are known in areas subject to drought, one appearing in Kenya, the other in Sudan.

In the rain forest, monkeys of the genera *Colobus* and *Cercopithecus*, together with canopy *Aedes*, comprise the reservoir. Undoubtedly this reservoir is maintained in a manner similar to the one in South America; only the cast of characters is different. *Aedes africanus* and *A. luteocephalus* are the significant sylvan vector-hosts in the vast reaches of the rain forests, while *Aedes deboeri* is suspected in the highlands of eastern Africa. Sylvatic transmission to man is the only route currently recognized. It takes place at the forest fringe under two conditions. Either man goes into the forest where a troop of canopy primates has left inoculum in mosquitoes of the fringe, or a porter monkey has inoculated mosquitoes in a banana plantation. *Aedes simpsoni*, the common vector in forest fringes and banana plantations, inoculates workers or transients in the area. An infected person may spark an epidemic in villages wherever the domestic vector-host, *Aedes aegypti* is present.

The occurrence of a wild reservoir in dry regions of East African lowlands and in areas subject to prolonged drought requires the postulation of a reservoir different from that in the rain forest. Few adult mosquitoes of any kind survive the drought, and even monkeys are said to be too scarce to be important components. In such a situation in Kenya, Lumsden (1955) called attention to the work of Haddow in which a lemuroid of the genus *Galago* (bushbaby) is the vertebrate concerned. Mosquitoes are unlikely to be significant since transmission occurs when they are rare. Furthermore bush-babies take refuge in cavities in trees during the day, where they are unlikely hosts for canopy mosquitoes. Lumsden suggests that some acarine resident in dens of the lemuroid is a likely vector. Since bushbabies sleep in different holes from time to time, some hospitable, sedentary arthropod capable of transmitting the virus seems to have possibilities as the means for carrying the virus through adverse seasons.

Epidemics occur among nomadic herdsmen on the plains of southern Sudan near the Nuba Mountains (Taylor *et al.*, 1955).

Presumably herdsmen acquire the virus during the dry season when they are concentrated around water holes at the foot of the mountains. Monkeys and baboons use the same water holes. Mosquitoes (possibly *Aedes luteocephalus*) transfer the agent to the nomads (Mattingly, 1958). As the rains come, the herds move out on the plain and near wooded valleys. Grivet monkeys are infected from the herdsmen. The high incidence of immunity in children of the tribesmen shows that the disease is not limited to one segment of the population as is the usual case at fringes of rain forests farther south.

The virus persists in a hospitable mosquito for the span of the life of the mosquito, although it is changed in some way. Davis *et al.* (1933) showed that the concentration of the virus was maximum shortly after it entered the mosquito. Boorman (1960a) noted that about 0.1 per cent of the virus appears in the hemolymph within less than two hours after an infective meal, and the remainder probably never leaves the food tube, where it is bound in by the peritrophic membrane. The small fraction of the virus that circulates in the hemolymph becomes fixed in some tissues and undergoes the "eclipse phase" so called by some authors. Within a few days the virus reappears in the hemolymph and becomes generally distributed. The mosquito becomes infective during this phase and remains so for life. For *Aedes aegypti* the pre-infective interval is 4 days at 37° C and 11 days at 23.4° C. This developmental interval for the virus in mosquitoes explains the observations recorded by Carter (1900) and by David Hosack as far back as 1814 that the incubation interval in man was about 5 days, but that the interval between the appearance of a first case and the occurrence of any secondary cases in an area was not less than 15 days. This difference represents the 5-day incubation in man and the 10-day interval in mosquitoes.

Transmission of the virus from a mosquito to a primate is by means of infected saliva introduced into the feeding puncture. Unquestionably this is the classical route in both the interhuman phase and the sylvatic one involving arboreal primates; however, it is not necessarily the only route. Findlay (1941) stated: "That mosquito bites are not the only means of transmission of yellow fever has been realized by the ease with which those who are not immunized become infected when working with the virus under laboratory conditions; . . . [for example] rhesus monkeys may develop spontaneous infection if they are confined in a room which has contained infected monkeys some months previously." Aragao (1939) suspected infected fecal droplets from mosquitoes as sources of infection in forests. The virus has been found viable for at least 12 days in excreta of bed bugs in the laboratory (Kassianoff, 1937).

Virus Uganda S has been shown by serological surveys to infect man, monkeys, and mosquitoes in eastern Africa, and foci have been reported in Singapore and Borneo. Infection of man with this agent is relatively common in parts of Nigeria. About 88 per cent of the children tested in one locality showed protection against the virus, even though clinical cases appear to be unknown. Apparently there is some relationship between the agent and that of yellow fever, since this virus may produce antibodies for the virus of yellow fever in man. It has been isolated from a collection of *Aedes* mosquitoes in Uganda. Over 40 per cent of the population in a village in Nigeria indicated possible prior infection by this organism (Boorman, 1958).

Aedes aegypti will harbor this agent for at least 79 days after a preliminary incubation period in the mosquito, according to Boorman.

Virus West Nile is a conspicuous cause of a dengue-like febrile disease in children of Egypt and in countries around the Mediterranean to the east and north. It probably is widespread over all of Africa and southern Asia to Singapore. Human infection is regular and commonplace in the Sudan and southern Egypt, and it is sporadic as island outbreaks in the northern part of the range (Taylor *et al.*, 1956). Infections of children by the virus renders them immune, so that in parts of Egypt over 70 per cent of the population more than four years of age show immune reactions. Since immunity results from an infection, it is assumed that man must not be a basic component of the reservoir.

Taylor and his co-workers proposed that a bird-mosquito reservoir was more likely the basic one. Certain birds circulate the virus in higher concentrations in the blood than is the case with man. The non-migratory hooded crow, buff-backed heron, domestic sparrow, and domestic pigeon, together with *Culex univittatus* and others of the subgenus *Culex*, probably comprise the resident reservoir. Since the disease in man is seasonal in northern Egypt and is general in southern climes, a migrant of some sort, possibly a bird, could account for the northward movement of the virus because a number of birds do migrate from tropical lands into zones of prevalence of this agent. Bird-mosquito-man transmission is possible through the medium of resident birds and *C. pipiens molestus* (Taylor *et al.*, 1956), because this mosquito feeds almost equally on man and birds. In Uganda a wild primate, blue monkey, is a likely component of the reservoir. *Culex vishnui* is the probable vector in Madras, India (Varma, 1960).

The ability of any particularly susceptible mosquito to become infective depends on the incidence of virus in the peripheral blood of the donor. When the titer of the virus in a vertebrate exceeds 3.5 logs, all mosquitoes become infected (Hurlbut, 1956). When the titer is at a level of 1.5 logs, only one in nine mosquitoes could ingest enough of the agent to become infective.

The fate of this pathogen in mosquitoes follows the pattern known for other viruses. The concentration declines during the first day or two after ingestion; on the third day it begins to rise; and by the seventh day it may reach a level somewhat higher than the initial dose ingested (Tahori *et al.*, 1955). The organism invades tissues of the head, thorax, abdomen, wings, and legs (Davies and Yoshpe-Purer, 1953). The most favorable temperature for the maintenance of the virus in a *Culex* mosquito is that between 25° C and 33° C; however, temperatures of 12–33° C did not inhibit transmission in the laboratory. After the fourth day transmission by salivation may occur at time of feeding.

Soft ticks, of the genus *Ornithodoros*, may harbor the virus, at least when inoculated by injection into the hemocoel, and all tissues as well as saliva and coxal fluid, may become infected (Hurlbut, 1956). No transmission could be demonstrated after ticks had ingested blood from a donor host that had virus circulating in titer high enough to infect mosquitoes.

Virus Wesselsbron is the cause of epizootics of a febrile disease of sheep in South Africa. Death is common, and losses among flocks may be very high. This virus is transmitted by means of at least two mosquitoes, *Aedes caballus* and *A. circumluteolus* (Kokernot *et al.*, 1958).

Virus Zika causes a degenerative disease of the central nervous system of primates in Uganda. It was first isolated in Zika Forest from monkeys and later from the canopy mosquito, *Aedes africanus*. During an outbreak of jaundice, it was isolated from humans in western Africa. Weinbren and Williams (1958) quote a description of pathogenic properties as follows: "There is a degeneration of nerve cells especially in the region of the hippocampus. Cowdry type-A inclusion bodies are found in areas of degeneration. Extensive softening occurs in the brain."

VIRUSES OF BUNYAMWERA GROUP

Viruses of the Bunyamwera group are known in nature only from their culicine hosts. They are encephalitic to weanling mice. All seem to be non-pathogenic for older mice and rabbits when inoculated intramuscularly; even so, they are immunogenic when inoculated into vertebrates. Antibodies have been found in humans for the Bunyamwera virus in Uganda, Tanganyika, and Nigeria (Bedson *et al.*, 1955). It was isolated from a pool of *Aedes* mosquitoes obtained in the Semliki Forest in 1943 (Smithburn, 1948). *Virus Cache Valley* was isolated in 1956 from a pool of *Culiseta inornata* in Utah. It is not infectious for chicks, but it may produce viremia in horses (Holden and Hess, 1959). The virus possibly occurs in islands of the Caribbean and in Brazil. The Kairi virus was isolated from a pool of *Aedes scapularis* from Trinidad, according to Holden and Hess. Other isolations have come from species of *Wyeomyia*, *Psorophora*, and *Culex* (Anderson *et al.*, 1960). The *Wyeomia* virus came from a pool of *Wyeomyia melanocephala* in Colombia in 1944. *Virus Germiston* came from collections of *Culex rubinotus* near Johannesburg, Union of South Africa, in an industrialized community (Kokernot *et al.*, 1960). *Virus Ilesha* known from Africa and *Virus Chitnoor* from India and Malaya are the other known representatives. There is reason to believe that viruses of many more forms are present in insects, so this list is presented with the idea that it indicates where investigations have led; we should see scores of new viruses added in the future.

VIRUSES OF GROUP C

Casals (1961) has designated as Group C six currently known viruses. They are *Apeu, Caraparu, Marituba, Murutucu, Oriboca,* and *Itaqui.* All are borne by mosquitoes and have been isolated from eastern Brazil. Some of them were described by Causey as representing this group of viral zoopaths. At least two, *Marituba* and *Oriboca,* become systemic in man and have been isolated in nature from man, other animals, and mosquitoes. The one called *Apeu* has been taken in the wild in mosquitoes.

Tick-borne Viruses

Tick-borne viruses (see Table 17) that cause encephalitis syndromes seem to behave very much alike. Rivers and Horsfall (1959) grouped the Eurasian forms into a complex and treated them as variants while the American form (CTF) was treated separately. With the exception of the causative agent of louping ill, all cause acute fever with varying degrees of psychic disturbances (Shubladze, 1958). Involvement of the central nervous system varies from slight to flaccid paralysis and death. Residual paralysis is a common sequella. Incidence of inapparent infections is reputed to be high. All of the viruses in this series have sylvatic reservoirs, and most have domestic ones as well. Apparently KF is known only from sylvatic orbits. The central European variants have transmission chains involving both ticks and milk.

Table 17. Viruses of the Tick-borne Group.

Name of Virus	Distribution
Diphasic meningoencephalitis (DM)	Russia, eastern Europe
Kyasanur Forest (KF)	Southern India
Langat	Malaya
Louping ill	Britain
Omsk hemorrhagic fever (OHF)	Siberia
Russian spring-summer encephalitis (RSSE)	Asia

Virus diphasic meningoencephalitis (syn. Central European tick encephalitis) causes a disorder of the central nervous system that is common in rural Slovakia and possibly elsewhere in eastern Europe. It may appear in man only as an influenza-like disease lasting 4–6 days, or it may show a later meningo-encephalitic phase usually involving the third to sixth cranial nerves. Foresters and rural residents are most often attacked. Libikova *et al.* (1960) found antibodies in domestic inhabitants as follows: man, 18 per cent; sheep and goat, 23 and 32 per cent, respectively; and old cattle, 50 per cent. He points out, also, that the percentage of domestic animals that may disseminate the virus is small. This small number is significant as far as man is concerned because many cases arise after persons have drunk raw milk from viremic animals. Milk from goats with inapparent cases is a particularly good carrier. According to Blaskovic (1960), man is the only sensitive indicator of a focus of this disease, because wild viremic hosts are inapparent ones.

Radvan *et al.* (1960) found that basic foci for this virus are clearly defined forested areas. These were sites in which the horn-beam-oak complex had been replaced by fir, where there was no undergrowth and the ground was covered by a deep layer of needles. Centers of foci with marshy growth dominated by alder are common features. Large numbers of the tick, *Ixodes ricinus,* are always present because of the abundance of its hosts.

Besides ixodid ticks the reservoir is composed of rodents, carnivores, and ungulates. Wild rodents of significance are species of *Apodemus, Clethrionomys, Microtus,* and *Sorex.* Other wild hosts include deer, badger, fox, and squirrel. Encephalitis in man increases as the number of rodents increases. Ixodid ticks are important in the propagation of the virus not only as a vector-host but as a means for carrying the virus from season to season (Rehacek, 1960). The virus has remained alive for nine months in unfed female ticks held at 4° C. It has survived in juvenile ticks throughout a winter and has even passed into a later instar.

Virus Kyasanur Forest is neurotropic and indigenous to the forest (of the same name) in Mysore, India. The known infested area is in the eastern foothills where rainfall is 30–80 inches annually. The forest is intermittent, tropical, evergreen, and deciduous, and is contiguous for hundreds of miles along the Western Ghats. It causes a disease in humans characterized by generalized aches and pains with petechial hemorrhages in the mucosa and overt hemorrhages from body openings. Symptomatology suggests a close relationship between this virus and the one causing Omsk hemorrhagic fever of central Asia. KF appears as explosive outbreaks and is entirely new and different from any other illness known in Indian history. It appears among persons a week or so after they have visited forested areas.

The reservoir is basically a tick-avian one, but several mammals may harbor the virus. The agent has been isolated from *Haemaphysalis spinigera,* a common parasite of birds in Kyasanur Forest. The black-faced monkey, *Presbytis entellus,* has been found naturally infected. Other wild animals showing neutralizing antibodies include palm squirrels and forest shrews. Humans are only accidental hosts.

Virus Russian spring-summer encephalitis (RSSE) causes severe encephalitic symptoms in man. The acute meningoencephalitic phase is common from the Far East westward throughout Russia.

Until recently, the disease was thought to be confined to northern latitudes of eastern Europe, and the USSR. It is now known from Malaya and Bombay State in India. While it is inapparent in its wild host, it is often acute in man. The disease is one of humans who enter forested areas as laborers, foresters, and campers.

Natural foci for this virus are swamp forests or taiga and savannas or wet steppes of Siberia and elsewhere (Blaskovic, 1960). Dense woods and distant steppe represent sylvatic foci, but domestic ones are known (Vereta and Sushkina, 1960). The reservoir is complex, involving ticks, mites, rodents, birds, hares, ungulates, and possibly others. Wild rodents have been thought to be the more important in sylvatic foci, but birds are now thought to be significant (Tagil'tsev, 1960). Starlings may be the principal porter of the pathogen to and between domestic situations. Goats, sheep, and cattle become infective and shed the pathogen in the milk of lactating animals.

Ticks are more often recognized vector-hosts, but hematophagous mites seem to be important components of the reservoir where nesting animals are concerned. The ixodid ticks, *Ixodes persulcatus, Dermacentor silvarum, D. pictus, Haemaphysalis japonica,* and *Hyalomma marginatum,* together with *H. detritum* and *Rhipicephalus turanicus,* contrive to spread the pathogen between wild vertebrates in the reservoir. Larvae of these ticks feed on murid rodents and on birds, while nymphs feed on hares (*Lepus,* etc.). Adults attack wolves, elk, domestic ungulates, hares, and even man. *Haemaphysalis concinna* and *Ixodes ricinus* are the vector-hosts of domestic orbits. In Malaya, where the disease is wholly sylvatic, the rodent, *Rattus rajah,* and its tick, *Ixodes granulatus,* comprise the reservoir (Smith, C. E. G., 1956a). Tagil'tsev (1960) incriminates several gamasid and laelaptid mites as vector-hosts in nests and burrows. He considers that their importance lies in the fact that these mites feed on the young of both rodents and birds, and transmission of the pathogen to young animals is more easily accomplished. He says further that in parts of the Siberian taiga 40 per cent of ixodid ticks bear the virus.

The virus is systemic in its ixodid hosts to the extent that it passes readily from stage to stage and through the gonads into the F_1 generation. It has persisted for 25 days in the gut of a tick without change in titer. In a particularly hospitable acarine host the virus multiplies, while in one poorly adapted no increase is apparent.

Virus is acquired by ingestion; within six days it has invaded the salivary glands, and then it may be transmitted by salivation at the time of feeding.

VIRUSES OF UNDESIGNATED GROUPS

Casals (1961) classified 25 viruses into nine groups that differ from each other but seemingly have no similarity to the preceding groups. He has called these "undesignated groups." Those known as *California encephalitis, trivittatus, Melao,* and *Be Ar 8033* form a group. It has been suggested that the first of these may belong to the Bunyamwera viruses. *Guama, Catu,* and *Bimiti* from eastern South America form a unit. *Bwamba* and *Pongola* viruses from eastern Africa are classed together. The geographically widely separated *Simbu, Oropouche,* and *Sathupera* species have similarities. *Turlock* from California and *Umbre* from India are similar. Colombia is the site of *Anopheles A* and *B* and nearby Trinidad is the known source of *Tr 10076*, all of the same tentative group. Trinidad is the type locality of three other (but similar) viruses all now bearing numbers. From Malaya come two grouped and numbered viruses. *Quaranfil, Chenuda,* and *Eg Ar 1034* form a group found in Egypt. All are too newly isolated for much information to have accumulated about them. At least the *Oropouche* virus of Trinidad has been found in man and howler monkeys in nature. *Mansonia venezuelensis* is a wild vector-host.

VIRUSES OF CURRENTLY UNCERTAIN GROUPING

Viruses which are parasitic in man, but whose position in the developing scheme of relationships has not been assessed, are included in Table 18. The Bwamba species has been isolated from human sera in several parts of tropical Africa. Bedson *et al.* (1955) lists Uganda, Tanganyika, and Kenya as sites for occurrence. Dick (1953) believes that arboreal primates and a flying, hematophagous insect comprise the basic reservoir. *Virus Guaroa* was isolated from human sera in Guaroa, Colombia, on the plains of the Orinoco Valley, where rainfall is some 160 inches annually. Nearly half of the residents reacted positively to neutralization tests (Groot *et al.* 1959). The virus is related to one, *Turlock* (?), commonly found in California. Better-known viruses in this group are discussed in more detail below.

Table 18. Viruses of Currently Uncertain Grouping.

Relation to Man	Name of Virus	Distribution
Pathogenic	Argentinian hemorrhagic fever	South America
	Colorado tick fever	U. S. A.
	Crimean hemorrhagic fever	USSR
	Hart Park	California
	Hemorrhagic fever (HF)	Far East
	Mengo encephalitis	Cosmopolitan
	Rift Valley fever (RVF)	Eastern Africa
	Sand fly fever (SFF)	Adriatic littoral
Presumably pathogenic	Culicoides	Trinidad
	Manzanilla	Trinidad
	Ndumu	Tongoland
	Psorophora	Central America
	Tahyna	Europe
	Tacaiuma	Brazil
	Witwatersrand	Africa
Non-pathogenic	African horse sickness	Africa and eastern Mediterranean Coast
	Blue tongue	Africa, U. S. A.
	Ornithosis	U. S. A.
	Rabbit myxoma	Cosmopolitan
	Nairobi sheep	Eastern Africa

Virus Colorado tick fever (CTF) is the one of this series known to attack man in the Western Hemisphere (Brown, 1955). Patients who were inoculated with this pathogen showed a biphasic temperature curve common to the European counterparts. It was discovered in 1930 and is now known from much of the area west of 100° West and north of 40° North. The range coincides with that of the wood tick (*Dermacentor andersoni*) (Kohls, 1956). Virus has been isolated from the ixodids, *D. parumapertus* and *D. occidentalis,* and the argasid, *Otobius lagophilus.* Wild vertebrates in the reservoir include Columbian ground squirrel, golden-mantled ground squirrel, pine squirrel, deer mouse, and chipmunk (Burgdorfer and Eklund, 1959). Incidence of infection in these rodents was as high as 13 per cent in some situations.

Rozeboom and Burgdorfer (1959) have found that this virus develops in tissues of the wood tick. When ingested by a tick in either juvenile stage, it will be retained until the imaginal stage. No significant differences were observed between virus concentrations in engorged and quiescent nymphs, but differences were significant between concentrations in nymphs and subsequent unengorged adults. Increases in titer occur during, or slightly after, ecdysis.

Virus hemorrhagic fever is an agent that causes disease in rodents and man, particularly in eastern and northeastern Asia. The disease is naturally rural and has plagued armies in both Manchuria and Korea amid the unsettled conditions since 1932. The Japanese and the Russians have indicated a rodent-arthropod reservoir. The mouse, Apodemus agrarius, and the vole, Microtus michnoi, seem to be the chief rodents in the sylvatic reservoir. The mite, Laelaps jettmari, has transmitted the virus from mouse to man, and apparently fleas may be involved in the inter-vole phase. Traub et al. (1954) did not commit any arthropod to the reservoir but suggested that trombiculid mites best fitted an explanation of a sylvatic-human phase of the reservoir. Excreta of infected rodents are a likely means of transmission from an acarine-rodent reservoir to man. Transmission by contact with a host or contaminated objects, food, or water seems improbable.

Virus Mengo encephalitis is the cause of a zoonosis in rats of various sorts, and occasionally it invades man. Dick (1953) reported that the virus has caused a widespread but non-clinical infection in at least three species of rats and is spread to man and monkeys in quarters. Mode of transmission in domestic situations seems to be through contamination of food with excreta from infected rats.

Virus Rift Valley fever causes enzootic hepatitis, a disease of antelope, sheep, cow, goat, monkey, and man over much of Africa and possibly Japan (Steyn, 1958). It causes most severe symptoms in sheep (Muspratt, 1956), as ewes abort and lambs often die. Symptomatology in man is shown by an acute fever of short duration, pain in the joints, and abdominal discomfort. Sequellae are low mortality and lifelong immunity. The virus has a mammal-culicine reservoir in both sylvatic and domestic phases. Daubney and Hudson (1933) protected sheep by keeping them under netting at night, whereas nearly all unprotected sheep nearby became infected within five weeks. Muspratt stated that natural infection of the following mosquitoes occurred in East Africa; Aedes dendrophilus, A. tarsalis, and Eretmapodites chrysogaster group In South Africa both A. caballus and Culex theileri harbor the virus in nature. Haddow (1956a) incriminated Aedes africanus and circumluteolus as vector-hosts. According to Dick (1953) Eretmapodites sp. may be significant in the sylvatic phase of the disease in central Africa. One of the African wild rats, *Arvicanthis abyssinicus* is tolerant to this virus and is easily inoculated with small doses. Possibly it is in the sylvatic reservoir.

Gillett and Mims (1955) have shown that the ability of mosquitoes to become infected depends on the concentration of the virus in the vertebrate. Concentrations up to 10^7 LD $50/0.03$ ml of blood resulted in infection in only about 3 per cent of the mosquitoes fed. At concentrations of 10^8 some 60 per cent became infective. The virus becomes undetectable in the mosquito about two days after ingestion, but it builds up later.

Virus sand fly fever (syn. phlebotomus fever, papatasi fever, and three-day fever) is the cause of an acute febrile disease of short duration in man. Headache, pain in eyes, infection of conjunctiva, and malaise characterize the disease. It is well known in areas under the direct influence of the Mediterranean climate. Its full range is said to lie largely in Palaearctica between 20° and 40° North between Italy on the west and central India on the east. This is the coincident range for its vector-host, *Phlebotomus papatasi*. Sometimes the incidence is high, as shown by the observations of Simić (1951) when he reported that up to 90 per cent of the people in certain areas of Serbia were affected in 1946. While the disease has long been known as a hazard to field armies and to transient peoples, it has not usually seemed significant to local health agencies. Presumably this is because the syndrome in adults may be a nondescript febrile illness. This is true even though immunity is unknown (Guelmino and Jevtic, 1953). Two immunologically distinct strains, the Sicilian and the Neapolitan, are known from the Mediterranean area (Sabin, 1955). The virus has been preserved in a viable state for nine years by freezing. It requires 7–10 days for incubation in the fly before it may be inoculated into man by salivation at the time of feeding (Bedson et al., 1955).

Viruses of currently unknown significance to man or other vertebrates represented by the list in Table 18 are included to show the incomplete state of our knowledge in this general field. Many more will be found in arthropods, and in time they will be assigned to complete reservoirs. This category is comparable to that in classification of fungi called Fungi Imperfecti wherein only one stage of the organism is known. It seems that in the case of the zoopathic viruses, discoveries are more rapid from the arthropodan component than from the vertebrate one. In time many fevers of undetermined origin may have their etiologies in viruses found first in the arthropod. Viruses known as *Anopheles A* and *B* were isolated from pools of *Anopheles boliviensis* in Colombia by Roca-Garcia in 1944. They cause encephalitic symptoms in mice. Friedlander *et al.* (1955) have characterized the B virus by electron microscopy. In 1954 the *Psorophora* virus was detected in a pool of three species of *Psorophora* collected in Honduras by Rodaniche (1956).

Viruses borne by arthropods but not parasitic on humans are the last four shown in Table 18. They are included as illustrations of species commonly having arthropods other than mosquitoes and ticks in their reservoirs.

Virus blue tongue is a distinct etiological entity of unknown affinity that derives its name from the characteristic symptom caused in sheep in Africa. The agent has both sheep and *Culicoides* spp. in its reservoir (DuToit, 1944). Wild-caught *Culicoides* have been used to transmit the agent at the time of feeding of the flies and by inoculating macerated flies into sheep.

Virus rabbit myxoma is the causative agent of myxomatosis, a disease of high mortality in rabbits of the Old World. Rabbits (*Sylvilagus*) of the Western Hemisphere, where the disease is indigenous, show a mild response in the form of cutaneous nodules (Fenner and Woodroofe, 1953). Elsewhere in the world where the virus has been introduced recently, the mortality among European rabbits (*Oryctolagus*) is usually 90 per cent or more. Populations of *Oryctolagus*, that have pestered Australians, have been greatly reduced by disease caused by this virus. Mortality of this rabbit in Australia may be of the order of 99.5 per cent in non-immune populations. The virus causing this disease is included here because of the extensive range of vectors associated with it.

The significance of arthropods in the reservoir is not wholly clear. Most of the evidence indicates a vector capacity only, but then one would expect other methods of inoculation. Puncture wounds such as those made by blood-sucking arthropods seem to be the only natural infection courts; yet when the virus was inoculated into confined rabbits, the agent killed up to 98 per cent of those in the compound but affected none outside. Button (1952) found that the virus spread to new territory only as rabbits spread. This would limit arthropod transmission to rabbit dens and would postulate spread by the transients.

Numerous insects have been suggested or incriminated as vectors of the virus, and conspicuous among them are mosquitoes. Ratcliffe (1955) and others have shown that several mosquitoes are possible vectors but that *Culex annulirostris* and *Anopheles annulipes* are the chief ones in Victoria and New South Wales. The former species maintains transmission in river valleys and around fringes of swamps. *A. annulipes* is important in the drier parts of the range because it takes shelter in rabbit burrows, where it has ready access to hosts. Other inhabitants of burrows that may act as vectors in Australia include the sticktight flea (*Echidnophaga* sp.), black flies (*Simulium* spp.), rabbit louse (*Haemodipsus ventricosus*), and a fur mite (*Cheyletiella parasitivorax*), according to Ratcliffe *et al.* (1952). Later Ratcliffe (1955) stated that black flies are chiefly responsible for the distribution of the pathogen over long distances in parts of Australia. Fleas voluntarily leave dead hosts and are able to transmit the virus for three days after becoming infected. There is general agreement that the rabbit flea (*Spilopsyllus cuniculi*) is the principal vector of the virus in Britain. Mosquitoes such as *Anopheles maculipennis atroparvus,* that survive the winter in domestic situations and also feed intermittently during the winter, accounted for outbreaks in domestic rabbits when infected rabbits were introduced. There are no known instances of transmission by mosquitoes in Scotland, but *Simulium reptans* could account for outbreaks. In winter, when rabbits were introduced into a warren infested with fleas 50 days after death of the previous occupants, they developed typical lesions. Myxomatosis could not be spread on the Scottish Hebrides Islands, where biting insects are absent. Corvine birds may perform an indirect function in transmission of the virus, as it seems that the rabbit flea will move from a dead rabbit to the scavenger bird, to which it clings for some time before dropping off.

Arthropods become contaminated when their mouth parts are inserted into infected epithelial cells (Fenner and Woodroofe, 1953). Rabbits serve as sources of inoculum for mosquitoes only when the course of the disease has progressed far enough to display changes in the skin. In the laboratory all mosquitoes feeding in primary lesions were positive for virus, whereas only 15 per cent of those feeding in secondary lesions became infective (Fenner and Woodroofe).

Mosquitoes often retain the virus for long periods (Andrewes *et al.,* 1956). Maximum concentration is present during the first day after ingestion, but infective doses may be retained in the mouth parts for 220 days. Virus is retained only in the head, and if artificially injected into the hemocoel, it does not multiply. Mosquitoes vary in their capability for retaining and transferring the virus. When *Aedes aegypti, Anopheles annulipes,* and *Aedes alboannulatus* were induced to probe three times each through the skin lesions, and later allowed to probe up to 21 times in succession on the backs of susceptible rabbits, *aegypti* was relatively inefficient. An examination of the maxillary stylets shows that there is a relationship between these structures and efficiency as a vector.

Virus Nairobi sheep disease causes a gastroenteritis of sheep and goats of eastern Africa. The reservoir seems to have only a domestic phase involving ovines and caprines and the tick *Rhipicephalus sanguineus* and *R. appendiculatus.* The agent may be ingested by any stage of the ticks and may persist by vertical transmission in the ticks (Lewis, 1946). When nymphs were permitted an infective meal, subsequent adults were able to transmit the virus for 871 days.

VIRUSES HAVING CASUAL ASSOCIATIONS WITH ARTHROPODS

A number of viruses listed in Table 19 may have some casual vector relationship to arthropods. All those listed have more reliable means of transfer, with the possible exception of *Virus equine infec-*

Table 19. Viruses Having Casual Associations with Arthropods.

Virus	Region	Vertebrate Host	Vector (Casual)
Newcastle	Laboratory	Chicken	*Ornithonyssus sylviarum*
Smallpox	Laboratory	Rabbit	*Cimex lectularius*
Unidentified pox (7 spp.)	Australia	Unknown	Culicidae
Equine infectious anemia or swamp fever	General United States United States	Equines Horse Horse	*Stomoxys calcitrans* *Tabanus sulcifrons* *Psorophora* sp.
Swine erysipelas	Russia	Hog	*Stomoxys calcitrans*
Encephalomyocarditis	Cosmopolitan	Rodents, primates	Culicidae (?)
Lymphocytic choriomeningitis	Laboratory	Mouse Many mammals Mouse	*Aedes aegypti* Bed-bug feces Louse
Poliomyelitis	Illinois United States	Man Man	Filth flies Cockroaches (3 spp.)
Vesicular stomatitis	Laboratory	Cattle	Tabanids, etc.

tious anemia. The anemia-causing virus, though, is vectored by large hematophagous Diptera such as tabanids. When mosquitoes are vectors, the resulting symptoms are benign. This list is included because of the possibility that in the presence of excessive populations of some arthropods, some of these viruses may attain outbreak proportions.

ADDITIONAL READINGS

RIVERS and HORSFALL (1959) is a collection of reviews by numerous authors on zoopathic viruses. This is essential reading.

CHAPTER 9

Protophyta II: Rickettsiales

GENERAL

This ordinal category now includes three families of similar microbes (Philip, 1956). Rickettsiaceae comprises several genera, two of which are of medical importance. Haemobartonellaceae comprises three genera of blood parasites. *Anaplasma* is considered to be in the family Anaplasmataceae. Formerly these groups have been placed with various microorganisms or have been left dangling according to the whims of authors. Nomenclature within the order is far from static and requires more insight into behavior of the organisms included in it before common agreement is reached.

RICKETTSIACEAE

Rickettsial agents, according to Rivers (1948) are characterized as microbes that are minute, pleomorphic, cocco-bacillary forms visible by means of light microscope. This group is similar to bacteria, in that species possess two nucleic acids designated RNA and DNA (Bell and Philip, 1952). All seem to have evolved in conjunction with arthropods, particularly acarines. Weyer (1952) said that the capacity to multiply in arthropodan tissues is so characteristic of rickettsiae that the trait is needed in defining them. Cowdry (1922) pointed out that the majority of arthropods that are hospitable to rickettsiae are hematophagous in habit. This provides the possibility of dual hosts and opens avenues of evolution toward other associations. In their further evolution some have become adapted to life in vertebrates, and some have come to survive dissociation from any organism for long periods. A few have found certain insects hospitable and seem to have left their primitive acarine hosts.

251

Glaser (1930) observed that rickettsiae in their arthropodan hosts may be extracellular, intracellular, or even intranuclear. They may occur as masses of cells inside host cells or, in the anomalous *Rickettsia quintana,* on epithelial walls. Some kinds may become systemic and others may be restricted. These organisms tend to become systemic in acarines and specific in insects. Some forms in insects occupy discrete bodies called mycetomes, and at the time of reproduction invasion of ovarian tissue is normal for these forms. Those that have become parasitic in vertebrates are able to enter ovarian tissues of acarines only.

Observers of rickettsiae in arthropods are reminded that obligatory symbiotic ones may exist in mixed culture with those pathogenic in vertebrates. Mere presence of the cells does not mean that the form is the pathogenic one.

Recognition of species of rickettsiae is possible in part by observing reactions of other organisms in contact with these bodies. Activity in a mixed culture with *Proteus* microbes has been used for some years, but as a diagnostic technique results leave much to be desired below the level of groups of species. Weyer (1952) has urged more consideration of the comparative behavior in live arthropodan hosts as a means for characterizing species. Some of the differential responses to injection into (1) body lice, (2) mealworms, and (3) vertebrates are shown in Table 20.

Rivers and Horsfall (1959) have arranged rickettsioses into five categories as shown in Table 21. The largest group is called the spotted-fever group, all agents of which are borne by acarines. Pathogens of the typhus group and trench fever are dependent on insects. Scrub typhus is mite-borne and Q fever is transmitted through acarines and fomites.

Coxiella burnetii

Coxiella burnetii (syn. *Rickettsia diaporica* and *R. burnetii*) causes an acute specific respiratory disease called Q fever, or coxiellosis or Balkan grippe. This disease is often serious in man but is rarely fatal. Normally it runs its course in 9–24 days. The pathogen is cosmopolitan and is now most often associated with cattle, sheep, and goats, from which it is transmitted readily to man. According to Luoto (1959) the disease has been found in over one-fourth of the commercial dairies in parts of the United States. Q fever has come to be an occupational hazard to handlers of ruminants and

Table 20. Differential Responses of Arthropods and Vertebrates to Coxiella and *Rickettsia* spp.

| Species | Family of Vector-Host | Pathology in Body Louse | | | Pathology in Fat Body of *Tenebrio* | Pathology in Man | |
		Epithelium of Gut Wall	Coelomic Cells	Systemic		Skin	Cells
C. burnetii	None or Ixodidae	Intracellular	Intracellular	Mortality slight	Intracellular	None	Intracellular Extracellular
R. akari	Dermanyssidae	Intracellular	None	None	Intracellular	Eschar, rash	Intracytoplasmic, Intranuclear
R. prowazeki	Pediculidae	Intracellular	None	Mortality variable	Intracellular	Rash	Intracytoplasmic
R. mooseri	Fleas, etc.	Intracellular	None	Mortality slight	Intracellular	Rash	Intracytoplasmic
R. rickettsii	Ixodidae	Intracellular	None	Mortality high	Intracellular	Rash on extremities	Intranuclear
R. conori Kenya form	Ixodidae	Intracellular	None	None	Intracellular	Eschar	Intracytoplasmic
Marseilles form	Ixodidae	Intracellular	None	Mortality high	Intracellular	Rash	Intranuclear
R. tsutsugamushi	Trombiculidae	Intracellular	None	None	None	Eschar on Europeans; no rash	Intracytoplasmic
R. quintana	Pediculidae	Extracellular	None	None	None	Rash on chest	?

their products. Herdsmen, abattoir laborers, and shearers of sheep
are particularly susceptible to attacks. Consumers of contaminated
milk are liable to infection. (Babudieri, 1959, gives a comprehensive review of knowledge of Q fever.)

Table 21. Groups of Pathogenic Rickettsiae.

Category	Name of Disease	Pathogen	Range
Q fever	Q fever, Balkan grippe	*Coxiella burnetii*	Cosmopolitan
Typhus group	Epidemic typhus, louse typhus, political typhus, Brill-Zinsser disease, recrudescent typhus	*Rickettsia prowazeki*	Cosmopolitan over cold climates
	Murine typhus, flea typhus, endemic typhus	*R. mooseri*	Tropicopolitan (humid)
Spotted fever group	Rocky Mountain spotted fever, New World spotted fever	*R. rickettsii*	Western Hemisphere
	Tick-borne typhus, boutonneuse fever, S. African tick-bite fever, Indian tick typhus	*R. conori*	Africa, Asia
	Siberian tick typhus	*R. sibiricus*	Asia
	Rickettsialpox, vesicular rickettsiosis, Kew Garden fever	*R. akari*	Probably cosmopolitan
	Queensland tick typhus	*R. australis*	Queensland, Australia
	Maculatum disease	*Rickettsia* sp.	U. S. Gulf Coast
	Infectious nephrosonephritis	*R. pavlovskyi*	Russia
Scrub typhus	Tsutsugamushi, Japanese river fever, mite typhus, scrub typhus	*R. tsutsugamushi*	Eastern Asia, Pacific Oceania, Australia
Trench fever	Trench fever, shin fever, five-day fever	*R. quintana*	Europe, North Africa, Mexico

Transmission of the agent to humans occurs primarily in domestic foci after contact with infected (1) parts of a ruminant (blood,
birth membranes); (2) secretions of ruminants (milk, saliva); (3)
excreta of domestic animals (urine, feces); or (4) dust in quarters
from hair and hide or dust raised by passage of herds. The agent
passes into the birth membranes of sheep, cow, and goat. From
these sources it reaches the litter in a stable and may infect persons

who clean the animal quarters. Transmission to man is actually seldom by direct contact; instead, the agent is usually inhaled in dust (Weyer, 1959). The dust raised by herds of sheep in transit has caused outbreaks in man in Europe. A focus of Q fever in man came from bottled milk in southeastern England, according to Weyer. Milk is a likely source in central United States where incidence in dairies may be very high (Luoto, 1959). Interhuman transmission is unusual but may be accomplished by way of urine and sputum. Weyer states that transmission among domestic animals is usually by direct contact.

Domestic foci occur where domestic animals are concentrated or confined on dry litter or in dry lots and pastures. Situations most often infested in the United States are stock yards, auction lots, fattening sheds, dairy lots, and hillside pastures. Domestic foci involving ungulates can be maintained only where frequent exchange of the stock is practiced. In southern California, such situations are a result of intensive dairying practice. Massive contamination of the establishments and frequent introduction of susceptible cattle in large numbers into the dry climates have created ideal foci. Welsh *et al.* (1959) have shown that viable rickettsiae may live for periods in excess of 100 days in soil in pastures where parturition has occurred. Water in surface pools may be positive for weeks. Foci are known among domestic fowls in Czechoslovakia. According to Syrucek and Raska (1956), migrating birds such as swallows introduce the agent to poultry farms by contaminated droppings. Wilcocks (1959) quoted reports from work done in Turkmen SSR to the effect that meat of fowls and shells of eggs could be sources of inoculum. In Europe this virus is disseminated when sheep are moved from mountain pastures to valleys. Also, on certain islands of the Mediterranean, the driving of goats through streets of villages distributes the pathogen to inhabitants. Boats transporting goats along the Pacific Coast of North America often become foci. Q fever is unknown in northwestern Europe and Ireland, where importation of domestic hosts is not practiced.

The current panzootic seems to involve only a domestic reservoir of ungulates or fowls. Ruminants are not particularly tolerant toward the pathogen, and unless introductions of suscepts is frequent, a focus disappears. Therefore a domestic reservoir can exist only as long as each focus is a link in an extensive system for exchange of sheep, cattle, and goats.

The number of susceptible wild vertebrates suggests that sylvatic reservoirs may exist in a number of regions. Among the birds susceptible to *Coxiella* are a number of species both resident and migrant. Overlapping the ranges of these birds are a number of susceptible rodents, carnivores, and insectivores. When we consider that at least a score of species of ticks representing nearly all genera have been found naturally infected (Weyer, 1959), the possibility of sylvatic reservoirs is enhanced.

Sylvatic reservoirs of *C. burnetii* are known in parts of Australia (Fig. 73), Europe, North Africa, and southeastern Asia. All that are currently known exist where a dry climate prevails, and most are at interfaces between arid or semiarid areas and grasslands (Proreshnaya *et al.*, 1960). Whereas the domestic reservoirs involve ruminants and fowls alone, the sylvatic ones center around small mammals (particularly rodents), ground birds, migratory birds, and some arthropods (Karulin, 1960). A stable sylvatic reservoir on Moreton Island near the east coast of Australia persists without importation of suscepts (Derrick *et al.*, 1939). A focus composed of tolerant and susceptible mammals occurs as bandicoot, rat, pig, and a few goats. Bandicoots harbor the agent and circulate it in the blood with no apparent injury to them. Their tick, *Haemaphysalis humerosa*, is abundant and is known to become infected naturally. This tick is able to maintain the agent transstadially and to transmit it in the generation acquiring the pathogen. Furthermore the tick infests a variety of animals including rodents, domestic animals, and the dollar bird (*Eurystomus*) that show varying degrees of susceptibility to rickettsia. Contamination of the environment by fomites from bandicoots is unknown. Ticks, therefore, seem to provide the contact between these marsupial suscepts.

Elsewhere, other likely reservoirs are less well known but seem probable because of the persistence of the agent without outside contact. *Coxiella burnetii* has been isolated from a gerbil (*Meriones*) and also from its tick (*Hyalomma savignyi*) in Morocco. Here again the tick seems to be essential. Raska *et al.* (1956) consider rodents such as *Apodemus* spp., *Microtus arvalis, Arvicola terrestris*, and lagomorphs of the genus *Lepus* to be important in the reservoir in Europe. Desert areas of south and central Asia have numerous foci where a rodent-acarine reservoir occurs (Zhmaeva *et al.*, 1955). Gerbils and *Hyalomma* ticks constitute one segment; sparrows (*Passer montanus*) and *Argas* ticks plus dermanyssid mites

constitute another. The agent survives in the feces and bodies of
dead ticks and mites for several months. Marmion (1954) referred
to reports that a reservoir, comprising a mountain rabbit, dormouse,
and a tick, *Rhipicephalus sanguineus,* existed in Spain. A natural

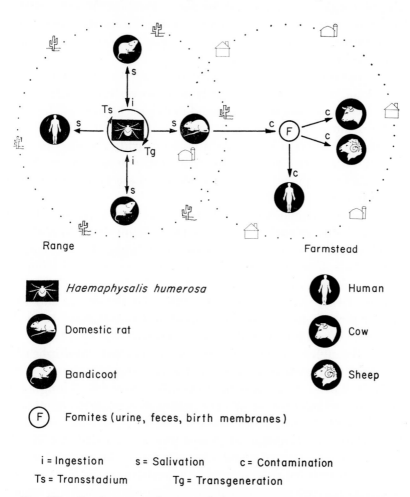

Range   Farmstead

Haemaphysalis humerosa   Human

Domestic rat   Cow

Bandicoot   Sheep

Ⓕ Fomites (urine, feces, birth membranes)

i = Ingestion   s = Salivation   c = Contamination
Ts = Transstadium   Tg = Transgeneration

Fig. 73. Overlapping sylvatic and domestic reservoirs for *Coxiella
burnetii* in eastern Australia.

focus has existed in the Crimea for a long time. An epidemic wave
was propagated from this area when extensive migrations of people
and their domestic animals took place during and after World War
II. Mountain pastures in Switzerland and western United States
may be foci for sylvatic reservoirs. Those in Switzerland involve

various ticks and the roe, while the mountain goat may be involved in the United States. Occasional cases in humans contracted in the mountains of Montana may have a sylvatic origin. Stoenner (1959) found an extensive sylvatic focus of this pathogen in arid areas of Utah. Serological evidence incriminates *Peromyscus maniculatus, Dipodomys ordii, D. microps, Onychomys leucogaster,* and *Eutamias minimus.* The tick (*Dermacentor parumapterus*) from these rodents has been found infected.

The possibility of *Coxiella burnetii* going to a wild reservoir from a domestic one seems logical in parts of western United States. Several *Dermacentor* and other ixodid ticks have been found infected in nature. Since their immature stages feed on wild rodents, those that feed on a tolerant wild rodent could provide the essential link and a sylvatic focus could exist. Altogether some 25 species of ticks and several species of dermanyssid mites are known to become infected in nature.

One sylvatic-human focus of Q fever has been reported (Pchelkina *et al.,* 1956) in northern Kazakhstan. During 1954 an outbreak was noted among workers in a labor force engaged in reclaiming virgin and abandoned steppe. The organism was isolated from the tick, *Ixodes crenulatus,* taken from a skunk in the area.

Rehn (1958) showed that ixodid ticks (*Ixodes ricinus* and *Dermacentor pictus*) are capable of supporting *Coxiella burnetii* in the laboratory. When larvae and nymphs ingested the agent, they retained it throughout their development to imagoes. Multiplication of the rickettsiae appeared to occur during engorgement and metamorphosis. Feces of the ticks bore infective forms for as long as six months after an infective meal. The pathogen becomes systemic and invades ovarian tissue. Some larvae of the F_1 generation contained viable rickettsiae. Infection of guinea pigs was carried out by (1) feeding them infected ticks and (2) inoculating them with feces of ticks. No transmission was effected by salivation.

Coxiella burnetii may become an intracellular parasite in tissues of numerous arthropods when infected in the laboratory. Weyer (1953) found that ticks, fleas, lice, bed bugs, and even larval mealworms could be inoculated successfully. Most species show infection only in the cytoplasm of the intestinal epithelium when inoculum is ingested. The organism may become systemic in acarines, particularly in argasid ticks, and cells and secretions of the coxal glands and those of salivary glands may support it. Ovarioles may become infected in argasid ticks and sometimes in ixodid ticks. When the agent is injected into the coelom of lice, for example, it invades the blood cells, the fat body, and the hypodermis. The parasite may survive for a time in some arthropods. Artificial inoculations in lice have survived and remained virulent for months. The agent has persisted in the tropical rat mite for six months and has lived as long as 75 days in dead mites. Davis (1940) reported that *Coxiella* survived for about three years in the argasid, *Ornithodoros turicata*.

The agent may pass from the normal hosts (ticks and mites) in either feces or eggs. Feces of all sorts of ticks may harbor the pathogen. When feces of ticks were applied to abraded skin, the rate of transmission was high (Smith, 1940). It may go into the F_1 and even F_2 generations in *Ornithodoros moubata* in the laboratory. Rarely does it pass to the F_1 in ixodid ticks. Dermanyssid mites are said to inject the pathogen at the time of feeding.

A domestic reservoir for this agent is possible. Daiter (1960) found wild-caught bed bugs in the epidemic areas of a Russian city naturally infested. These insects were shown to become infected by feeding on guinea pigs in the acute febrile stage of the disease. Ones bearing the pathogen sustained it for 231 days. The agent is excreted by them for at least two months. It multiplies in the bed bugs and passes from instar to instar. Proof of capability as a vector was not given.

Rickettsia prowazeki

Rickettsia prowazeki is the causative agent of a typhus syndrome that is variously called epidemic or louse typhus, Brill-Zinsser disease, Brill's disease, and jail fever, among others. It is restricted to areas where parts of the year are cold, and reaches its peak rate of transmission in late winter. Persons of all ages are susceptible. As a devastator of populations it has had few equals in Europe, where historically it has decided wars and quieted rebellions. Among the armies fighting across Europe it had no peer as an arthropod-borne disease. Napoleon, the Kaiser, and Hitler all had cause to regret typhus in their conquests to the east. At least once in this century it depopulated part of eastern Europe when it took millions of lives as an aftermath of World War I. The prevalence of the disease corresponds so closely to the declines in economic and political conditions that it has been referred to as *political typhus*. Political prisoners in several concentration camps of central Europe felt the heavy hand of jail fever when inadequate diets and indescribable filth set the stage for outbreaks late in World War II. In 1942 after three years of war, populations of North Africa, particularly Algeria, suffered enormous casualties.

Weyer (1959) has summarized the state to which this disease has been reduced in European societies. Use of antibiotic therapeutic preparations has greatly reduced the mortal effects of the disease. Residual toxicants lethal to lice have gone far to eliminate lice from all who accept treatment. Use of immunizing injections has been successful in reducing infection even in the presence of vector-hosts. In spite of all control efforts typhus is still widespread.

According to Borman (in Rodenwaldt, 1952), typhus was and continues to be endemic in countries wherever people live in privation or abject poverty. When there are many who wander aimlessly from one disreputable haven to another, their malnourished bodies and attendant lice make a vast, mobile reservoir. The reservoir is self-contained when such people live wholly with their own kind. When their wanderings bring them into close contact with other people equally unclean and malnourished, the disease spreads (Fig. 74). Even in normal times the entire area of eastern and southeastern Europe, inclusive of Asia Minor, is said to be a coherent endemic area. Epidemics expand to peripheral areas in times of stress such as economic collapse.

Since World War II, aboriginal people of southern Africa have suffered an epidemic of typhus (Gear, 1954). The restless nature of the people causes them to move about a great deal, and in their travels they stop to rest in wayside kraals. The pathogen may be left by a human carrier at a kraal to infect the residents, or a transient suscept may acquire it while at a rest stop. Funerals of the victims of typhus provide the means for spread of the disease, since the mourners crowd into the hut of the deceased one and some may come away infected. They in turn bear the pathogen to other quarters.

The reservoir for *Rickettsia prowazeki* apparently involves only man and his louse, *Pediculus humanus humanus*. The head louse and the crab louse may be secondary vector-hosts. Man is an excellent vertebrate host in certain parts of the range because all the essentials for the reservoir are provided. Man can and does become tolerant toward the pathogen where the Brill-Zinsser syndrome finds expression, as it does in urban slums of eastern Europe. In fact, any community that has suffered an epidemic of typhus "remains a potential reservoir for the rickettsiae for the lifetime of the infected generation" (Gear *et al.*, 1952). Transients carrying the rickettsiae

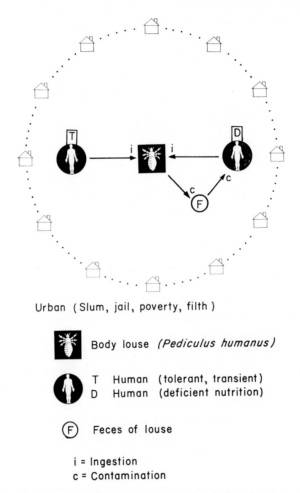

Urban (Slum, jail, poverty, filth)

Body louse *(Pediculus humanus)*

T   Human (tolerant, transient)
D   Human (deficient nutrition)

Ⓕ   Feces of louse

i = Ingestion
c = Contamination

Fig. 74. Common interhuman reservoir for *Rickettsia prowazeki* in any of its endemic centers.

may distribute them all over the world. Positive proof of this transfer was obtained when smears of lymph nodes of an emigree were taken 20 years after possible infection (Price, 1955).

Coincidence of epidemic typhus and malnutrition has been suspected from time immemorial. Fitzpatrick (1948) has shown that susceptibility in rats in the laboratory increased with nutritional deficiencies as follows: (1) low protein intake with or without adequate vitamin-B group; (2) normal protein intake and one-tenth normal intake of vitamin-B group; (3) complete diet except reduction of either pantothenic acid, riboflavin, or thiamin. These deficiencies in a human population accompany prolonged overcrowding, poverty, and filth. The introduction of a human carrier into such a situation and an increasing incidence of infestation provides both the tinder and the breeze necessary to cause this biological conflagration.

Epidemiologists have always been concerned with the ways and means of maintaining the parasite between epidemics. The possibility that rickettsiae in extra-human hosts, called by different names, may change their physiology in a man-louse reservoir has been reviewed by Price *et al.* (1958). This is not the case with *Rickettsia mooseri* at least. The most likely possibility for survival of the pathogen is in the asymptomatic human. Gear *et al.* (1952) have demonstrated that rickettsiemia may be shown in a latent carrier after many years. Wilcocks (1959a), in his summary of typhus conditions, calls attention to the observations of Kostzewski in Poland where the number of recrudescences in the first few years after illness is small, but a distinct rise in incidence occurs 10–15 years later. Many have experienced attacks 30–40 years later, and such persons could initiate an epidemic. Extra-human reservoirs may be involved in tropical areas to account for human outbreaks in times of stress (Reiss-Gutfreund, 1956). A larger percentage of domestic animals such as zebu, sheep, and goat gave higher titer in agglutination tests than did humans in a routine survey in Addis Ababa, Ethiopia. Furthermore six strains of the agent were isolated from the ticks *Amblyomma variegatum* and *Hyalomma rufipes* collected from zebu cattle. These strains were readily transmitted to lice in the laboratory.

Rickettsia prowazeki is a parasite of the epithelium of the gut of an arthropod regardless of whether the host is a louse, a tick, or a flea. The feces become infested and when dried may retain viable parasites for at least a year. The agent is pathogenic in lice and may become lethal to them as a result of the desquamation of intestinal epithelium. First the epithelial cells enlarge, then the nuclei disappear before sloughing begins. When more than 10,000 organisms form an infective dose, death may ensue within 48 hours. Smaller doses require a longer time as the organisms may increase at least 100-fold at 34.5° C. When inoculated into *Xenopsylla*, the agent appears in the epithelium within 24 to 48 hours and persists throughout the life of the flea without apparent injury. When inoculated into the coelom of lice, the organism has been observed to pass through eggs into nymphs at least in the first instar. Hog lice and crab lice are suitable laboratory hosts for this parasite when inoculated intrarectally. Death of these lice follows inoculation. In the case of hog lice, only a few cells may be invaded before death ensues. Explants of louse tissue will support this rickettsia for several days, but after repeated passages through them, the organism ceases to invade cells of the epithelium when inoculated into lice. Instead, it grows extracellularly in the manner of *R. quintana*.

Transmission of *R. prowazeki* is effected from man to louse by ingestion at times of feeding. In reverse the agent enters abraded skin when fresh or dried feces of infected lice are rubbed into the skin by scratching.

Rickettsia mooseri

Rickettsia mooseri (*R. typhi* W. and T., not A. and M., *muricola*, *manchuriae*) is the cause of a disease called endemic, flea, or murine typhus. Basically the disease is one of the warmer, more moist parts of the world, where it occurs sporadically in man. Mohr *et al.* (1953) have said that the disease is significant in the United States only where the mean January temperature is no less than 8.3° C. While distribution is basically tropicopolitan, isolated cases have occurred elsewhere. Weyer (1959) in his summary said that between 1931 and 1946 about 42,000 cases occurred in the United States. For the most part the disease is one of farmsteads, at least in southeastern United States. Since 1944 the disease has been on a decline, and in one southeastern state the annual incidence declined from 1256 to 41 cases in ten years as a result of campaigns against it.

Seasonal incidence of disease caused by this agent varies in different parts of the world, according to Weyer. It is perennial in the tropics, but in temperate climates transmission is commoner in summer and early fall. In southeastern United States the disease is most likely to appear between May and August.

The reservoir seems to be restricted to mammals, acarines, and fleas. Among the more tolerant mammals are bandicoot, opossum, cat, dog, and rabbit. The literature is at variance as to which is

most significant, but certainly rodents, and particularly rats, constitute the extensive mammalian part of the domestic reservoir. The
southern cotton rat, *Sigmodon hispidus,* having both feral and
domestic tendencies, may well be an important component of the
rural reservoir in southern United States.

The deer mouse (*Peromyscus polionotus*) is in the sylvatic phase
of the reservoir in states along the Gulf Coast (Brigham, 1937). The
exact role of the house mouse in maintaining this parasite is confused, for it is considered significant in North Africa and China but
is of doubtful significance in the United States, according to Weyer.
Rattus rattus and *R. norvegicus* are the mammals of importance in
domestic situations the world around.

Arthropods in the reservoir include fleas, mites, and possibly
ticks. The disease caused by this rickettsia is often called flea typhus
because fleas, particularly *Xenopyslla cheopis,* seem to be the arthropods most often responsible for transfer of the agent, in domestic
situations at least. Weyer lists a number of other fleas as secondary
vector-hosts. In the Indonesian tropics a trombiculid mite (*Schöngastia indica*) is important in the passage of this agent among wild
rodents. The dermanyssid mite, *Ornithonyssus bacoti* may be a
normal part of the reservoir at times. Weyer noted that the ixodid
tick, *Boophilus australis,* could become part of a domestic reservoir
in Java.

There is a question whether this rickettsia is basically sylvatic
or domestic. Actually the situation may vary according to whether
the center is tropical or temperate. Le Gac (1951) has shown that
in central Africa the agent attacks humans, but only after feral rats
have been forced into domestic situations following the periodic
burning of the savannas where the rats reside. In this area the
reservoir would seem to be sylvatic.

Rickettsia mooseri is essentially a parasite of the intestinal epithelium of fleas and other insects. It must become systemic in mites
because in both a trombiculid and a dermanyssid, it has passed to
the F_1 generation through the egg. In fleas the organism lives in the
gut and the malpighian tubules, but in lice it lives only in the gut.
Since the microbe is unable to penetrate the peritrophic membrane,
it passes through that part of the mid-gut lined by it and enters cells
to the rear before spreading anteriorly. In *Xenopsylla cheopis* the
rickettsia may increase 16-fold within three days and has been
known to survive 52 days. The agent is not lethal to fleas but is so to
the rat louse (*Polyplax*). Some exotic hosts are bed bug and *Tria-*

toma sp. Louse feces that were air-dried held live rickettsiae for 250 days (Kitaoka and Shishido, 1950).

The means are uncertain by which *R. mooseri* is transmitted to rodents and humans, according to Weyer. It is possible that humans acquire the pathogen by eating food contaminated by urine of rats. House rats could not be infected in the laboratory by food contaminated by feces of fleas, but they became infected when fed bread contaminated by urine of rats or humans. Other experiments were unable to produce infection in rats by such contamination. The most probable means for transmission is by feces of fleas. Contaminated feces, when rubbed into abrasions or punctures of the skin or mucosa, could account for transfer as it does for *R. prowazeki.*

Rickettsia rickettsii

Rickettsia rickettsii (syn. *R. brasiliensis, R. typhi* A. and M., not W. and T.) causes diseases in the New World that are known under many names. The most common name is Rocky Mountain spotted fever (RMSF). Elsewhere the disease is called Brazilian spotted fever, exanthematous fever, petechial fever, and Felsengebirgs-fleckfieber. This pathogen exists in the United States outside of New England. It is best known in the mountainous regions of the United States. It extends through Mexico and Central America across Colombia and Venezuela to Brazil. Mortality of 20 per cent and more is common. This is a severe, acute, infectious disease of the small peripheral blood vessels. A rash appears, and spots may become necrotic on the extremities. Without question RMSF causes greater damage to tissues on the surface of the body and to those of the brain than does any other rickettsial disease (Rivers and Horsfall, 1959).

Transmission of this rickettsia to man, like its counterparts in the Old World, occurs only through the agency of ticks during frost-free parts of the year (Weyer, 1959). At low altitudes in the Rocky Mountains, peak transmission takes place in April and May. In the mountains the active season is in summer. Hunters, fishermen, and foresters are most likely to be infected. Over most of the remainder of the United States transmission is effected in summer when people of all ages may be afflicted. The period of maximum morbidity is in July.

At least four general sites for transmission of this rickettsia are known in the United States. The one best studied is found in Montana where natural reforestation followed the massive lumbering operations that had denuded the hills. Human cases in this area are largely among adult males whose activities take them into this kind of environment. Beck (1955) has reported that areas for transmission in the Great Basin of Utah extend from high altitudes downward through the foothills to the desert. Here again, human cases occur among transients in sylvatic situations. Eastern foci are either urban or coastal. Urban outbreaks occur among persons of all ages who range through heavily vegetated, vacant lots. Coastal foci center around diked areas that were formerly salt marshes, where persons of all ages may be involved. Scattered cases may occur elsewhere in the United States among persons who have ranged into areas that have recently returned to a natural state.

The reservoir for *R. rickettsii* seems to involve all small mammals and their ticks that live in runways in dense vegetation where the area is reverting to a natural state. Rodents, rabbits, skunks, and possibly a few birds are hospitable to the pathogen in varying degrees. Beck has listed 12 mammal hosts for mountainous regions of Utah, 11 others for the foothills, and 17 more for the desert. A total of 40 mammals may play some part in perpetuating the pathogen. One species, *Peromyscus maniculatus* ranges all three areas and seven of those in the foothills inhabit the desert. Over much of the United States, rabbits (*Sylvilagus* spp.) and field mice (*Peromyscus, Microtus,* etc.) constitute essential mammals in sylvatic reservoirs. Dogs and ranging domestic rodents play at least secondary roles in transporting infected ticks to domestic environments (Price, 1954).

Apparently any tick that infests mammalian hosts for the rickettsia is a potential vector-host. In mountainous areas of the United States *Dermacentor andersoni* is the significant bridge between wild mammals and man. Other western vector-hosts, at least in sylvatic foci, are *D. parumapertus* and *Haemaphysalis leporis-palustris. Dermacentor variabilis* is the vector between the wild reservoir and humans all over eastern United States. In southwestern United States *Amblyomma americanum* seems to be significant as a vector-host. In Mexico and southward other ticks such as *Rhipicephalus sanguineus, Amblyomma cajennense, Ornithodoros nicollei, Otobius lagophilus,* and possibly others are vector-hosts.

Transmission both to a tick and from a tick to a vertebrate takes place at the time of feeding. The agent enters the gut of a tick with the blood. From here it soon spreads to all parts of the body, including the salivary glands. The tick may transfer the agent by salivation while feeding in a later stage and even a later generation. Vertical transfer within a tick is possible because the agent is non-pathogenic to the many different tissues, including those of the ovary that it invades. Passage from one generation to another has not decreased the virulence of this pathogen (Price, 1953).

Tissues of both ticks and humans are amply hospitable to this rickettsia, and the association is sufficiently durable to provide long-term reservoirs for it. Price (1954) stated, furthermore, that the agent lives over the winter in tissues of nymphal and adult ticks. *D. variabilis* as an unfed adult has sustained the organism for eight months without appreciable loss. It has lived 620 days in the tissues of *Ornithodoros turicata* and 345 days in *O. furcosus* (Brumpt, 1936a). The organism has been passed through four consecutive generations of *O. parkeri* and then was transmitted to a vertebrate by the vertically infected ones, thus showing that it is systemic. Since it lives so well in ticks, Ortiz-Mariotte and Varela (1949) have found them to be suitable for maintaining the pathogen for preparation of vaccines.

Price *et al.* (1958) have shown that this pathogen may survive in human lymphatic tissue for 12 months. Recrudescences may occur from such latent infections long after original inoculation. Such prolonged retention of the parasite by man probably has no significance to the reservoir, but it indicates that some other verte-brate may harbor this agent similarly.

The behavior of this organism in two exotic hosts is character-istic. It readily develops in the hemocoel of larval *Tenebrio* when artificially inoculated. In the body louse it develops profusely in cells of the intestinal epithelium, and it causes death of lice more rapidly than any other species of rickettsia except the form of *R. conori* which is the cause of Marseilles fever (Weyer, 1954).

Rickettsia conori

Rickettsia conori (syn. *R. megawi, blanci,* and *pijperi*) is ap-parently a complex of variants which causes rickettsioses known by at least twelve different names. Weyer (1954) considered that dif-ferences between forms within the complex were sufficient to cast doubt on the validity of a single binomial designation. The form in southern Africa that is the agent for South African tick-bite fever has been named *R. conori pijperi* because it is distinct. The form that produces boutonneuse fever or Marseilles fever occurs over the

Mediterranean littoral; that which causes Abyssinian or Kenyan typhus and South African tick-bite fever occurs south of the Sahara Desert. In eastern Asia, that which is responsible for Indian tick typhus and urban exanthematic fever of Saigon is present. For the purpose of this discussion, the several entities are considered as subspecific. The benign syndrome is characterized by a fever and a maculo-papulous eruption, especially of the head. An eschar forms at the site of inoculation in most cases, and a rash may spread over the whole body.

Transmission of this pathogen occurs during the warmer parts of the year outside the tropics and any time of year in the tropics (Weyer, 1959). In Spain the form called boutonneuse fever occurs from May to October with peak incidence in August and September. Agricultural workers primarily are afflicted. Seldom does the disease occur far inland (Caputo, 1957).

The reservoir for this rickettsia is imperfectly known. In the Mediterranean area, foci are rural and domestic. Caputo (1957) noted a focus along the Ligurian coast where farmers were frequently infected from a domestic reservoir by way of the dog tick, *Rhipicephalus sanguineus*. Foci in South Africa are presumed to be sylvatic (Gear, 1954) where the wild host is probably some rodent, and the ticks are *R. evertsi* and *Amblyomma hebraeum*. In Kenya the domestic rat (*Rattus rattus*) may be the transient that brings the pathogen into situations where *Haemaphysalis leachi* is the vector to man. *Rhipicephalus sanguineus* has no part in transmission in this area (Weyer, 1959). This species taken from various animals has been found bearing the rickettsia. Some from burrows of *Otomys angoniensis* and one from a leopard were positive in Kenya (Heisch *et al.*, 1957). Hoogstraal (1952) reported that *R. simus simus* is a significant component of feral reservoirs in Africa. Timms *et al.* (1959) described an infection in a person in Kenya wherein symptoms of this typhus occurred seven days after removal of a specimen of *R. simus* from the thigh. Immature stages of this tick become infected when they feed on rodents near domestic situations, and they may transit the agent by adults that develop from them. In the tall-grass country of eastern Africa, *R. pulchellus* is suspected as a vector-host. It has a range of wild suscepts and is brought to a domestic situation on dogs. The Indian form has been isolated from *R. sanguineus, Haemaphysalis leachi,* and *Ixodes ricinus. Dermacentor nuttalli* taken from *Citellus undulatus* were positive for this rickettsia in Tuva Republic, Russia, according to Piontkovskaia and Mischenko (1959). Since at least six species of burrowing rodents may be hosts of this *Dermacentor*, a tick-rodent reservoir is considered a possibility in central Asia. Possibly any species of ixodid tick is a component of a reservoir if it feeds on a vertebrate hospitable to the agent.

Rickettsia conori is a systemic parasite in its acarine hosts and may pass from stage to stage even to the F_1 generation. Weyer (1954) observed the fate of two variants of this agent in the human louse, an exotic host. The variant from South Africa and Kenya invades the epithelium of the gut but is non-injurious. The form causing boutonneuse fever causes the epithelium to become detached, and the infected lice die in three to seven days.

Transmission from tick to man is accomplished mainly by salivation into the feeding puncture (Weyer, 1959). Inoculum obtained by crushing ticks may be rubbed into the eye and cause infection.

Rickettsia akari

Rickettsia akari (syn. *Dermacentroxenus murinus*) is the cause of a mild febrile disease somewhat like chickenpox. The syndrome is variously known as rickettsialpox, vesicular rickettsiosis, and Kew Garden Fever. It was first noted as a distinct entity in New York during the summer of 1946. Since then it has been reported in cities over much of the United States. Jackson *et al.* (1957) found a form in a sylvatic focus in Korea. Very likely the agent is widely distributed. The disease is indicated by a rash and generally by a primary lesion (eschar) at the site of inoculation. Crusts may form over the papules, but later scarring is absent.

Domestic foci in the United States are multiple residences of middle-income people in large cities (Nichols *et al.*, 1953) (Fig. 75). Infested buildings have central garbage incineration in the basement, with garbage disposal by way of chutes from the apartments. Usually garbage is incinerated each morning after having accumulated in the cold incinerator for a day. Mice are able to live in abundance in the accumulations in the burner and the chutes. Dermanyssid mites often line the walls of the incinerators and the ducts.

All outbreaks in cities so far have occurred in suburbia. Nichols *et al.* (1953) show that transient mice may account for this distribution. While it is true that the house mouse has a very limited range from its normal habitat, it sometimes ranges widely. Nightly excursions in one instance took mice as far away as one-half mile to a wheat field and hedgerow. Such movements could take them to the range of wild rodents and their parasites. However, no sylvatic focus is known in the United States.

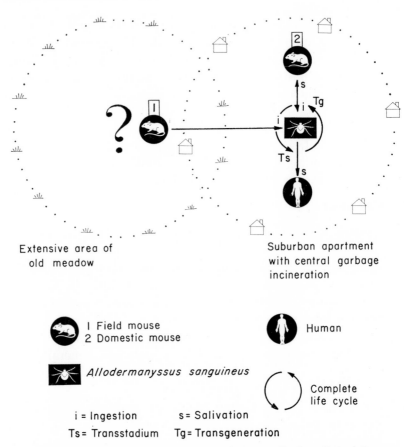

Fig. 75. Reservoir for *Rickettsia akari* in suburban United States. Question mark in the sylvatic situation means that details are currently unknown.

Rickettsia akari has its domestic reservoir in the United States in mice and the mite, *Allodermanyssus sanguineus*. *Rattus norvegicus* is a factor in Russia (Weyer, 1959). The house mouse is tolerant toward the agent. When ample food is available, large populations of both mice and mites occur. Any cause for sudden decline in mice, such as a campaign against them, causes the mites to disperse, and then human residents of the focus are attacked. Infected mites transfer the agent to humans, and an outbreak occurs.

The sylvatic focus in Korea (Jackson *et al.*, 1957) involves the reed vole (*Microtus fortis*). The chain of transmission is unknown, but ample dermanyssid mites are present to account for transmission in lairs of the vole.

This rickettsia is an intracellular parasite of mites that is acquired by ingestion. It invades the epithelium of the gut, causing the invaded cells to rupture either into the lumen or into the hemocoel. Those cells loose in the hemocoel may invade ovarioles and remain in the egg to the F_1 generation at least. Other cells invade the salivary glands, whence they pass by salivation into another suscept at the time of feeding.

Besides the usual mite hosts, the body louse and larval *Tenebrio* have proved hospitable when inoculated intrarectally. The organism will pass readily from the lumen of the gut into the hemocoel of both lice and larval beetles. It develops extracellularly in the hemolymph of the louse, but it invades the fat body of the larval beetles. Those that remain in the gut multiply in the cells, but they do not destroy the whole epithelium as do those of *R. prowazeki* (Weyer, 1952). *Rickettsia akari* is erratically present in the lumen of the gut and the feces.

Rickettsia australis

Rickettsia australis causes a disease of man known as Queensland tick typhus, an entity similar to boutonneuse fever. Serological tests indicate also a relationship to *R. conori*. The disease is recognizable by a general papular rash with a small eschar forming at the site of inoculation. Persons affected have crossed the Atherton tableland of northern Queensland where the whole area is said to be heavily infested by the ixodid tick, *Ixodes holocyclus*. Marsupials, particularly bandicoots, and a rodent (*Uromys*) may be infected in forested areas.

Rickettsia pavlovskyi

Rickettsia pavlovskyi is the causative agent of infectious nephrosonephritis. It is normally parasitic in a reservoir of steppe rodents, ticks, and mites in Russia, but it occasionally attacks man (Grokhovskaya *in* Pavlovsky, 1955). The agent has been isolated from burrowing rodents and ticks, *Ixodes laguri*, taken from their burrows. It seems that ticks of the genus *Dermacentor* spp. are responsible for transfer of the agent to man. One center for an outbreak in man was a small village in a neglected deciduous forest. Possibly both mites and ticks act as vector-hosts by vertical transmission of the microbe. Such was observed through the F_1 generation in the laboratory where a dermanyssid mite, *Haemogamasus glasgowi*, harbored the agent for a year and still transmitted it to the F_1 generation. Similarly, ticks of the genera *Ixodes* and *Dermacentor* were able to infect the F_1 generation through the reproductive system (Korshunova *in* Pavlovsky).

Rickettsia tsutsugamushi

Rickettsia tsutsugamushi (syn. *R. orientalis* and *R. tamiyai*) is the cause of tsutsugamushi disease, scrub typhus, Japanese river fever, and ezo fever. It is probable that the binomial as used here includes several variants. At any rate, four types of syndromes have been named as follows: *Niigata* (or classical), *Kochi* (or Shikoku), *Shichito*, and *Tsurumi*, all of which are named for different parts of Japan. The disease known as twenty-days fever in Mie Prefecture may also be a form of the disease. Presumably the classical form is the one distributed elsewhere in Pacific Oceania (Sasa, 1954). At present tsutsugamushi disease is known in southern and eastern Asia, all of Japan, and islands southward to northern Australia. The numerous foci are located in a rough triangle bounded by lines from Japan to New Hebrides to western India.

According to Philip (1948), tsutsugamushi disease was second only to malaria as a cause of casualties in the Pacific theaters of war (1941–1945). The military task force that struck the Schouten Islands suffered nearly 1500 casualties from this disease within six months. On Ceylon one British division had 756 casualties as a result of a four-day training exercise. The mortality rate varies according to the type of the disease. The Niigata or classical type shows a mortality rate of 20–40 per cent in Japan; the Kochi type may have a rate of 60–70 per cent. The Shichito type is seldom mortal. A primary lesion or eschar is usual on Europeans and rare on Asiatics. Pulmonary symptoms are usually present. Recurrent attacks may occur within a few years after the initial attack.

From all indications, *R. tsutsugamushi* exists solely in a trombiculid-mammalian reservoir. Its tolerant mammalian hosts include shrews, rats, voles, and bandicoots. In the laboratory, gerbils, hamsters, and monkeys are very susceptible. Man also is very susceptible. Price *et al.* (1958) have isolated this organism from lymphatics of humans up to 15 months after inoculation, during which time recrudescences may occur at any time. While this does not suggest that humans play any part in a basic reservoir, it does indicate that the lymphatics may be the site in vertebrates where the agent lies dormant.

Within a general area of infestation such as that along the north shore of New Guinea, limited areas of intensive transmission of this rickettsia are called "typhus islands" (Harrison and Audy, 1951). These areas are ecological complexes providing harborages for populations of rodents where the mite component can be maintained as a large population.

The four epidemiological types of this pathogen mentioned above occupy reservoirs that range over certain ecological interfaces (Sasa, 1954). The Niigata type involves man at interfaces between giant grasses and scrub (Figs. 76 and 77). In Japan such sites are on the flood plains of major rivers wherever they flow across flat terrain. The reservoir in Japan consists of the vole, *Microtus montebelli*, and the mite, *Trombicula akamushi*, with *Rattus norvegicus* and *Apodemus speciosus* in supporting roles. On New Guinea the interfaces between elephant grasses and scrub on broad alluvial plains provide sites for the reservoir composed of bandicoot and *Rattus* sp., especially *R. browni*, and the mite *T. deliensis*. In Burma and Assam, shrews and *R. rattus*, together with *Schöngastia ligula* and *T. deliensis*, constitute the reservoir in the edges of forests.

Outbreaks of tsutsugamushi disease occur at different times of the year according to the habits of the vector-hosts (Weyer, 1959). The Kochi-type disease affects man in summer and involves man along coastal areas of Shikoku, Japan. Areas for maintaining a reservoir are those where narrow bands of scrub border cultivated areas which lie between steep hills and the coast (Fig. 78). *Rattus norvegicus* and *Trombicula tosa* comprise the reservoir as far as it is known. The Shichito-type disease is transmitted to man by *T. scutellaris* in autumn and winter and occurs in a reservoir at the interfaces of residential back yards and either fields or forests in Japan and the Pescadores Islands. Summer transmission is by way of the vector-host *T. akamushi*. Presumably *R. norvegicus* and possibly *Apodemus speciosa*, together with *T. scutellaris*, constitute the reservoir. Tsurumi type may well be the most widely distributed in

Japan, but the exact nature of the reservoir is uncertain. The beginning and the end of the monsoon provide favorable conditions in Assam and Burma. The Indian form appears most commonly from

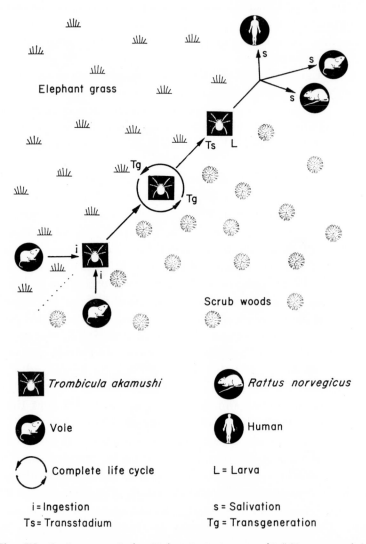

Fig. 76. Basic reservoir for *Rickettsia tsutsugamushi* (Niigata type) in Japan at an interface between grass lands and scrub woods.

June to November, the maximum abundance occurring in September. Tropical and subtropical climates permit year-round transmission.

A jungle focus appears in Malaya, where jungle rats (*Rattus muelleri* and *edwardsi*) and several species of Insectivora, together with *Trombicula akamushi*, constitute a sylvatic reservoir. A sylvatic-domestic phase of the reservoir is known in Java, where areas

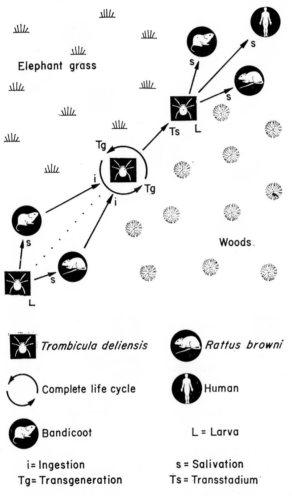

Elephant grass

Woods.

Ts L

Tg

Tg

i

i

s

s

s

L

L

🟫 *Trombicula deliensis*

⚫ *Rattus browni*

⟲ Complete life cycle

⚫ Human

⚫ Bandicoot

L = Larva

i = Ingestion
Tg = Transgeneration

s = Salivation
Ts = Transstadium

Fig. 77. Reservoir for *Rickettsia tsutsugamushi* in New Guinea at interfaces between elephant grass and woodlands.

of high grass bordering canals permit domestic and wild rodents to have overlapping ranges. *Rattus rattus argentiventer* and *R. r. jalorensis*, together with *T. akamushi* and *Schöngastia indica*, make up the normal reservoir. In Korea, some 17 per cent of *Apodemus agrarius* were found infested with *Rickettsia tsutsugamushi,* according to the summary of Weyer.

This rickettsia has only trombiculid mites as its vector-hosts as far as is known. The organism is ingested by the mites from a dermal source in a thin-skinned mammal or bird. It passes through the gut

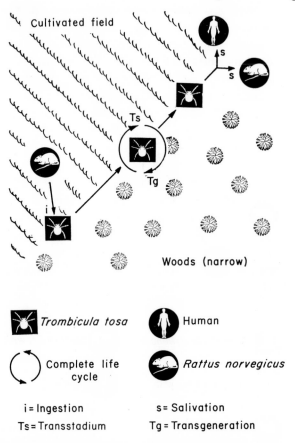

Fig. 78. Reservoir for *Rickettsia tsutsugamushi* (Kochi type) in Japan at interfaces between cultivated fields and bands of woods.

wall and becomes systemic. Since neither nymphs nor adults feed on birds or mammals the agent must pass to larvae of the F_1 generation to be transmitted. At the time of feeding the agent is injected with the saliva. Body lice have been infected by intrarectal and intracoelomic inoculations (Weyer, 1958). The hemolymph proved to be a suitable medium in which several strains of this organism could multiply. The organism was maintained by serial passages among lice, and no pathology was evident.

Rickettsia quintana

Rickettsia quintana (syn. *R. wolhynica, pediculi,* and *wiegli*) is the causative agent of trench or shin fever. The disease probably occurs in the same parts of the world as louse typhus. Its epidemiology and vector relations compare with those of typhus except that humans are the only vertebrates in the reservoir (Weyer, 1959). It is definitely known to occur in Europe, North Africa, and Mexico. Strangely enough, the disease is rarely familiar to residents or clinicians in endemic centers, where distinct symptomatology is absent. During times of war and economic distress, infestation is more common in populations unaccustomed to it. A carrier then brings the agent into the potential reservoir, where clinical manifestations soon appear. The disease runs a course through an advancing army when it occupies an area seeded with the pathogen. This happened to the German army in both World War I and II, and the Allied armies became infested during the seesaw operations on the western front in 1915–1916. In the British army about 200,000 cases occurred in 1916–1917. In all, the Allies suffered about 1,800,000 cases of trench fever in World War I. Trench fever was said to be second only to influenza as cause of casualties from disease on that front.

The reservoir need be only man and body lice. Much of the human population is tolerant and may carry pathogens in a viable state for years (5–8 years, according to Rodenwaldt, 1952). Such persons have been known to infect lice 100 or more months after a primary attack. The attack rate is directly proportional to the degree of infestation by body lice in a susceptible human population. No wild reservoir is known, but *R. quintana* may be maintained in the laboratory in rhesus monkeys and their lice.

This parasite behaves somewhat specifically in lice. It infests the mid-gut as do other rickettsiae, but it lives extracellularly and never invades the epithelium. It is not lethal to lice. The agent appears as a mat layer on the face of the intestinal epithelium. Rickettsiae become dislodged and contaminate the contents of the gut and feces. This microbe will not survive either in the tick, *Ornithodoros moubata,* or in the mealworm (Table 20).

Transfer of the pathogen between hosts is similar to that of *R. prowazeki*. Man-to-louse transfer takes place as the louse ingests infected blood, while louse-to-man transfer is less direct. Fresh feces from parasitized lice when rubbed into the skin provide the principal medium for transfer. Dry feces retain the agent for a long time and may well provide a means for delayed transfer to man. Man-to-man transfer is possible by rubbing contaminated urine or saliva into abraded skin.

ANAPLASMATACEAE

This family is the cause of anaplasmosis, a febrile blood disease of ruminants of tropical and adjacent areas. The genus *Anaplasma* is the one best known. These are coccoid parasites found in ruminants in the periphery of red corpuscles. The parasites are variously considered to be protozoan, viral, and rickettsial. In Bergey's Manual they are listed as members of Rickettsiales in the Protophyta. At least five species have been recognized as follows: *A. marginale*, a cosmopolitan parasite of cow, zebu, buffalo, antelope, and deer; *A. centrale*, parasitic in cow in Natal; *A. argentinum*, in cow in Argentina; *A. ovis*, in sheep and goat in Algeria; and *A. rossicum*, in bovines in the Caucasus. They are found to be systemic in ticks of the genus *Boophilus* and at least six other genera of ticks taken from ruminants (Piercy, 1956).

Routes of transmission seem to involve both physical and biological vectors. Poisson (1953) noted that contaminated instruments or contaminated mouth parts of arthropods such as those of ticks and tabanids were usual agents of transmission. Vertical transmission at least to the F_1 generation has been demonstrated for *A. marginale* in four genera of ticks. *Boophilus annulatus* is thought to be a natural component of the reservoir of this agent. If this is true, systemic infection of the tick is required, because this is a one-host tick that boards only one host in its lifetime.

HAEMOBARTONELLACEAE

This group of parasites attacks the blood-vascular system of a number of different kinds of mammals, including man. They are represented by the genera *Haemobartonella*, *Grahamella*, and *Eperythrozoon*. Phylogeny of the group is uncertain, but Breed (1956) has placed the family in Rickettsiales of the Protophyta. *Haemobartonella* spp. attack red cells but never cause cutaneous eruptions. *Eperythrozoon* spp. appear as minute chains around the periphery of red cells or are free in the plasma in rodents, ruminants, etc. *Grahamella* spp. produce 8–20 cells within the red cells of rodents, insectivores, canines, bovines, and primates without apparent symptoms.

Arthropods are known to be associated with transmission in all kinds of these genera, but little is known about details. *Haemobartonella* spp. are carried by fleas (for *canis*) and lice (for *muris*). *Grahamella bovis* is known to enter the tick, *Boophilus calcaratus*. *Eperythrozoon* of rodents may live in lice and mites in the laboratory, and *E. wenyoni* of bovines has been found in ticks of the genus *Hyalomma*.

ADDITIONAL READINGS

RIVERS and HORSFALL (1959) must be examined for details of rickettsial agents, particularly for clinical manifestations.

WEYER (1959) is essential for any study of the agent causing Q fever (coxiellosis).

BORMAN's account in RODENWALDT (1952) is necessary reading for knowledge of the situation about typhus, especially in Europe in recent times.

HARRISON and AUDY (1951) deal with tsutsugamushi as a zoonotic disease of major significance. The significance of interfacial niches is brought out.

CHAPTER 10

Protophyta III: Spirochaetales

GENERAL

The order of microbes Spirochaetales is placed by Breed (1956) in the class Schizomycetes (bacteria and related forms) of the division Protophyta. Included are unicellular organisms, each cell being an elongate spiral mass without a rigid wall. Motility is achieved by means of an elastic axial filament or modified fibrillar membrane. Cells divide transversely. While more definitive reasons for generic and specific taxa are needed, it is here considered that three generic ones, *Borrelia*, *Treponema*, and *Leptospira* include vertebrate pathogens that are related to Arthropoda. *Borrelia* species require arthropods in their reservoirs, while the other genera have more casual and secondary relationships.

Borrelia

Borrelia spp. are elongate unicellular organisms that assume the shape of a spiral. Externally they are provided with polar flagella. No nucleus is present, and the chromatin is dispersed in the cytoplasm. Multiplication is by transverse division. In habits they vary from zoopaths through commensals to free forms.

Most observers agree that the genus *Borrelia* contains several species even though they are morphologically indistinguishable. Classification, to the extent that it is known, is based on biological differences. Differentiation is based on the relative specificity of each spirochete for an acarine host, according to Brumpt (1936) and confirmation by others. For example, each of the species *Borrelia turicatae*, *B. parkeri*, and *B. hermsi* may live extrinsically only in *Ornithodoros* species having the same specific names. This point of specificity for an acarine host is of more significance to the epidemiologist than to the clinician because of a need to know the source of a particular pathogen. The forms with which we are concerned cause relapsing fevers in vertebrates and are associated with ticks or lice, as presumably all *Borrelia* evolved with the Acarina (Baker, 1943). Even now nearly all species live part of their lives in soft ticks, particularly those of the genus *Ornithodoros*. The common exception is the complex called *B. recurrentis* that now develops extrinsically in the body louse.

Borrelia spp. are systemic parasites in their arthropodan hosts such as lice and argasid ticks of the genus *Ornithodoros* (Burgdorfer, 1951). They are ingested with the blood and move passively into the mid-gut. Within a few days the organisms begin to move out of the gut and into the hemocoel, where their numbers increase in the hemolymph by accrual from the gut and by cell division of the arrivals. In ticks particularly, the parasite may invade various organs such as salivary glands, coxal glands, central ganglion, Gené's organs, gonads, and malpighian tubes. One species, *Borrelia duttoni*, thrives in the salivary glands of nymphal ticks but tends to vacate these glands in adults. The central ganglion is a particularly hospitable tissue for *B. duttoni* at least (Feng and Chung, 1939), but it does not seem to be so suitable for *B. turicatae* (Varma, 1956a). Once in the coelomic organs, spirochetes may live for years. Pavlovsky and Skrunnik (1951) reported that two ticks from a strain of *Ornithodoros tholozani* retained spirochetes for 14 years and then effectively transferred them to guinea pigs. These same observers reported that the agent in *O. tholozani* could pass to the F_2 generation and was still infective for guinea pigs.

An infective tick may transmit its spirochetes to vertebrates at the time of feeding by (1) irrigating the feeding puncture with contaminated saliva or (2) irrigating the feeding site with contaminated coxal fluid. Burgdorfer proposed that both methods of transfer were effective for nymphs, but in the case of adult ticks, contaminated coxal fluid bore most spirochetes to the wound in the skin. Varma (1956a) stated that contaminated coxal fluids of *O. turicata*, *parkeri*, *hermsi* and *tholozani* probably played no part in transmission of *Borrelia* because none of these ticks excretes coxal fluid while feeding.

Louse-borne spirochetes are probably derived from tick-borne forms (Wolman and Wolman, 1945). Several existing species may develop in exotic hosts such as lice and bed bugs. Spirochetes, when in lice, pass from the gut to the hemocoel, but they do not seem to enter any of the organ systems, as they do in ticks. Spirochetes may escape infected lice only through the infected hemolymph that is freed when a louse is crushed, since neither saliva nor feces bear spirochetes (Chung and Weir, 1938). When infected hemolymph is rubbed into abraded or punctured skin by scratching, the agent is transferred.

Table 22. Borrelia Known to Infest Arthropods.

Species of *Borrelia*	General Distribution	Natural Arthopodan Host
crocidurae	Central Africa, Turkey	*Ornithodoros erraticus* (small)
dipodilli	Kenya	*O. erraticus* (small)
merionesi	Sahara, Dakar	*O. erraticus* (small)
microti	Iran	*O. erraticus* (small)
hispanica	N. Africa, Spain	*O. erraticus* (large)
duttoni	Trop. Afr., Madagascar, Senegal, Arabia	*O. moubata*
latychevyi	Central Asia	*O. tartakovskyi*
persica	Central Asia	*O. tholozani*
babylonensis	Near East	*O. tholozani* (Babylonian form only)
caucasica	Caucasus	*O. verrucosus*
normandi	North Africa, S. Tunisia	*O. normandi*
dugesi	Mexico	*O. dugesi* (only)
brasiliensis	S. America	*O. brasiliensis*
venezuelensis	C. and S. America	*O. rudis*
talaje	Mexico into U. S.	*O. talaje*
turicatae	Texas	*O. turicata*
hermsi	U. S. (western)	*O. hermsi*
parkeri	U. S. (western)	*O. parkeri*
recurrentis	Cosmopolitan	*Pediculus humanus humanus*, *Cimex lectularius*

Relapsing fevers are difficult to diagnose because the variable symptomatology simulates so many other conditions. Chills, fever, sweats, and generalized pains are usual, while nausea, vomiting, and headache are common symptoms. Convulsions may accompany paroxysms in children. A persistent sense of coldness is reported by many. A febrile period of about three days is followed by an afebrile period of about eight days. A series of relapses follows for a few months in untreated cases. Frequently the disease is mistaken for respiratory infection because pneumonia is a common sequella. No attempt is made herein to characterize the several syndromes.

The forms of *Borrelia* known to cause the various relapsing fevers are given in Table 22. It is recognized that some of these are variants

within a complex, but they are given as separate entities for geographical reasons.

Borrelia crocidurae

The *Borrelia crocidurae* group is a complex of four variants,
crocidurae, dipodilli, merionesi, and *microti,* that cause the so-called
"tick relapsing fever" in sylvatic foci of Turkey, northern Africa, and
central Africa. The occurrence of these agents in man is relatively
rare. All forms occur in burrowing rodents of one sort or another.
Gerbils of the genera *Dipodillus* and *Meriones* are particularly significant hosts in the Sahara and northward. In Dakar, *Crocidura,
Golunda,* and *Mus* species become the primary vertebrate hosts.
Without exception, *Ornithodoros erraticus sonrai,* the so-called
"small form," is the common arthropodan host for all. Hospitable
species in the laboratory include *O. canestrinii* and *O. lahorensis* as
well as the human body louse. Lice have been said to be naturally
infected (Heisch, 1950). In all the susceptible ticks the agent
becomes systemic and may be transmitted to the F_1 generation
(Colas-Belcour and Vervent, 1955) by way of the ovum, or to a vertebrate by way of the feeding puncture. Neither *O. moubata* nor
O. erraticus "large form" are hospitable to this pathogen. Among
laboratory animals, adult guinea pigs and adult rabbits are immune
to this organism (Baltazard *et al.,* 1950).

Borrelia hispanica

Borrelia hispanica is the cause of human relapsing fever in areas
bordering the Mediterranean Sea and extending along the Atlantic
littoral for a short distance both north and south of the Straits of
Gibraltar. The fundamental component of the reservoir is *Ornithodoros erraticus erraticus,* the so-called "large form" of various observers. This is the only spirochete associated with this tick (Baltazard
et al., 1950), and its range and that of the spirochete coincide. Less
specific, but essential in one form or another, are burrowing mammals such as gerbils, hedgehog, jackal, and wild rats. Many other
vertebrates may be infected in the laboratory. Even acarine hosts
are more numerous than is the case for most *Borrelia.* Among them
are *O. savignyi, O. moubata,* and *Rhipicephalus sanguineus.* Sucking
lice may harbor the pathogen and presumably a man-louse reservoir
is a distinct possibility (Garnham, 1958). This *Borrelia* may survive
for five years in a tick (*O. nicollei*) (Davis and Mavros, 1955), and

it may be transmitted through the eggs to the F_1 generation. Transmission to vertebrates is normally effected by salivation or contamination of the skin by coxal fluid.

Borrelia duttoni

Borrelia duttoni is the causative agent for the sporadic relapsing fever of man in tropical Africa, Madagascar, and the southern part of the Arabian peninsula. This pathogen has no known domestic or sylvatic vertebrate hosts, according to Geigy and Herbig (1955). Walton (1955) reported otherwise for an area of Kenya near the Tanganyikan border, where the pathogen occurred, but human cases were rare. He found that the carrier tick, the eyeless tampan (*Ornithodoros moubata*), was restricted to an area of some eight square miles where about 90 per cent of the houses were infested. These were houses in which domestic fowls lived with the people. Some of the ticks recovered from these buildings were infected with *B. duttoni*. Here seems to be a domestic reservoir involving ticks but not humans. Geigy and Aeschlimann (1957) stated that rats played no part in any natural reservoir in Tanganyika. The wart hog, a natural host for one of the variants of *O. moubata*, cannot be regarded as a reservoir animal, because none of a large series of ticks taken from their burrows has been found infected (Geigy and Mooser, 1955). Both domestic and wild rats of several genera may be successfully infected by the organism in the laboratory, but ticks do not seem to be able to transmit the agent by biting (Geigy and Aeschlimann, 1957). The human body louse, *Pediculus,* and a monkey louse, *Pedicinus longiceps,* are hospitable to the parasite and may transmit it to their respective vertebrate hosts if it is crushed and the hemolymph is spread over an abraded area (Heisch, 1950 and 1950a).

In contrast to the little that is known about the reservoir, a great deal is known about the fate of the pathogen in its acarine host. The general fate of this parasite in ticks is as follows. The spirochetes are ingested with the blood and lodge in the mid-gut. Then within a short time they penetrate the gut wall and enter the hemocoel. After the twelfth day none is left in the gut. Active multiplication of the parasite takes place at 25°–30° C, and invasion of several organs takes place. Varma (1956a) assessed the degree of acceptability of organs of *O. moubata* to *B. duttoni*. Salivary glands, coxal glands, and the central ganglion were nearly always invaded, while the gonads were invaded in nearly two-thirds of the ticks. About one-fourth or less showed infection of malpighian tubules and Gené's organ. Sarasin (1959) reported that spirochetes enter any firm tissue in the body cavity and live in intercellular spaces. When the oocytes are involved, the parasite is intracellular; however, entry into oocytes takes place prior to the formation of the tunica propria, according to Aeschlimann (1958).

Borrelia duttoni may leave the body of the tick that ingested it by way of saliva, coxal fluid, or eggs. Feces are devoid of any forms (Feng and Chung, 1939). Spirochetes may be inoculated directly into the blood stream with the salivary fluid or may contaminate the feeding puncture by infective coxal fluid (Varma, 1956). Burgdorfer (1951) has shown that nymphs transfer the agent more often by salivation, and that adults do so largely by way of coxal fluid. Vertical transmission between generations is commonly recognized. Geigy et al. (1956) found that transmission in this fashion had possibly taken place in one instance over a period of several years, but that such transmission resulted in loss in virulence by the time the spirochetes had reached the third lineal descendant of the tick which had acquired the infection from a vertebrate. Eggs may be invaded by spirochetes until the formation of the vitelline membrane.

Lice, too, may harbor the pathogen provided the rate of ingestion exceeds the rate of destruction by digestive fluids of the lice (Heisch, 1955). The few spirochetes that escape into the hemocoel begin to increase markedly in number between the sixth and the eighth day. No organs are invaded as is the case in ticks (Mooser and Weyer, 1954). No pathologic symptoms were apparent in lice, nor was the spirochete adversely affected, even after 21 passages through lice. Heisch (1955a) observed "curious granules" in cells attached to the fat body, especially in the head of lice infected with this spirochete, and the pathogen is often concentrated in, on, or near these masses.

Borrelia latychevyi

Borrelia latychevyi is the cause of Asiatic human relapsing fever. It ranges over central Asia east of the Caspian Sea to Afghanistan and Tadzhikistan. This is largely an area of mountainous desert and semi-arid, rocky land where the parasite leads a sylvatic existence. It has been isolated from Ornithodoros ticks taken in several different locations. The organism is only slightly pathogenic to man but causes high mortality in new-born rabbits in the laboratory (Baltazard *et al.* 1952). It will not infect adult guinea pigs, a fact that makes it unique among those species that live in *Ornithodoros.*

Baltazard *et al.* isolated this agent from several batches of *Ornithodoros tartakovskyi* collected in northeastern Iran near Meshed. The ticks came from burrows occupied by rodents, tortoises, lizards, and toads. Seven of 56 lots of ticks tested were infected. Three of the seven came from burrows of *Meriones,* and four came from burrows that had been abandoned. No natural infections were noted among the wild rodents, but *Meriones, Microtus,* and *Rhombomys* spp. could be infected readily by subcutaneous injections.

Maintenance of this agent seems to depend on *O. tartakovskyi,* but *O. tholozani* in one of its forms may play some part. Transmission is by way of the saliva and feeding puncture. Coxal fluid is emitted several minutes after the tick has left its host, and even though it bears spirochetes, it is an unlikely factor in transmission (Baltazard *et al.,* 1952).

Borrelia persica

Borrelia persica causes central Asian spirochetosis, a disease of man in rural and settled areas in and near the rocky fastnesses around the Caspian Sea and areas southwest toward the Mediterranean. Babudieri (1957) has reported differences in the epidemiology of the rural and urban forms. Victims of the former are goatherds, nomads, road-building crews, and wanderers who have sought shelter in some of many caves found throughout the country (Fig. 79). Caves in this area are more in the nature of cavities naturally or artificially excavated. The floors are sandy and dry except in the interstices and small grottoes along the walls. Many of these caves are occupied during the winter by goatherds and their flocks. This is a disease of winter occupants in these environs.

Relapsing fever in towns affects residents who have a history of staying at home instead of wandering, according to Babudieri. A characteristic niche favoring this pathogen in Jordan is a village in which dwellings are cave-like, windowless chambers with earthen floors. Many of the abodes are in ruins and cracks are abundant; hence the chambers are ecologically identical with the caves outside the towns. Peak frequency of disease in the towns is in the summer.

The reservoir for *B. persica* is uncertain but may be composed of some burrowing rodent such as the spiny mouse (*Acomys*), hedgehog, and sand rat (*Psammomys*) and some strains of the argasid tick, *Ornithodoros tholozani*. The urban form may survive in domestic rats, humans, and these ticks. It is possible that *O. coniceps* is part of the reservoir in Jordan, according to Babudieri. Transmission to a vertebrate is by salivation.

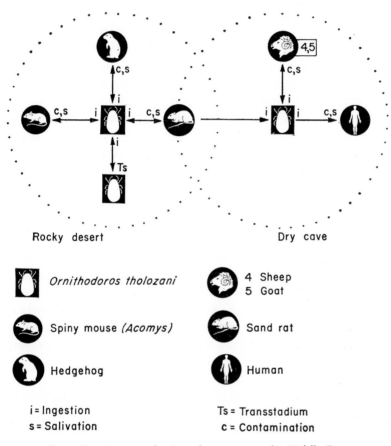

Rocky desert Dry cave

	Ornithodoros tholozani		4 Sheep 5 Goat
	Spiny mouse *(Acomys)*		Sand rat
	Hedgehog		Human

i = Ingestion   Ts = Transstadium
s = Salivation   c = Contamination

Fig. 79. Reservoir for *Borrelia persica* in the Middle East.

Bourgain (1950) considered the ticks themselves to be of major importance in maintaining this spirochete because of prolonged association. Survival of the organism for 10 years has been recorded, and survival for 5–7 years is commonplace. Pavlovsky and Skrunnik (1945) found that transmission to vertebrates was effected in the laboratory even 12 years after infection of the ticks.

Borrelia hermsi

Borrelia hermsi is the cause of occasional cases of relapsing fever in man in the mountainous area of the United States west of the one hundredth meridian, and it has a normal sylvatic existence (Davis, 1941). Human cases occur in the mountains at elevations up to at least 3000 feet. The disease has historically occurred among occupants of newly opened summer cottages (Herms and Wheeler, 1936). Known wild hosts include *Sciurus douglasi* and *Eutamias* sp. in California. The only known arthropod in the reservoir is *Ornithodoros hermsi*. Any feeding stage may acquire the agent and any subsequent one including the F_1 may be infected, but the rate of infection is low. The normal means of transmission presumably includes contaminated coxal fluid, but direct transfer by contaminated blood smeared on the body may induce infection.

Borrelia parkeri

Borrelia parkeri is the cause of relapsing fever in western continental United States from Kansas to Texas to the West Coast throughout the range of its tick host, *Ornithodoros parkeri*. It is known only in its sylvatic phase, but components of the reservoir are unknown. Effective acarine hosts include only *O. parkeri* as far as is known. The spirochete becomes systemic and the salivary system is invaded. No vertical transmission to F_1 is known. *O. turicata* will harbor the parasite but is unable to transmit it either vertically or horizontally. A hybrid F_1 of *O. parkeri* ♀ × *O. turicata* ♂ was able to transmit it.

Borrelia talaje

Borrelia talaje is the causative agent of Mexican relapsing fever in Mexico and in southwestern United States. It exists in a sylvatic phase among burrowing rodents and the tick, *Ornithodoros talaje*. No other tick from the Western Hemisphere is known to harbor this agent except possibly *O. dugesi* (Davis, 1956).

Borrelia turicatae

Borrelia turicatae is the cause of a form of endemic relapsing fever in the southern Great Plains of North America. Its basic reservoir seems to be the tick, *Ornithodoros turicata*, in which it may persist for years in the same individual; it may even reside indefinitely in the tick. Davis (1943), for example, found nearly 100 per cent of ticks bearing spirochetes in the F_5 generation. Caves seem to provide the usual site for the ticks, particularly those that have housed sheep and goats. Three persons in a collecting party were bitten by ticks in one cave, and all became ill with typical spirochetosis. Other ticks transmitted the pathogen while feeding on a caged rabbit in the laboratory. The agent is adaptable to life in sucking lice in the laboratory (Heisch, 1950).

Borrelia venezuelensis

Borrelia venezuelensis is the cause of relapsing fever variously called neotropical, Colombian, or Venezuelan relapsing fever. Little is known of its reservoir except that the only significant tick is *Ornithodoros rudis*. In this tick the spirochete may pass to the F_1 generation. Vertebrate hosts include man, rat, striated monkey, opossum, armadillo, cow, and horse.

Borrelia recurrentis

Borrelia recurrentis is the causative agent of cosmopolitan relapsing fever in humans. Presumably man is the only vertebrate in the reservoir, and the body louse seems to be the only significant arthropod. According to Martini *in* Rodenwaldt (1952), four principal foci are known, namely Oriental, Eurasian (vast area east of Germany and southward to Arabian peninsula), North African (especially Ethiopian) highlands, and South American Andes. The Eurasian focus coincides with that for *Rickettsia prowazeki*, as would be expected since both agents depend on body lice for interhuman transfer. Apparently the spirochete responds to the vertebrates differently according to source. A form from northern Africa may develop in guinea pig and rabbit, while an Ethiopian one would not do so until the reticulo-endothelial system of the vertebrate was blocked. The Ethiopian and Chinese strains cannot be transmitted by the tick, *Ornithodoros moubata,* while Eurasian and South American ones may be. These variations in reaction to ticks seem strange in view of the fact that most forms from ticks may be harbored by lice.

Sparrow (1955) has observed the fate of spirochetes in lice as follows: A single blood meal from a patient during the attack of fever is sufficient to infect a louse. Within a few hours the gut is clear and all live spirochetes are present in the hemolymph, where rapid multiplication follows. The spirochetes remain in the hemolymph for the life of the louse.

Transmission is entirely dependent on getting contaminated hemolymph from lice in contact with abraded or scarified skin. In nature this means that lice must be crushed, as is often done by scratching. The act of scratching both abrades the skin and crushes an occasional engorged louse. This peculiar method of transmission suggests an adaptation of the parasite and is the cause of speculation about the origin of this form in arthropods.

Sparrow (1955) revived the earlier speculation of Nicolle and Anderson that epidemic louse-borne relapsing fever originates after the infection of lice by one of the tick-borne spirochetes. *Borrelia hispanica* normally found in *Ornithodoros erraticus erraticus* was adapted to lice and was transmissible by hemolymph in the manner of *B. recurrentis*. One natural strain was found to be as readily adapted to lice as is *B. recurrentis*. There were clear cases where lice acquired infection when they were fed on patients with subclinical infections. This is considered a mutant strain that remained infective for lice and caused only inapparent infections in guinea pigs and attenuated infections in rats. If such is possible in other parts of the world, an adequate explanation of a reservoir will require more understanding of all spirochetes.

Treponema

The genus *Treponema* is a group of spirochetes that causes cutaneous and more involved lesions in vertebrates. They have only vertebrates in their reservoirs, and transmission for the most part is vertical.

Insects are casually associated with at least three species of these spirochetes in the moist tropics. The importance of flies in the epidemiology is debatable (Barnard, 1952). Certainly flies of the genera *Hippelates* (Chloropidae), *Musca* (Muscidae), and *Siphunculina* (Oscinidae) may and do ingest *T. pertenue*, the agent of yaws, and then regurgitate it to reinfest their labella. Furthermore these flies frequently feed on the human skin about any moist area. *T. carateum* of the tropical Caribbean littoral has been associated with *Hippelates* flies. Even *T. pallidum* may become a skin invader when it is associated with *Musca* sp. in Africa or with *Hippelates* in the Western Hemisphere (Brumpt, 1949).

T. pertenue, the cause of yaws, a tropicopolitan disease, has a significant relationship to flies. Barnard (1952) has reviewed the literature on the transmission of yaws from the sixteenth century to the middle of the twentieth century. Throughout these 400 years, flies of various sorts have been suspect. Hackett (1957) has evaluated the several routes of transmission as follows: Direct transmission by contact or by congenital means is easy and frequent especially among indigenous people. Transmission to new arrivals in a focus might be explained by indirect paths. Insects, particularly flies that feed on exudates from lesions, may be disturbed and then feed on the skin of another person and thereby contaminate the skin of the new host. Interrupted feeding of some of the blood-sucking flies might be a suitable means for mechanical transfer. Dogs may pick up the agent by licking or rubbing against a lesion and then transmit it. Contaminated inanimate objects such as floor coverings, bedding, vegetation along paths, dust, and even water may convey the pathogen.

Kumm (1935) has shown that the eye gnat, *Hippelates pallipes*, becomes infected readily with this spirochete when it feeds on moist exudate bearing abundant inoculum. The spirochete disappears from the food tube within a few hours and at no time becomes systemic as does *Borrelia*.

Leptospira

Leptospira icterohaemorrhagicae causes infectious jaundice or Weil's disease in man. The agent is usually transferred by means other than arthropods, but some ticks may become infected (Burgdorfer, 1956). Once a tick has become so, the organism may persist for over 500 days as a systemic parasite. Laboratory transfers to guinea pigs were readily produced by injection of macerated ticks. Virtually all organs of *Ornithodoros* ticks such as salivary glands, central ganglion, coxal glands, ovaries, and excretory tissues harbor the organism.

ADDITIONAL READINGS

Martini's account in Rodenwaldt (1952) discusses cosmopolitan relapsing fever in its current phase.

Sparrow (1955) should be consulted for the origin of spirochetes, particularly those that currently live in lice. Since lice become vectors only when crushed, they are improbable original hosts for spirochetes.

CHAPTER 11

Protophyta IV: Bacteria

GENERAL

Bacteria are independent microscopic cells devoid of discrete nuclei. Their forms are either elongate, short, or round. Often the cells adhere as pairs, tetrads, blocks, or chains. In all cases they reproduce by fission two or three times an hour when in suitable media and at an optimum temperature. Many have the capacity for prolonged resistance to unfavorable climatic and nutritional pressures. A large segment of the group is parasitic in vertebrates.

Vertebrate pathogens of this group are for the most part casually or only facultatively dependent on arthropods as vectors. In only three instances are they either wholly or partially obligate associates. Casuals either adhere to an appendage or surface of a vector or are ingested and thereby contaminate the contents of the food tube. From such association a bacterium becomes dislodged (if on a surface) or expelled orally or anally (if ingested), and consequently it may contaminate the food, the body, or the environment of its vertebrate host. In some instances the carrier retains the bacterium until it in turn is ingested by a susceptible vertebrate. Only *Brucella* spp. invade arthropod tissues and are expelled by ways other than through enteric openings. Table 23 is a listing of species of bacteria that may contaminate some arthropod and in consequence may be conveyed to another suscept or at least to the food of a suscept. Cockroaches are particularly significant in this regard. Roth and Willis (1957) reported an instance in which cockroaches were directly responsible for an outbreak of gastroenteritis. All cases had been inoculated by milk from one dairy. The bottle caps became contaminated in storage because they were overrun by infected

Table 23. Bacterial Pathogens of Vertebrates Associated to Some Degree with Arthropods.

Agent	Disease	Associated Arthropod
Pseudomonas aeruginosa, etc.	Blue pus	Cockroach (2 spp.)
Staphylococcus aureus	Abscess	Cockroach (3 spp.), erytheid mite
Diplococcus pneumoniae *	Pneumonia	Cockroach, bed bug, flea (lab.)
Streptococcus faecalis, etc.	Endocarditis	Cockroach
S. pyogenes	Joint ill (sheep)	Screw-worm
Escherichia coli	Gastroenteritis	Cockroach (2 spp.), house fly
Paracolobacterium aerogenoides and *coliforme*	Gastroenteritis	Cockroach (2 spp.)
Proteus mirabilis	Gastroenteritis	Cockroach
P. morganii	Summer diarrhea	Cockroach (1–3 spp.)
P. rettgeri	Fowl typhoid	Cockroach
P. vulgaris	Abscess, etc.	Cockroach (1–3 spp.)
Salmonella anatis, etc.	Gastroenteritis	Cockroach (1–3 spp.), tick, house fly, flea
S. enteritidis *	Dysentery	Flea, ticks
S. typhosa *	Typhoid	Cockroach, house fly
Shigella paradysenteriae	Dysentery	Cockroach, house fly
Pasteurella pestis *	Plague	Cockroach, flea (100 + species)
P. tularensis *	Tularemia	Ticks and flies
Clostridium perfringens	Gas gangrene	Cockroach
Mycobacterium leprae *	Hansen's disease or leprosy	Cockroach, tick, gnat, flea
M. phlei	Abscess (guinea pig)	Cockroach
M. tuberculosis	Tuberculosis	Cockroach (?), house fly
Nocardia sp.	Nocardiosis	Cockroach
Brucella abortus *	Brucellosis	Tick, cockroach (?)
Corynebacterium pseudotuberculosis	Gaseous lymphadenitis (deer)	*Dermacentor* ticks
Bartonella bacilliformis *	Carrión's	*Phlebotomus*

* Discussed in text.

cockroaches. When the caps were stored in containers and kept free of roaches, the outbreak ceased.

Pasteurella

Pasteurella tularensis

Pasteurella tularensis causes tularemia in humans in both Nearctica and Palaearctica. It causes the usual symptoms of a febrile disease including nausea, vomiting, and rise of temperature, and it may be fatal. Carlé (1951) characterized four phases of tularemia in man: In Phase 1, which is ulcero-glandular, (1) necrosis occurs at the infection court such as a puncture, scratch, or cut, and (2) a swelling of lymph nodes occurs. Phase 2 is ocular-glandular and involves irritation of the conjunctiva and swelling of the lymph nodes and salivary glands of the head; this follows the rubbing of inoculum into the eyes. Phase 3 simulates typhoid with pneumonic symptoms and follows inhaling air-borne inoculum. Phase 4 simulates grippe and follows oral contamination.

Tularemia is a zoonosis that is distributed in patches or tularemic islands within its range. The map shown by Carlé indicates a close association with flood plains of streams and rivers and with bodies of fresh water. Foci are known along all the major rivers of northern Europe and western Asia. They exist from the tundra at 65° North southward to the Caucasus.

The vole (*Arvicola terrestris*) is the mammal responsible for maintenance of *P. tularensis* in palaearctic foci, according to Carlé. It is relatively tolerant and is known to provide chronic porters. It survives well during epidemics when *Microtus*, rats, and other hosts die out. Ixodid ticks (particularly *Dermacentor silvarum*) parasitic on voles are likewise important carriers because they retain the pathogen for as long as 18 months, then pass it from stage to stage, and may pass it to offspring of the generation that initially became infected. Ticks are also capable of transferring the pathogen to other rodents. Thanks to fleas, lice, ticks, and mites, other mammals (sand mouse, hare, skunk, fox, wolf, and others) may be involved.

In northern Russia the wild reservoir is the arctic hare and its tick, *Dermacentor marginatus*. Transmission begins in the spring when overwintering ticks board the hares. Respiratory infections of man occur during the winter in commercial establishments where hares are processed for human food. Some transfer to man is effected when partially cooked meat of these animals is eaten (Myasnikov and Tsareva, 1959).

The reservoir of this pathogen in the lower reaches of the valley of the Don River in Russia is a complex one, according to Carlé (1951). Rodents of the genera *Arvicola*, *Microtus*, and *Muris* are the basic vertebrates. Of these *A. terrestris*, the greater vole, is the tolerant one responsible for interepidemic survival of the agent. This is a water rat that lives in the dense vegetation of flood plains; it lives in subterranean tunnels during the day and may forage in water or above ground during the night. High water, possible from March to May, crowds these voles on knolls and even on floating logs. During the floods, voles are both concentrated and exposed above the ground in the daytime, and they are easily attacked by biting flies. The oral appendages of the flies become contaminated as the agent is transmitted by interrupted feeding. During the night, mosquitoes, such as *Anopheles bifurcatus* and *Aedes* spp., may become infected and may harbor the parasite. Later they void virulent bacteria in feces, which may contaminate various surfaces or water. Mechanical transfer to humans was reported in the midsummer of 1937, when the Don spread over its flood plain, causing the greater vole to be exposed to attack by horse flies and deer flies, *Haematopota* and *Chrysops*. Fishermen and agricultural workers were inoculated by the contaminated mouth parts of flies that had first fed on sick voles shortly after the flood.

Transmission to *Microtus* and *Muris* species takes place during times of high water when displaced voles move into areas occupied by the upland rodents. Nest parasites such as ticks, mites, and fleas effect transfer to the new hosts. Ticks retain the pathogen and become a part of the reservoir, since they transmit it vertically through various stages and possibly to the next generation.

Transmission between vertebrates through ingestion of contaminated water or grain is common. When any infected rodent dies in water, in shocks of grain, or in stored grain, contamination of the material occurs. Should man or a rodent ingest contaminated water or inhale the contaminated air, transmission of the organism may follow. Even the steppe lemming may become infected when a migrating horde arrives at a river in flood. Sick animals may die in streams or in domestic situations along the subsequent route of march.

There is a sylvatic-domestic phase in the Caucasus involving a chain from vole through striped mouse to the house mouse by way of ticks and fleas. Domestic-human phases involve transmission by either (1) contaminated hides, fur, or meat to human skin, (2) contaminated dust, or (3) contaminated water. An interhuman phase may occur where an extensive infestation of the body louse exists and lice are free to move about among the people, because this louse maintains the bacterium easily (Price, 1954).

Outbreaks of tularemia in the United States may involve a variety of transmission chains. A horizontal route through hares and their tick, *Haemaphysalis leporis-palustris,* is known in Alaska. Another horizontal chain may exist in rabbits and their lice. The usual intersylvatic reservoir in the United States is maintained in a complex of

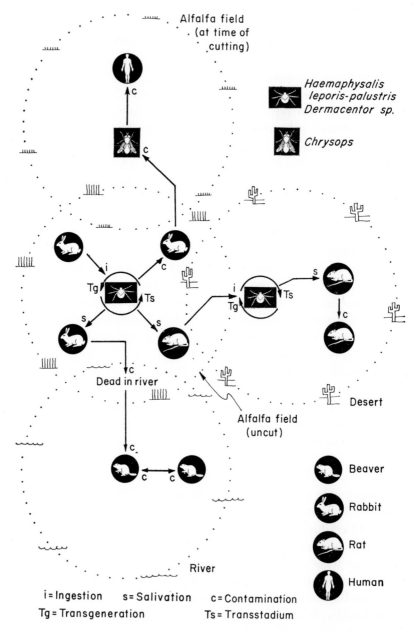

i = Ingestion   s = Salivation   c = Contamination
Tg = Transgeneration   Ts = Transstadium

Fig. 80. Reservoir and transmission chains for *Pasteurella tularensis* in the Great Basin of western United States.

rabbits and wild ground birds together with *Haemaphysalis* and sometimes *Dermacentor* and *Amblyomma* ticks. A little-known chain may depend on carnivorism among desert rodents (Vest and Marchette, 1958). When the mortality among the vertebrates is high, some die in streams, the water then becomes contaminated, and outbreaks among beavers have resulted. Under some conditions a sylvatic-human phase occurs. In the Ozark region a summer season of transmission from small mammals to man is by means of ticks, mostly *Amblyomma*. Later, an autumn season for transfer to humans occurs when infected rabbits are dressed for cooking. In the Great Basin of western United States, transmission to hay cutters occurs when contacts between infected rabbits and man is provided by the deer fly, *Chrysops discalis*, which acts solely as a vector (Fig. 80).

Pasteurella tularensis becomes systemic when ingested by ticks. When nymphs of *Ornithodoros* spp. ingest the organism, the bacterium invades the epithelium of the gut, salivary glands, central ganglion, coxal glands, excretory system, and ovaries. Excreta from coxal glands and anus may contain massive concentrations of bacteria. Hopla (1955) showed that this bacterium increased in numbers in nymphal *Amblyomma* but decreased in adults. Body lice infected by ingestion retained the bacteria in the gut even while molting and for as long as 35 days. There was a gradual decline in numbers.

In laboratory infections the extent of pathogenesis is variable according to the arthropod involved (Price, 1957). Normally the epithelium of the anterior third of the gut is invaded in the body louse. The first evidence of intracellular development may appear as early as the fourth day or even much later. No evident injury is caused while the agent is in the gut; however, after it has gone into the hemocoel, the louse dies within a week. Epithelial invasion of the bed bug is in the posterior part of the mid-gut and only occasionally in the malpighian tubules; however, the bacteria multiply in the anterior part of the lumen of the gut. Ticks showed infection of epithelial cells of the rectal sac, lower intestine, diverticula, and malpighian tubules. No invasion of the salivary glands was apparent in either ticks, bed bugs, or lice.

Pasteurella pestis

Pasteurella pestis is the causative agent of plague, a disease that manifests itself in some five forms. Bubonic plague or black plague is

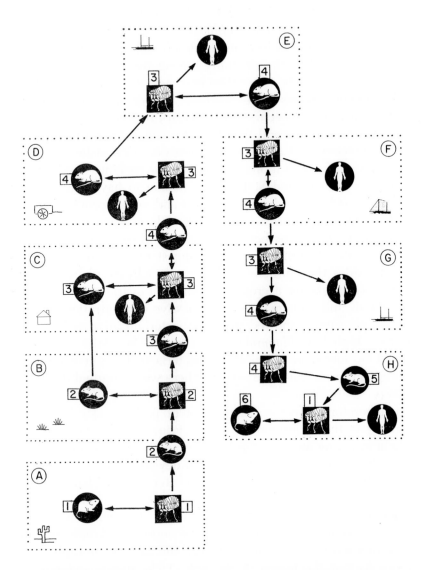

Fig. 81. Chains of transmission for *Pasteurella pestis* from its basic sylvatic reservoir (A) by way of transports for grain to a port in a semi-arid area to a new sylvatic reservoir. Transmission is from flea to vertebrate by regurgitation, vertebrate to flea by ingestion, and from vertebrate to vertebrate by contamination. A, desert; B, steppe; C, domestic-inland; D, grain transport; E, Port A; F, grain ship; G, Port B, etc.; H, semi-desert area. See explanation of symbols at the bottom of the facing page.

characterized by swellings (buboes) of the axillary lymph nodes and a high mortality rate. The second type has been called *pestis minor* since it is relatively benign, and the patient usually remains ambulatory. The very malignant pneumonic form localizes in the pulmonary system and often causes hemorrhages of the lungs; this form is a result of inhaling inoculum. The fourth, the septicemic form, appears with a high fever and hemorrhages of the mucosa of nose, mouth, and intestine, and terminates in death. The Andean form usually appears in pueblos in the Andes Mountains. It is an inflammatory sort which produces malaise, vomiting, and often death.

Plague has had a long history of periodic devastation of southern Asia. It has spread along trade routes and into most parts of the world, where it is commonly known as port plague because of its frequent appearance in them (Fig. 81). It has spread along both caravan routes and sea lanes, and has been particularly associated with transport of grain. On several occasions the disease swept across Europe with disastrous results. Following the Parthian War in Asia Minor in A.D. 165, one of the early pandemics spread across western Europe. Another struck Europe by way of Turkey beginning in the year 542. The most devastating outbreak swept westward in the mid-fourteenth century and left about one-fourth of the population of western Europe dead in its wake. The prolonged pandemic culminating in the mid-seventeenth century reportedly killed over 300 thousand persons in one year in the city of Naples alone. Over 10 per cent

1 *Neopsylla setosa et al.*
2 *Ceratophyllus mokrzecki et al.*
3 *Xenopsylla cheopis*
4 Any local flea on wild burrowing rodents
5 Any local flea on wild roving rodents

I. Suslik *(Citellus)*
6. Any colonial burrowing rodent

3 Any domestic rodent
4 *Rattus spp.*

Human

2 Sand mouse *(Meriones)* et al.
5 Any roving wild mouse

of the population of London died from the disease a few years later. Scarcely over 200 years ago, about 50,000 persons perished from plague in Marseilles, France.

The most recent pandemic is thought to have begun its explosion in Yunnan near the Tibetan border and then spread halfway around the world (Link, 1955). About the middle of the nineteenth century the disease must have been domestic. It had reached the port cities of Hong Kong, Calcutta, and Bombay by the middle of the last decade of that century. Marine transport took it to ports all over the Pacific, including at least one on the West Coast of the United States. It spread westward to ports in Arabia and around the Mediterranean.

Plague presumably came to North America about 1899, where it first occurred in San Francisco as an outgrowth of an oriental pandemic. By 1907 the pathogen had moved inland and was killing wild rodents. Since that time the agent has spread widely among burrowing rodents in the dry parts of the United States and Canada west of the one hundredth meridian. It is now a potential danger to persons who live in areas of wild rodents or who visit remote recreational areas currently so popular in the far western United States.

Rites of exorcism have long been performed under the direction of many religions in efforts to avoid the plague. At the dawn of urban history, priests of the Philistines instructed their followers to make and worship images of the mice that marred their land in times of plague. Marcus Aurelius, an emperor of Rome, tried to stem the destruction of an epidemic in A.D. 165 by ordering massive slaughter of Christians for reasons not obvious to us but popular at the time. Quarantines of areas and masking of individuals had their advocates. For centuries functionaries in the healing arts prescribed that persons should move from the epidemic area for protection. The people were advised to leave the area early in the epidemic, stay away a long time, and return slowly. While this was good advice for some individuals, the mass of people remained in a stricken area and suffered through the epidemic.

Plague exists as a sylvatic zoonosis in colonial burrowing rodents (Levi and Rall', 1960). Foci occur where there are extensive areas occupied by stable populations of a single basic host. In such situations the pathogen actually is able to occupy only parts of the range of the basic host. In other words, in any one endemic focus the basic host has a range greater than that of the pathogen. The secondary hosts permit the pathogen latitude for expansion. The steppe-desert interface of Asia north and east of the Caspian Sea is one such massive area (A, Fig. 81), and a similar one is in western China. We have reason to believe that domestic plague of historical European outbreaks came from sylvatic foci of the pathogen in the steppes of central Asia. South Africa, South America, and southwestern United States have extensive sylvatic foci.

Bacteriaemia of rodents varies in both degree and duration as the transmission chain varies (Levi and Rall', 1960). When the pathogen is passed from individual to individual within a species (suslik to suslik), bacteriaemia is always high regardless of size of dose. Only when the infecting dose is massive as a high degree of bacteriaemia shown by the suscept when the donor is another species. The pathogen persists for a longer period of time when passage is intraspecific (e.g., gerbil to gerbil) than it is when passage is interspecific (suslik to gerbil). Transmission is said to be favored the longer the bacteria persist in a host.

Between rodents the pathogen passes by one of four possible means to a suscept according to Levi and Rall' (1960). Food contaminated by the parasite when ingested may cause infection. An active rodent may become contaminated from direct contact with a dead one in a burrow. Air-borne bacilli may be inhaled to cause respiratory symptoms. Lastly, contaminated fleas regurgitate the pathogen into suscepts while attempting to feed. In nature this flea-rodent chain is essential to maintain a focus of infection.

In the literature abundant evidence may be found of routes of transmission that are reversible between domestic and sylvatic foci. The reservoir recedes periodically to these basic foci. On the other hand, *P. pestis* of port plague seems to have gone from domestic foci to wild ones in the United States, South America, South Africa, Madagascar, and elsewhere.

The reservoir relationships for the plague bacillus differ little in basic pattern the world over. As a rule, there is an essential, burrowing, colonial rodent which belongs to the Sciuridae or Gerbillinae. Intermediate or accessory species belong to the Muridae, Jaculidae, and rarely Leporidae, and these disperse the pathogen in times of outbreak. The interplays are often complex and may involve scores of species of mammals in vast semidesert areas of the world.

Central Asia, considered to be the original site of plague, has sylvatic reservoirs for the pathogen of several independent sorts localized in extensive sandy zones (A and B, Fig. 81). Tikhomirova *et al.*

(1935) have characterized one such situation at a steppe-sand interface in Russia. Some 18 species of rodents range the steppe, and
seven range the sandy zone. They all meet at the interface or in an
intermediate zone. *Citellus pygmaeus*, a suslik, is dominant in the
grass-wormwood zone of the steppe, and *Meriones* (*Pallasiomys*)
meridianus, the sand mouse, dominates the sands. Thirteen or more
species of fleas with a range of hosts have been taken from the burrows of the suslik, and about 12 species with general feeding habits
live with the sand mouse. The sand mouse is tolerant to the bacterium and may harbor infections for extended periods. A flea of
varied host range, *Ceratophyllus mokrzecki,* has been found infected
in nature. The mouse and its fleas move from the sandy zone into the
intermediate one and thereby overlap the range of the suslik and a
dozen or more other rodents. The suslik is susceptible to plague and
at least one of its fleas, *Neopsylla setosa*, with a range of rodent hosts,
becomes infected naturally. The bacterium survives in the hibernating suslik. In eastern Russia and Mongolia the marmot (*Marmota*)
and its fleas, comprise an essential part of the sylvatic reservoir. The
fleas get on sheep dogs on the range, and are transmitted by them
to domestic (i.e., camp) situations. Machiavello (1954) listed over
60 species of mammals from Asia and European Russia that have
been found spontaneously infected with *Pasteurella pestis*.

Kartman *et al.* (1960) found that in a basic focus in California,
P. pestis spreads to contiguous areas by movements of wild rodents
carrying their fleas to domestic rats and other rodents. No extensive
spread was noted.

North America is an area into which *Pasteurella pestis* was introduced. The pathogen invaded ports along the West Coast of North
America, and then it presumably moved into sylvatic reservoirs.
Regardless of how it became established, it has been recovered from
over 60 species of wild rodents and a half-dozen lagomorphs.
Holdenried and Quan (1956) assessed the reservoir capacities of
common rodents in a semidesert part of New Mexico and have rated
them according to tolerance for the bacillus. Two species of *Tho-
momys,* two *Citellus,* one *Microtus,* and one *Onychomys* are moder-
ately resistant. At least 11 species are more or less susceptible. This
complex fauna of overlapping ranges, together with numerous fleas,
can and does provide a vast reservoir comparable to that in deserts of
central Asia.

The North American reservoir for plague exists in western Canada, western United States, and Mexico. The sylvatic existence of plague bacteria was first observed in 1903 in Contra Costa County, California, and by 1909 epidemic proportions were observed in ground squirrels (Link, 1955). Evidence of spread outside California was noted in 1934, when a sheep herder became ill with plague in Lake County, Oregon. Prairie dogs (*Cynomys mexicanus*) were reported to be heavily infected in Mexico in 1954 (Kartman *et al.*, 1958). Sheep herders, campers, prospectors, and others who range into areas where there are large populations of burrowing rodents may become afflicted.

Kartman *et al.* (1958) explained how plague may well progress from sylvatic to domestic foci in western United States. These observers call attention to the fact that transient rodents overlap ranges of both wild rodents and domestic rats. Expanding suburbs and increasing tendencies for people to settle in even more isolated areas will eventually bring man and his attendant rats into proximity to colonial wild rodents. Peripatetic field mice, whose ranges span the distance between wild and domestic foci can act as porters. Wilderness areas are ever more appealing to campers now that roads and trails have made many of them accessible. Infected fleas may move directly from burrows or rodents to the campers, and human illness will result.

Introduction of *Pasteurella* into South America resulted in the organism's invading a wild reservoir where it has largely remained. In Peru and Ecuador the agent spread from ports along rail lines into the highlands where both sylvatic and interhuman phases have become established. Transmission in the latter phase is accomplished by *Pulex irritans* as it was in much of medieval Europe. The wild reservoir in Argentina is complex, involving at least six genera of rodents and rabbits, while the Brazilian reservoir involves rodents, cats, and marsupials, according to reports.

Rodenwaldt (1952) noted the occurrence of rat plague in Spain, where recurrent domestic-human transfer continues without any apparent sylvatic phase. Elsewhere in the world, foci dependent solely on this phase soon die out. Ports and cities along lines of communication where this is the only phase must have repeated introductions through channels of commerce if the foci are maintained (A, Fig. 81).

The reservoir relations of *Pasteurella pestis* in southern Africa has been analyzed by Davis (1953) as follows: Plague in the domestic phase is incapable of persisting without periodic renewal from a sylvatic phase. The strongest link between the phases is the multimammate mouse, *Rattus natalensis,* a species that is equally at home in domestic and peridomestic haunts. In the former haunt it overlaps the range of domestic rats, and in the latter it commingles with gerbils (mainly *Tatera* sp.). The causative agent of plague thrives in the gerbils, *Tatera* and *Desmodillus,* by way of two fleas (*Xenopsylla* spp.) common to their burrows. These fleas feed readily on wandering mice. Infected mice in turn initiate infection in domestic rat fleas and thence domestic rats.

According to Fyodorov (1960) plague in man in central Europe was in proportion to the incidence of wild rodents. More specifically, species of *Marmota* and *Citellus,* the colonial, burrowing rodents are the mammals of importance. Both were very common in the steppe areas of the continent at one time. Even as late as the second decade in this century, ground squirrels constituted a grave menace to agriculture in much of Russia. The plow and the harrow have driven these rodent pests to submarginal land, and the only large areas still held by them are the trans-Caspian lowlands. As the ground squirrels were displaced, plague became progressively less frequent. Disappearance of European foci progressed from west to east.

The passing of urban plague in England was associated with changes in the architecture of dwellings (Rodenwaldt, 1952). Frame construction of houses was the rule in London, for example, prior to the great fire of 1666. After the fire, masonry largely replaced wood in construction. *Pulex irritans* was considered to be the medieval vector and it throve in the early dwellings but was not adapted to houses of masonry construction. Incidentally, this flea is said to be the one of greatest significance as a vector in much of northern Africa and on the western slope of the Andes.

Bacot and Martin (1924) found that, with the onset of hot weather, incidence of plague declines in many parts of the world. Where the heat is accompanied by dryness, the rate of decline is more rapid. Their explanation is that inoculated fleas that have left a dead host live only a short time where temperature is high and moisture is low. The shorter the life of the vector, the less the chance it has of finding a new host.

Pasteurella pestis is able to maintain itself in the gut of species of fleas common on rodents the world over. Some species of fleas provide more suitable media for development than others, but all seem to be susceptible. Bacot and Martin (1914) have reported on infection of fleas as follows: A day or two after a flea has taken a meal of infected blood, clusters of minute brown masses appear in the mid-gut and proventriculus. These masses are more firm and jelly-like than the over-all mass in the gut, and they are teeming with plague bacilli. Quite often, especially in some species of fleas, the masses of bacteria and blood about the bases of the proventricular spines collect until the valve into the mid-gut is so choked or "blocked" that little or no blood is able to pass during the act of feeding. Such blocked individuals attack any and all hosts repeatedly, but the ingested blood goes no further than the esophagus, which often becomes greatly distended during the act of feeding. The blood in the esophagus of a blocked flea that has recently fed keeps the new blood seething in the esophagus by continuous, strenuous action of the pharyngeal pump (Holdenried, 1952). Bacteria in the plug in the proventriculus come to be mixed with the new blood and thereby contaminate that in the anterior part of the gut and oral appendages. Quan *et al.* (1954) stated that, within two days after an infective meal, the bacterial count in the gut of *Xenopsylla* ranged from 1 to 6 million. Proventricular blocks associated with empty and constricted stomachs occurred as early as two days after an infecting meal. Not all species become blocked by infective meals of blood; yet some fleas even in this condition are successful vectors to vertebrates because infected fleas may retain viable bacteria anywhere in the food tube from mouth parts to feces. Munshi (1960) questions the significance of blocking as the primary cause for transmitting the bacilli.

Infected fleas are affected differently by plague bacilli. When blocking occurs, as Kartman *et al.* (1956) have shown, death of the flea follows within about 5–8 days. Neither nutriment nor sufficient liquid gets to the mid-gut, and the flea literally dehydrates. First, the flea shrinks in size; then it dies. In the meantime it feeds many times a day on any accessible host. Some fleas that live on wild rodents may retain viable bacteria for several months, particularly in winter.

Transmission of plague bacilli from flea to vertebrate may be accomplished by any species, whether individuals are blocked or not. To qualify as a vector, a species must supply infective doses of parasites to an adequate number of vertebrates to maintain the reservoir. This can be done by individuals when blocked, or it may be done equally well when massive numbers of fleas bearing few bacteria in their stylets repeatedly attack a vertebrate host. The order of importance of the several modes of transmission has been stated by Burroughs (1947) as follows: (1) feeding by blocked fleas, (2) massive feeding by fleas with contaminated mouth parts, (3) contamination of abraded skin by feces or contents of crushed fleas, and (4) ingestion of contaminated fleas. Successful infection of a vertebrate by the two latter methods is considered rare.

Even though many species of fleas may become infected with plague bacilli, only a few in any one locality seem to be significant in the reservoir. Quan, Miles, and Kartman (1960) found nine species at a focus in California; yet only two were consistently infected (93 per cent of the population). Of the 111 fleas positive for *P. pestis*, only 19 per cent were positive by animal inoculation (Quan, Kartman, *et al.*, 1960). Rate of infection ranged from a few organisms to millions in each flea. A meal of low bacteriaemia was assumed to be the cause of low incidence in a flea, but they are able to rid themselves of the agent at some stage after an infecting meal.

The significance of insects other than fleas in reservoirs of plague bacilli is not clear. Certainly some other insects ingest and harbor the pathogen. Bed bugs have harbored the pathogen for five months (Hall, 1937). Lice, too, have been found naturally infected. Infections among lice of man and rodents have been reported (Girard, 1943). Certain triatomine bugs harbor the bacteria and probably transfer them by means of contaminated mouth parts while feeding in nests of wood rats, for example (Ames *et al.*, 1954).

Shigella

Shigella spp. cause enteric fevers in humans. Among the more important ones are those that cause summer diarrhea in children. These agents are spread when contaminated food and liquids are ingested. Food may become contaminated directly by food handlers or by insects such as cockroaches and flies. Insects may contaminate food with bacteria from their body surfaces or from their food tubes by way of feces. Either the bacteria become dislodged and fall on foods or they are deposited on food with feces. Watt and Lindsay (1948) incriminated the house fly as a primary vector of *Shigella* by comparing incidence of dysentery in towns where flies were kept from dwellings with others where no suppressive measures were employed. Prior to initiation of the test, all towns had similar high incidences of the disease. During the first year those towns where flies were suppressed had a significantly lower incidence of dysentery. When the group of towns was reversed in the experiment and suppression of flies was applied to towns previously untreated, the incidence of disease was also reversed. Enteric fevers were the only diseases showing this relationship to flies during the experiment.

Salmonella

Salmonella, a group of causative agents of food-borne disease of man, needs no arthropod to insure survival, but circumstantial evidence causes certain ones to be suspect. Muscoid flies are most often suspected. Olsen and Rueger (1950) found that S. *oranienburg* survived on the surface of the American roach 78 days, and in its feces 199 days. When the organism was put on either crackers or dry cereal, it remained viable 60–90 days. S. *pullorum* survived passage through the house fly (Gerberich, 1952). S. *bovis-morbificans* has been obtained from the roach, *Periplaneta americana* in Australia. Eskey *et al.* (1951) obtained S. *typhimurium* from sticktight fleas taken from both domestic rats and hogs on a hog ranch. Presumably the larvae had ingested the agent and had passed it transstadially. Argasid ticks have been experimentally infected with this species. S. *enteritidis* has been taken from fleas removed from a wild chipmunk, from *Rhipicephalus sanguineus* in a kennel, from *Ornithodoros* ticks, from body lice, and from rat fleas. S. *enteritidis* undoubtedly is pathogenic to rat fleas, killing them within 40 days.

Salmonella typhosa

Salmonella typhosa, the causative agent of typhoid fever, is a contaminant of food and water that frequently causes outbreaks of disease, especially where disposal of human wastes is carelessly handled. Foods may be contaminated by human porters (called typhoid carriers) or by insects that feed both on wastes and on human food. Water is usually contaminated in shallow wells or springs.

The extent of the role of insects as vectors of this *Salmonella* is not clear. Where unlimited contact is maintained by insects between human wastes and prepared human food, typhoid bacteria may be transferred. However, other means for contamination of food are common in these situations. Outbreaks of typhoid have been traced to insects where no other agent for transferring the pathogen seemed likely. Herms (1923) reported an outbreak among patrons of a center distributing dairy products. Contamination of the dairy presumably came from a pit privy used by a typhoid carrier not connected with the dairy. Flies bearing S. *typhosa* were found in both the dairy and the privy. The water supply was free of the agent. Bitter and Williams (1949) quoted an Italian observer to the effect that the Oriental roach was the only logical vector between families in an urban area where there were neither flies nor contaminated water. Typhoid bacteria were recovered from the feet and bodies of the roaches collected from pit privies. Likewise these bacteria were recovered from bread and cheese on which contaminated roaches had fed.

Brucella

Brucella abortus, the causative agent of brucellosis in cattle and humans, has a natural vertebrate-arthropod reservoir. Galouzo and Rementsova (1956) quote instances of recurrence of brucellosis in livestock in parts of Russia long after removal of all infected cattle. Ticks infected with the microbe have been found in these areas. The sylvatic reservoir includes such vertebrates as burrowing rodents, *Citellus* (3 spp.), *Spermophilopsis* sp., *Microtus arvalis*, and *Rhombomys;* gazelle; crow, sparrow; snake, lizard, toad, tortoise. It also includes numerous ticks such as *Hyalomma* (5 spp.), *Dermacentor* (3 spp.), *Boophilus calcaratus*, and *Ornithodoros lahorensis*, all of which have been found naturally infected. The pathogen passes readily from one generation to the next in ticks, as has been observed in the laboratory. After ingestion by ticks, the organism becomes systemic and causes infective feces, coxal fluid, and saliva. Many of the ticks named above infest, serially, lizards and rodents or bovines. All of the essentials for a zoonosis are provided in the combination. The usual means of transfer of the agent, to man at least, is contaminated milk or other objects.

MISCELLANEOUS

Mycobacterium leprae

Mycobacterium leprae, the cause of Hansen's disease or leprosy, is not known to have a reservoir requiring arthropods. Numerous observations have shown that various arthropods ingest the bacteria while feeding on active lesions. Naturally infected *Amblyomma* ticks and pubic lice have been found in Brazil. The most significant potential association is that with cockroaches. Moiser (1946) reported that *Blatella germanica* may feed on the insensitive tissue of a patient to the extent of causing scarring. The bacteria survived 19 days in the gut and remained viable up to 16 months in the feces. As many as 23 per cent of roaches in wards of a leprosarium in Southern Rhodesia were infected.

Diplococcus pneumoniae

Diplococcus pneumoniae, the causative agent of pneumonia, has no known arthropod in the natural reservoir, but it can live in and on the bodies of insects such as cockroaches (Roth and Willis, 1957). Epshtein *et al.* (1935) found the pathogen may be ingested by bed bugs and fleas and remain viable. In such instances the epithelium of the gut becomes coated and cells are invaded by the microbe. The flea, *Ceratophyllus fasciata*, permitted the agent to propagate "intensively" and to infect the gut for at least 25 days.

Bartonella bacilliformis

Among the Bartonellaceae, the one best known is *Bartonella bacilliformis*, the causative agent of bartonellosis or Carrion's disease of humans. The disease may express itself in all ranges of virulence from benign to a fatal anemia. At one end of the scale is the inapparent case of a subclinical carrier while mortal Oroya fever, a hemolytic febrile form, is at the other. Between the extremes is the benign form, *verruca peruviana* (or *peruvana*) with its cutaneous eruptions. This disease is called "verruga" in nearly all of the early literature.

The pathogen is resident in distinct ecological islands along the western slope of the Andes Mountains. In the Peruvian zone (6°–13° South) the "islands" consist of canyons such as that of the Rimac River at elevations between 2,000 and 10,000 feet where the climate is said to be that of perpetual spring because the temperature ranges between 53° and 60° F (Shannon, 1929). The steep walls of canyons permit an average of about eight hours of sunlight each day. The canyon floor is lush with vegetation, but the walls are xerophytic. The Colombia-Ecuador zone is near the equator. It is one of plateaus slashed by ravines with vertical walls.

The exact composition of permanent reservoirs for this *Bartonella* is unknown. Vertebrates known to be susceptible include field mouse

(*Phyllotis*), "gopher" (*Citellus tridecemlineatus*), squirrel (*Sciurus*), dog, man, and monkey. The only ones of these known to be naturally infected are the field mouse and man. Herrer (1953) reported that squirrels, when inoculated in the laboratory would yield the pathogen from the skin up to 10 days after inoculation even though the animals showed no nodules. He suggested that this observation might have some bearing on maintenance of this parasite in nature. Rodents show a high degree of tolerance, and the pathogen has been recovered from skin cultures taken at sites of inoculation. Man, too, shows all ranges of tolerance including carriers for prolonged periods, (Weinman and Pinkerton, 1937). The incidence of disease suggests a basic sylvatic origin with a sylvatic-human phase.

At least four species of sand flies (*Phlebotomus*) have been found bearing the pathogen in nature. Infected males and unengorged females have been found even though males are not blood feeders at all. Females that are initially free of the agent may become infected after a meal on infected mammals in the laboratory. The organisms have been found among the chitinous spines of the pharynx, on the epithelial lining of the gut, in the buccal cavity and on the mouth parts (Hertig, 1939). Intracellular invasion of mid-intestinal epithelium is known but may be uncommon. *Phlebotomus* may transfer the agent while feeding, presumably by way of contaminated mouth parts; however, feces of the flies may bear live pathogens.

ADDITIONAL READINGS

Roth and Willis (1957 and 1960) should be studied for an understanding of the role of domestic roaches as the vectors of enteric bacteria. The significance of these animals has been little realized in relation to urban cultures.

West (1951) recounts the effect of house flies as vectors of enteric bacteria. Under primitive conditions muscids must still be regarded as of paramount importance.

Carlé (1951) is a comprehensive account of tularemia as a zoonosis. Chains of transmission are explained thoroughly. The paper is difficult to read because some of the expressions are colloquial, but for understanding the role of wild animals and invertebrates in the chains of transmission, there is no better account.

Hirst (1953) is a book dealing with the ecology of the plague organism. The history and current status is explained. More recent details may be had from the several references cited.

CHAPTER 12

Protozoa

GENERAL

The animal kingdom contains four phyla that have representatives depending on arthropods for nourishment and transport. Of these, the phylum Protozoa is represented by a large number of microscopic vertebrate parasites that live in arthropodan hosts. The classes Mastigophora and Telosporasida are particularly rich in species with this dual association. The class Sarcodina has one genus, *Entamoeba*, that has at least a casual association with certain insects. The class Piroplasmasida has only the one order Piroplasmorida. In it are parasites of ungulates and of some birds. Most of the arthropodan associates are parasites in the blood-vascular systems of vertebrates and they are obligatory parasites of arthropods. Those that are enteric pathogens of vertebrates tend to be casually associated with these invertebrates.

Protozoa (Hall, 1953, and Kudo, 1954) are unicellular (or noncellular, according to definition) animals that exist singly or in colonies of like components. Those of most significance in medical entomology live singly or in aggregations for parts of their lives as intracellular parasites in red corpuscles of vertebrates, or they live in tissues and organs of blood-feeding arthropods. Reproduction is both gametic and non-gametic (budding, fission, multiple division). Nuclei of varied forms are present in all components. Organelles may be present or wanting. The class Sarcodina has pseudopodia, agametic reproduction, and indefinite form. Mastigophora have flagella as locomotor organelles. Telosporasida have spores and lack contractile vacuoles, and they reproduce both agametically and

Table 24. Categories of Protozoa of Significance to Medical Entomology.

Class	Order	Genus	Reservoir (General)		
			Vertebrate	Invertebrate	(Vector only)
Sarcodina	Amoebida	Entamoeba	Mammal	(Vector only)	
Mastigophora	Protomastigorida	Leishmania	Mammal	Insect	
		Trypanosoma	Mammal, bird	Insect	
Telosporasida	Coccidia	Hepatozoon	Mammal	Mite, tick, flies	
		Haemogregarina	Reptile, fish	Acarine	
		Karyolysus	Reptile	Acarine	
		Aggregata	Squid *	Crab	
		Schellackia	Lizard	Acarine	
		Lankesterella	Frog, sparrow	Acarine	
	Haemosporidia	Plasmodium	Bird, mammal	Mosquito	
		Haemoproteus	Bird, reptile	Culicoides, hippoboscid fly	
		Hepatocystis	Arboreal primates	Argasid tick (?)	
		Leucocytozoon	Bird	Simuliid fly	
Piroplasmasida	Piroplasmorida	Babesia	Bovine, equine, canine	Tick	
		Theileria	Bovine	Tick	
		Aegyptianella	Bird	Argas tick	

* Non-vertebrate.

gametically. The various genera parasitic in vertebrates and known to be associated with arthropods are given in Table 24.

In the discussion that follows, only the groups that are well known will be considered in detail. Many of the species may be known in the vertebrates or have been subjects for descriptive biology, but only a few have been subjects for bionomic studies. Those less well known will be grouped for discussion at generic or higher levels (Table 24).

Many species of Telosporasida parasitic in an arthropod-vertebrate reservoir have two forms in their vertebrate hosts, namely, a vegetative one called *trophozoite* and a reproductive one called *gametocyte*. There may be repetitive generations of trophozoites by *schizogony*, or direct division of the units. The gametocytes, however, must give rise to *gametes*, two of which unite to form a *zygote* before the schizogonous cycle may be initiated again. Those forms of entomological significance that have gametic reproduction produce zygotes in the arthropodan component. The zygote then proliferates in the arthropod in a *sporogonous cycle*. Mastigophora, however, have agametic reproduction in arthropods.

The sarcodine, *Entamoeba histolytica*, that causes amoebiasis in humans, is seldom thought of in connection with arthropods because it has no obligatory biological relationship with them. Under certain situations, however, it may use insects as vectors. Roth and Willis (1957) reported that viable cysts had been found in cockroaches in Egypt, Venezuela, and Peru. Recognizable, viable trophozoites have recovered from vomit drops of muscid and calliphorid flies, according to Pipkin (1949). Roberts (1947) noted that cysts of *E. histolytica* can and do become lodged in the pseudotracheae of flies; they remain there in a viable form, and they may become dislodged later by regurgitation of fluids. While it is conceded that polluted drinking water and contaminated food handlers are the main carriers in urban areas, the importance of flies in rural areas, particularly the rural tropics, must not be discounted (Roberts, 1947).

MASTIGOPHORA: PROTOMASTIGORIDA

The class Mastigophora is so diverse that many representatives are difficult to assign to the group. All bear flagella for a part or all of their development. Since we are concerned with only two zoopathic genera, *Leishmania* and *Trypanosoma* of the order Protomastigorida, characterization is simplified. Representatives are colorless, elongate forms with one flagellum. Reproduction is by longitudinal fission, and gametes are absent.

To medical entomologists Trypanosomatidae is the most important family in the order. This family is zoopathic for the most part, but only the genera *Trypanosoma* and *Leishmania* require both arthropods and vertebrates in their cycles. Species of *Trypanosoma* are polymorphic, with a maximum of four forms known. The four forms are *leishmanial, leptomonadal, crithidial,* and *trypanosomal.* The first is ovoid and lacks a flagellum. Leptomonadal forms are elongate with a short flagellum. In the crithidial form, the flagellum has a short undulating membrane. The flagellum runs the entire length of the body along the edge of an undulating membrane in the trypanosomal form. *Leishmania* has only leishmanial and leptomonadal forms. Since some genera (*Crithidia, Leptomonas, Herpetomonas*) are confined to invertebrate hosts, one must be careful in studying parasitized arthropods that these strictly arthropodan associates are not confused with those forms parasitic in vertebrates.

Leishmania

Representatives of the genus *Leishmania* cause syndromes variously called Oriental sore, kala azar, and espundia. Kirk and Lewis (1955) said: ". . . they are morphologically indistinguishable, and it is doubtful to what extent they can be distinguished by cultural, biochemical and serological methods or by animal inoculation." In a review of the Russian work of Latychev and Kryukova, Wilcocks (1956) said that human leishmaniae may have evolved from *L. donovani* (a viscerotropic form) to one of its forms, *infantum* (less viscerotropic), to *tropica* (viscerotropism dormant), and to *brasiliensis* (viscerotropism absent). For the purposes of this volume the forms will be considered separately.

Leishmania donovani. Leishmania donovani (syn. *infantum*) is the cause of leishmaniasis in man, that is variously called kala azar, visceral leishmaniasis, and dermal leishmanoid. The disease is widespread, but only Bengal and Assam have been ravaged by distinct epidemics. Three main types of the disease are recognized. Classical kala azar is confined to India where it affects adult humans only. Mediterranean or infantile kala azar affects children and occurs in Portugal, on the Mediterranean Coast, and in the Middle

East, southern Asia, China, and South America. The Sudanese form has a sylvatic origin and affects adults only. The classical form of the disease is manifested as a prolonged fever accompanied by enlargement of the spleen and liver, and it frequently terminates in death. The phase called dermal leishmanoid sometimes appears among treated cases, when lesions of the skin are present though there is no internal evidence of the parasite.

Manson-Bahr *et al.* (1959) reported that the Sudanese, Kenyan, and Brazilian forms may be of a kind. The Kenyan representative of the group differs from the Indian in that during the visceral stage of the disease the skin appears to be more regularly or extensively involved.

This pathogen has either a sylvatic or a domestic reservoir, according to its geographic location. In foci of eastern Asia, which are strictly sylvatic, infections in humans are sporadic and never familial, and are contracted by workers on alluvial plains. Infections from northwestern China to southern Russia, and westward to the Mediterranean, are sporadic and rural, and the pathogen comes to man from canines. Sudanese foci are strictly sylvatic in wooded country with a high water table (Fig. 82). Transients through these areas, such as woodcutters, foresters, and personnel of military patrols, are most susceptible. Some of the Sudanese foci are so sharply delimited that they are known and are shunned by the resident population. These areas are recognizable by the patches of yellow, sandy soil known as "azaza" islands, found on plains of clay soils that are subject to massive cracking (Kirk, 1956). Foci in Bengal and Assam are in populous areas devoted to rice culture, where streams and canals interlace the countryside and patches of bamboo and small groves are abundant. In India, reservoirs are strictly domestic.

Sylvatic reservoirs are usually canine-*Phlebotomus* ones. Some burrowing rodents are significant. Both kinds of vertebrates live in cavities along with species of sand flies (*Phlebotomus*). The jackal is the Asian vertebrate of importance, and a fox (*Lycalopex*) is the Brazilian one. A ground squirrel (*Xerus*) is the vertebrate in the reservoir of a form in Kenya which is said to be very similar to *L. donovani* (Heisch, 1957). Apparently any *Phlebotomus* that frequents burrows may be a vector-host in the reservoir.

Domestic reservoirs have come into being in areas where the expanding human populations and their accompanying dogs have replaced wild canines. The wild *Phlebotomus* found lodgment in the domestic environs. *Phlebotomus papatasii, argentipes,* and *perniciosus* are adaptable species in southern Asia or around the Mediterranean (Fig. 83). Cats are said to enter the domestic reservoir in parts of South America. All three of the vertebrates, man, dog, and cat, may have chronic dermal leishmaniasis following the acute

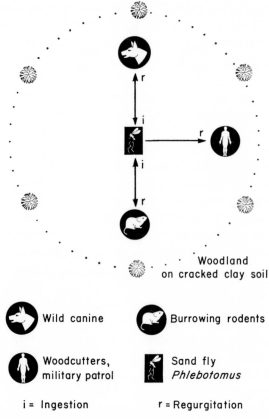

Woodland
on cracked clay soil

Wild canine   Burrowing rodents

Woodcutters,   Sand fly
military patrol   *Phlebotomus*

i = Ingestion   r = Regurgitation

Fig. 82. Reservoir for *Leishmania donovani* in Sudan.

visceral phase, and when these animals are numerous, ample inoculum is provided for any sand flies that are present. When domestic conditions encourage these flies to remain in a building that houses active cases, repeated inoculation is possible.

Visceral leishmaniasis is a chronic disease in northeastern Brazil, where outbreaks occur in valleys of the foothills (Deane, 1958). Transmission chains of the agent are primarily rural, but urban transmission is known. In rural situations the pathogen occurs in a domestic orbit. Pet dogs have particularly high levels of parasitism of the skin, but in foci of parts of Brazil wild foxes (*Lycalopex*) are naturally infected. They range widely and introduce the pathogen into distant domestic foci, where dogs and humans may contract the disease.

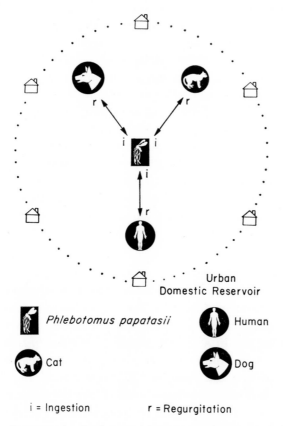

Phlebotomus papatasii

Urban
Domestic Reservoir

Human

Cat

Dog

i = Ingestion   r = Regurgitation

Fig. 83. Reservoir for *Leishmania donovani* in foci around the Mediterranean.

The exact function of *Phlebotomus* in the reservoir of *L. donovani* has been under study since 1922, when coincidence of kala azar and *P. argentipes* was first noted. Subsequent efforts to infect flies of the genus showed variations in susceptibility of different species as well as of the same species under different conditions. By 1925 Christophers *et al.* had learned that these flies ingest forms that develop into a flagellate stage at times. Leishmania move forward in the food tube to the fore-gut where clumps of them begin to multiply, especially in the proventriculus. Smith *et al.* (1940) found that after an initial infective meal, flies maintained on a diet of raisin juice grew an internal culture of the leptomonadal form suitable for transmission. Often under these conditions the proventriculus is "blocked" so that food fails to pass into the stomach on subsequent feeding. Blocked individuals seldom live longer than a day or two. When fed on a diet of blood only, following the infective meal, the flies contain only a few flagellates that are retarded in development and exhibit a low order of infectivity to vertebrates.

Transmission of *L. donovani* is accomplished by contamination of the feeding punctures by flagellates from the food tube. Blocked flies are particularly effective in returning the pathogen to man, because they make repeated attempts to feed. Ingested blood cannot pass into the mid-intestine; instead, it mixes with the contaminated contents of the fore-intestine, and the mixture may be regurgitated into the wound. Not all transmission is effected by blocked flies, but larger doses of parasites are injected by them. Laboratory transmission has been obtained when muscids were fed alternately on contaminated buccal and nasal mucosa and then on normal mucosa.

Leishmania tropica. This is a complex of forms that causes sporadic cutaneous leishmaniasis in man. The true relationship among the forms is unknown; therefore, for convenience in this discussion, the forms are considered as trinomials as follows: *L. tropica tropica* causes oriental sore in Asia and Africa; *L. tropica brasiliensis* causes espundia in South America; *L. tropica guyanensis* causes a cutaneous form in Guiana and Peru, and *L. tropica mexicana* causes aural leishmaniasis in Mexico. Whatever the form, the principal symptom is a necrotic lesion at each site of inoculation. The disease runs a prolonged course and leaves its mark on the victims as permanent scars. This characteristic scarring has impressed medical practitioners throughout the history of medical literature of Asia. Pringle (1957) stated that the middle Asian pandemic originated in Transcaspia near Afghanistan, where the disease called "Balkh sore" has been known since the eleventh century. It reached the Iranian plateau about 1830.

Cutaneous leishmaniasis caused by the several forms is basically a zoonosis, the cause of which is vectored to man from wild rodents at least in Asia. When the typical form of the parasite is introduced from the wild, it causes the "moist" sore. The "dry" sore occurs as a result of domestic or interhuman transmission. In middle Asia the type form appears commonly in rural settlements adjoining a desert (Fig. 84). It is infrequent in similar settlements surrounded by cultivated areas. The basic reservoir for the type form involves burrowing rodents such as gerbils (*Rhombomys* and *Meriones*) and suslik

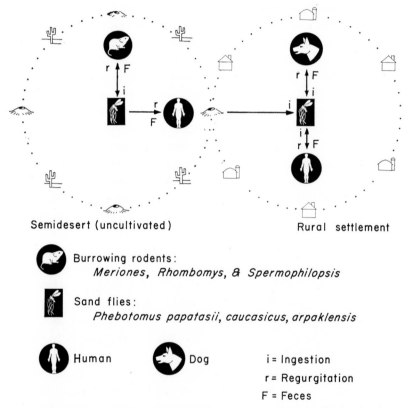

Semidesert (uncultivated)   Rural settlement

Burrowing rodents:
Meriones, Rhombomys, & Spermophilopsis

Sand flies:
Phebotomus papatasii, caucasicus, arpaklensis

Human   Dog   i = Ingestion
                            r = Regurgitation
                            F = Feces

Fig. 84. Reservoir for *Leishmania tropica* in the Middle East.

(*Spermophilopsis leptodactylus*) together with sand flies such as *Phlebotomus papatasii, P. caucasicus*, and *P. arpaklensis*. The rodents live in burrows in the margins of desert areas, but populations cannot be maintained in cultivated lands. In Morocco the vertebrate reservoir is a squirrel (*Xerus getulus*); in Tunisia it is another rodent (*Ctenodactylus gondii*), according to the account in Rodenwaldt (1952). In Iran and Iraq, *P. sergenti* is regularly associated with the distribution of this pathogen.

Transmission of the type form is directly proportional to the persistence of association between susceptible vertebrates and sand flies. The review by Hoare (1955) indicated that burrowing rodents are basic to the reservoir of the type form because (1) they are tolerant and (2) transmission is perennial. Vector flies develop in the deep burrows the year around, and adults are continually available as vectors between rodents. The season for transmission to man is usually restricted to fall. Domestic transmission of the form that causes "dry" sore occurs in towns and cultivated oases; however, little is known about details of the route. Presumably dogs become infected from the sylvatic reservoir; interhuman transfer is also a probability. In either event domestic, nocturnal *Phlebotomus* flies transmit the agent to man as they feed. The account in Rodenwaldt (1952) states that the cause of the urban "dry" form is transmitted at night. People who sleep covered except for their appendages have sores on the extremities, whereas those that sleep lightly clothed may have sores distributed widely. This indicates that the flies feed on any exposed body surface during the night.

Leishmania tropica brasiliensis of South America has a sylvatic reservoir in the agouti (*Dasyprocta*) and the paca (*Caniculus*) and the sand fly (*Phlebotomus intermedius*, among others); however, the importance of this reservoir remains to be proved. Dogs and other domestic animals are likely components of domestic reservoirs. Man may be the only vertebrate involved in French Guiana, where he is frequently tolerant to the point of being asymptomatic. In parts of Brazil the pathogen invades communities where charcoal is made from wood. Workers become infected while felling trees to be used in the charcoal manufacture (Wilcocks, 1957).

The literature is in general agreement that the typical forms of this pathogen develop in flies of the genus *Phlebotomus* in the same manner as those of *L. donovani*. Leptomonads may be found throughout the gut, and they are known to survive for 35 days. Shoshina (1953) found leptomonads literally packed in the hind-gut. At times they were evacuated with feces. She concluded that *L. tropica* is normally evacuated by certain flies while feeding and that the infective forms enter the body either through abraded skin or the feeding puncture.

Trypanosoma

This genus contains a number of species that depend on insects for their transmission to vertebrates. Some species have a cyclopropagative development in the food tube resulting in metacyclic forms which are expelled either through the mouth parts or with feces through the anus. Others do not propagate in the food tube but do contaminate the mouth parts. The former group requires an interval of time between ingestion and transmission. The latter group requires that feeding on the hosts be interrupted momentarily for dependable transmission. Arthropods in the reservoirs for the various forms include tsetse, tabanids, hippoboscids, other biting flies, mosquitoes, triatomine bugs, and fleas.

Trypanosomiases of both humans and domestic animals have determined the culture of tropical Africa (Buxton, 1955). Potential invaders as the horse-borne Arabs were stopped at the first fly belts. The Dutch migrating from the south were forced to take rough overland routes instead of the smoother grasslands because of nagana, a devastating disease of livestock. The lines drawn between the pastoral and the woods tribes is one drawn by *Glossina morsitans* in southwestern Sudan. Historically, inland transport in Africa has been by human porter instead of beast because of nagana. Even today fly belts prevent extensive rearing of the livestock so necessary for relief from the widespread malnutrition of central Africa.

Trypanosoma gambiense. This is the cause of classical or Gambian sleeping sickness in man. The disease may be acute, but it is more often chronic and may last for months or even years. All lymphatic tissues may be involved, and invasions of the central nervous system are common in the late phase of the disease. Cases have been reported from much of Africa between 15° North and 15° South, and from the Atlantic Coast to about 35° East. This represents an area of about five million square miles. Actually specific foci within this area are very numerous, but far less than half of the whole area is involved.

Human trypanosomiasis has depopulated whole areas of equatorial Africa when the combined effects of death and sterility exceeded the reproductive rate in infested zones. In advanced stages of epidemics, the inhabitants dispersed in characteristic patterns (Morris, 1952). Areas along main rivers became depopulated because of death and migrations upstream to sites along the headwaters, or on to divides. The new situations imposed changes in the culture of crops and in domestic habits. Deforestation incident to the demands of agriculture led to erosion of the more sloping land, and soil exhaustion was the consequence. The former sites of habitation were rapidly reclaimed by the bush and big game animals

Populations of tsetse changed, and trypanosomes that infect game replaced those which had driven man away.

The Gambian trypanosome has man and one or more species of tsetse closely associated with him as its basic reservoir. The association must be so intimate that the tsetse feeds on man often and repeatedly. A dependable supply of flies and either a dense human population (16–80 per square mile) or repeated visits by humans to a fly-ridden site furnish the necessary combination of hosts. Sites for contact between man and flies are usually in zones where vegetation is in transition as at margins of woods and thickets where the feeding flies range. Man is so tolerant that he may sustain the parasite for months or even years while remaining physically active. When an ambulatory patient is also a transient, he may become a ready source of food and inoculum for tsetse as he moves along the trail. A chain of transmission is maintained when both sick and healthy persons are transients.

Glossina palpalis and *G. tachinoides* are the most significant species in all foci in the bush near streams or large lakes. The former is the only known vector-host in eastern Africa. *Glossina tachinoides* is the usual vector-host in the thickets and groves surrounding pockets of water on savannas. The incidence of disease is determined by the frequency of contact between man and tsetse rather than by numbers of flies. Significance of focus, therefore, depends more on man's visits to the haunts of a suitable tsetse than on the potential of a particular site for producing flies.

The more significant specific foci for transmission of this trypanosome may be grouped around about ten situations. (1) Fords in larger streams on principal routes of travel may concentrate people in tsetse zones (Fig. 85). (2) Woodland villages in small clearings near streams assure repeated domestic contact. (3) Large villages surrounded by moats that are choked by vegetation permit a lively exchange of pathogens. (4) Common washing and bathing sites provide temporary but excellent sites for transmission, especially at water holes after streams are dry. (5) Persons fishing from shore or from canoes in rivers account for some. (6) Farmers are subject to attack when they tend crops growing in dry river beds. (7) Cultivation of crops on small patches of cleared woodland rather than on large permanent tracts results in more disease. (8) Frequent and mass use of ritual groves may mean repeated contact. (9) Settlements of dense populations near roads which lead through forests and along which many transients pass, are good sites for transmission. (10) Camps for laborers employed in alluvial mining operations have shown very high rates of disease. In all of these instances humans enter the habitats of the flies.

Mulligan (1955) illustrated the maxim that disease follows in the wake of a population explosion when he showed how Gambian sleep-

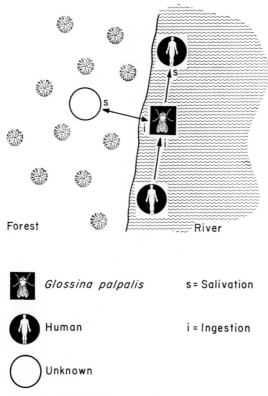

Fig. 85. Site for transmission of *Trypanosoma gambiense* along a river bank in central Africa.

ing sickness expanded from two basic foci in northern Nigeria to an area-wide disease during the present century. With the quieting of intertribal mayhem, walled settlements and restricted agriculture gave way to expanding towns and decentralized agriculture. The settlements came to be connected by interlacing trails, highways, and other rights-of-way, and residents became frequent travelers. Tsetse were already present everywhere in the area. Now man likewise was everywhere on the move. For a time, sleeping sickness was virtually an occupational disease of the traveler, miner, and farmer. As various farming enterprises became established the everyday activities around the homes brought residents in contact with infected tsetse. The focus of trypanosomiases that had been isolated at the confluence of the Niger and Benue rivers spread in all directions. The focus in the Lake Chad Basin expanded south until the two merged in Zaria Province.

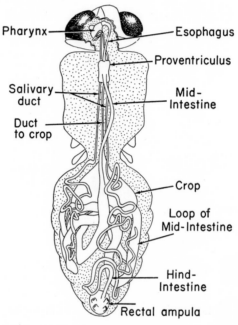

Fig. 86. Diagram of food tube of *Glossina*. (After Patton and Cragg, 1913.)

Curiously enough, the wetter coastal areas where forests predominate are devoid of Gambian sleeping sickness. This is known to be the case along the south shore of Lake Chad at about 5° South. *Glossina palpalis* is abundant enough, but the flies disperse widely and seldom attack man. Where a savanna extends to the coast, foci occur as usual.

The possibility of a sylvatic reservoir must be considered, but the exact nature is unknown; however, enough evidence is available to make antelopes suspect. Certainly some wild vertebrate is indicated for Sesse Island in Lake Victoria, where, according to Buxton (1955), the agent maintained itself for five years in the absence of man. This agent has been cycled through ungulates for five years without loss of virulence toward man.

Trypanosoma gambiense is cyclopropagative in the digestive system of tsetse (Fig. 86). The agent is ingested as the trypanosome form. It is included in the blood meal within the peritrophic membrane. Shortly after ingestion, this form first moves caudally inside the membrane, then into the space between the membrane and the epithelium, where the protozoan clings to the epithelium and begins to multiply. Gradually the pathogens move forward to the region

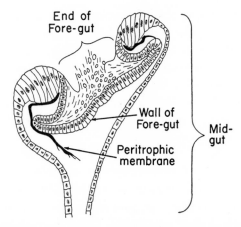

Fig. 87. Diagram of the zone of formation of the peritrophic membrane in a muscoid fly. (After Patton and Cragg, 1913.)

between the fore- and mid-guts where the peritrophic membrane is formed (Fig. 87). They invade the proventriculus by penetrating the membrane at the site of its formation. Cellular multiplication begins as the early crithidial forms divide in the fore-gut and labral gutter. In some manner this form enters the salivary canal from the labral gutter. Shortly afterward, it invades branches of the salivary ducts, where the metacyclic form is produced. The pathogens pass with salivary injections into vertebrate hosts as a tsetse feeds. Preinfective time in a fly is 18 days or longer.

Wijers (1958) recounted conditions required for *Glossina palpalis* to become infected with *T. gambiense*. The fly must take its first blood meal on a person bearing a large number of infective trypanosomes (short, stumpy forms) in the peripheral blood. It must then live at least 18 days in order to be a vector. Transmission rate is highest late in the dry season, when people concentrate about water holes.

Trypanosoma rhodesiense. This is the cause of Rhodesian sleeping sickness, which is an acute disease of man, usually fatal within a few weeks. Rarely is the disease mild. It produces a fever, a rash, and an ulcer at the site of the injection. Within a week or ten days after onset of symptoms, affected persons become too ill to leave their beds. The area of common occurrence extends from the equator to 20° South, and from 25° to 40° East, which is generally east of the *T. gambiense* area.

Morris (1960) noted that the north shore of Lake Victoria has been subject to recurrent outbreaks of Rhodesian sleeping sickness since 1940. Early in this century this area was depopulated by Gambian sleeping sickness, and then reverted to brush. Simultaneously it was populated with game which harbored the pathogens. The Rhodesian sickness struck persons who lived nearby or who went into the area for timber, meat, and fish. The disease is always of remote rather than populous areas.

The reservoir for *T. rhodesiense* is sylvatic and involves some game animal and one of several species of tsetse (Fig. 88). While details of the fundamental reservoir are unknown, wild animals that circulate this and similar trypanosomes are Thomson's gazelle, dik-dik, bushbuck, duiker, and jackal. Other animals that may harbor this pathogen are serval cat, hyena, porcupine, cane rat, hyrax, and ant bear (Fairbairn, 1954). The domestic guinea fowl retains inoculum for at least three months. Tsetse responsible for transmission of the agent are *Glossina morsitans, swynnertoni, pallidipes,* and *longipalpis.*

Transmission to transients occurs in areas inhabited by game animals that are far removed from the habitations of man. Fishermen, hunters, and collectors who range into these remote areas are most likely to become afflicted. Man is an unlikely source of inoculum because he is bedridden while infective and not available to flies. In general, this pathogen strikes humans in the hotter months and in the warmer sites.

Trypanosoma rhodesiense develops in the tsetse as does *T. gambiense.* The first part of the cycle in *G. morsitans* may be completed at 16.5° C, but a final invasion of salivary ducts will be carried out only when the temperature is 26° to 30° C. No infected flies could be found where mean temperatures ranged between 19° and 25° C

(Nash and Page, 1953). *G. tachinoides* is a more efficient vector when the temperature is about 37° C (Duke, 1933). In the Congo watershed the infection rate of flies was two and one-half times as high in warm valleys as on cooler plateaus.

Transmission of the pathogen is effected by salivation at the time of feeding. Fairbairn and Burtt (1946) established the minimum

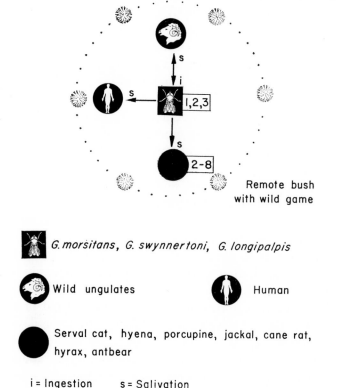

Remote bush
with wild game

G. *morsitans*, G. *swynnertoni*, G. *longipalpis*

Wild ungulates   Human

Serval cat, hyena, porcupine, jackal, cane rat, hyrax, antbear

i = Ingestion   s = Salivation

Fig. 88. Sylvatic reservoir for *Trypanosoma rhodesiense* in Eastern Africa.

infective dose to be 300–450 metacyclic forms for a susceptible person and a much higher dose for a resistant one. Rate of transmission varies according to the strain of pathogen concerned. A single *G. morsitans* extruded over 11,000 infective forms during each of two successive salivary-extrusion tests.

Trypanosoma vivax. *Trypanosoma vivax* (syn. *cazalboui* and *viennei*), together with *T. congolense,* causes most of the nagana of domestic stock in equatorial Africa. The French word *souma* is sometimes used to designate the *vivax* syndrome. Cattle, horses, sheep, and goats are easily infected, and the disease may be chronic before terminating in death. Pigs are not affected. *Vivax* and *congolense* commonly occur together and are grouped together in discussions. In some situations the first may be dominant, in others the second. The form called *viennei* causes a bovine trypanosomiasis in Venezuela and islands of the southern Caribbean.

Transmission patterns of the African form are similar to those of *T. congolense*. Presumably transmission by tsetse after cyclopropagative development is normal. When tsetse are involved, the disease is seasonal and corresponds with a rise in populations of the fly. In Nigeria transmission is most common either at the height of the rainy season or toward the end of it. Whenever tabanids act as vectors, the height of new infections may be during the early dry season following the maximum emergence of flies. Over parts of the range new cases of the disease appear with an increase in *Glossina* and continue as the season for horse flies comes. Some tribesmen are alleged to prevent transmission by keeping their cattle permanently enclosed in huts. The South American form depends on tabanids as vectors, and no cyclopropagative phase is known.

The cyclopropagative phase of the African form in tsetse is distinctly different from those that cause human trypanosomiasis as well as *congolense* in that all development takes places in the mouth parts. The agents cling as rosettes to the inside of the food canal, while the metacyclic forms are in the salivary canal of the hypopharynx. The time of development is shorter by some days than for the other forms. At 29° C only five days are required to produce infective forms, and at 22° C the time required is only about 12 days.

A similar species, *T. uniforme,* causes nagana in eastern Africa. Because its behavior so closely parallels *T. vivax,* it is placed in the *vivax* group in the genus.

Trypanosoma congolense. *Trypanosoma congolense* (including *dimorphon*) is the cause of nagana in many wild and domestic ungulates. Godfrey (1961) recognized three types of this parasite depending on length of the pathogen, its degree of parasitemia, and its order of pathogenicity. The type called *congolense* is short, has low degree of parasitemia, and is lightly pathogenic. On the opposite extreme is the type *dimorphon* with its long cells, high incidence of parasites, and severe pathogenesis. An intermediate form is between these extremes. Pigs as well as horses, goats, and sheep are susceptible. It is fatal to mature cattle and chronic in calves and possibly yearlings. This parasite together with *T. vivax* causes far more disease of cattle than does *T. brucei*. The principal reason for this difference seems to be that the latter is less common in tsetse. If cattle are brought into contact with game animals in fly belts, they generally become infected with either *vivax* or *congolense*. In some areas infections occur even when no big game is present, as some other animal is presumably in the reservoir as well. Hyena and monkeys may be involved in the chain.

Flies such as tsetse may tear the surface and malpighian layer of the skin and thereby provide an infection site. Tabanids cut and slash capillaries in a manner that produces a similar subsurface hemorrhage. Transmission to a vertebrate follows inoculation of the trypanosomes into the dermal hemorrhage.

The relative importance of the various biting flies as vectors is unclear. Certainly tsetse of all sorts may be significant over most of tropical Africa. In western Uganda, where the tribesmen keep their cattle in compact herds, the importance of interrupted feeding of the hordes of tabanids must be considered. Likewise the "sudd," a vast clay plain in southern Sudan, produces swarms of tabanids and no tsetse; yet it experiences epidemic nagana. Since tabanids as well as tsetse swarm over savannas of much of Africa they both could be significant. The more effective vectors among the tsetse are *G. morsitans* (and its subspecies *submorsitans*), *caliginea*, *longipalpis*, and *austeni*.

Cyclical development of *T. congolense* in tsetse is similar to that in *T. gambiense* except that metacyclic forms are produced in the salivary canal of the hypopharynx instead of in the glands proper. Also, the cycle is somewhat shorter than it is for the latter species, possibly because it exists only as a contaminant of the mouth parts in tabanids. Tsetse are vector-hosts, while tabanids are vectors only. This trypanosome causes swelling of the salivary glands of tsetse even though it does not enter them directly.

A related form, *T. simiae*, is fatal to pigs and wart hogs. Sheep and goats are tolerant toward it. While the agent is transmitted after a cyclical phase in *Glossina morsitans* it is readily vectored as trypanosomes by tabanids in areas where wild pigs are present even though *Glossina* are missing.

Trypanosoma brucei. This is the causative agent of a form of nagana in livestock and wild game in central Africa, and it, too, is of basic veterinary significance. Its effect on domestic animals varies from an acute fatal disease in horses, dogs, and sheep to an asymptomatic condition in pigs. Some strains of the pathogen are more severe than others. Unfortunately very little is known about the characteristics of basic foci or the routes for transmission. The reservoir may involve all the usual domestic animals and numerous species of big-game animals together with any sufficiently abundant tsetse. Flies most frequently involved in transmission are *Glossina morsitans, palpalis, pallidipes, tachinoides,* and *brevipalpis.* Tabanids may be involved in transmission when abundant.

Culwick *et al.* (1951) have shown that *T. brucei* in mixed culture with *T. gambiense* or *T. rhodesiense* will "eliminate" both of the associates. This may account for limits on distribution of the latter species. *T. gambiense* is not so restricted because humans seem to be the chief component of the reservoir. This organism has the same developmental pattern as that of *T. gambiense* and *T. rhodesiense* in the tsetse.

These three organisms cause some lesions in the salivary glands, but no shortening of life has been noted. The glands may be swollen up to four times normal size, and they appear chalky or brown to black, according to the duration of infection.

Trypanosoma evansi. This is the cause of surra or gufar in domestic livestock and wild ungulates in Africa, Asia, and South America. It is particularly common in camels, but attacks cattle, water buffalo, horses, and dogs. It seems to be restricted to the camel in Sudan. The disease is often serious in semidesert areas, particularly following the rainy season. The Camel Corps of the British Army of World War I suffered enormous casualties. Transmission of the agent is most frequent in the vicinity of watering places where horse flies are abundant. Nomads in both Sudan and the Middle East have practiced keeping herds of dromedaries away from fly belts because of the disease. Patton (1920) cites an instance where a drove of camels was pastured by day outside the fly belt of the Euphrates Valley. Each night the animals were driven some five miles to and from a watering site in order to avoid the flies and surra. The occurrence of swarms of horse flies in southern Sudan regulates massive movements of camels each season. Mechanical transmission of this trypanosome is accomplished by horse flies primarily; and by the muscids, *Stomoxys* and *Haematobia,* to some extent. Even though this agent depends on flies for transmission, no development of the agent occurs in flies.

Trypanosoma rangeli. *Trypanosoma rangeli* (syn. *ariarii*) is the cause of a trypanosomiasis in man, dogs, and rodents from Guatemala to Argentina. Wild hosts include *Cebus* monkeys and opossums. Humans are tolerant toward the parasite and pathogenesis is unknown. Knowledge of the reservoir and chains of transmission is incomplete.

This trypanosome lives part of its life in blood-sucking bugs, particularly *Rhodnius prolixus.* The organism is ingested with blood and multiplies in the gut as "long crithidia." In time, these pathogens enter the hemocoel where further development takes place. Later, they penetrate the salivary glands and enter the salivary ducts where they become metacyclic trypanosomes. Under favorable conditions, the pathogen becomes infective 16–28 days after entering a bug. Nymphs infected in the first instar rarely showed metacyclic forms in less than a month, while 4–5 months may be required.

T. rangeli is pathogenic to bugs that it invades. According to Grewal (1956), bugs are unable to molt if the hemolymph has been massively invaded, while lesser populations of this organism in the hemolymph will retard molting. Pathogenicity was associated with invasion of cells of the hemolymph where leishmanial forms of the parasite are produced. In time, the hemolymph becomes milky. When salivary glands are invaded, the glands change in color from a cherry red to whitish.

Trypanosoma lewisi. This is a cosmopolitan parasite in a rodent-flea reservoir that is non-pathogenic to humans. It is introduced here to illustrate an adaptation of this group of agents to a different arthropod. Several members of the genus *Rattus* are naturally infected. Gerbils support this trypanosome in Tunis. The agent has a normal cyclopropagative phase in the epithelial cells of the mid-gut and on the surface of the hind-gut of fleas, ked, sucking lice (*Haematopinus*), and ticks (*Ornithodoros*). In the flea, *Nosopsyllus fasciatus,* the propagative phase requires 5–6 days at room temperature. During this time multiple fission occurs in the mid-gut for 1–3 days and metacyclic forms are produced from crithidia attached to the lining of the hind-gut. These infective forms pass with the feces. The agent is pathogenic to fleas during the time of invasion of the epithelial cells.

Trypanosoma cruzi. *Trypanosoma cruzi* (syn. *Schizotrypanum*) is the causative agent of a chronic blood disease called Chagas' disease that is limited to the Western Hemisphere from about 41° South to 31° North. In Chile this cause of trypanosomiasis is domestic and has been considered the cause of the most important disease related to arthropods. In the northern part of its range, on the other hand, it is known only from sylvatic foci. The disease is virtually unknown among humans in the United States even though the pathogen is abundantly distributed in its sylvatic reservoir in southwestern United States. Symptoms are often vague and diagnosis is frequently difficult. Exhaustion with or without myocarditis is a common complaint. More overt symptoms are fever and unilateral swelling of the eyelids or some other part of the face. A note of some historical interest suggests that Charles Darwin suffered from this disease for over 40 years.

Trypanosomes causing Chagas' disease become systemic upon inoculation into humans. They circulate in the blood for about two weeks after onset, and later they invade muscles such as those of the heart, where they may propagate in masses. Both leishmanial and crithidial forms have been found in the hearts of wild hosts (Deane, 1958a). Positive identification by examination of blood films is often impossible because of the scarcity of the parasites in the blood.

Chagas' disease is a zoonosis having both domestic and sylvatic phases (Fig. 89). Hoare (1955) noted that the armadillo (*Dasypus*) and opossum (*Didelphis* spp.) are the chief vertebrates in the reservoir of the pathogen. At least eight South American marsupials of three genera are involved. Clark and Dunn (1932) in their review said that 40–50 per cent of the armadillos examined in Brazil were infected. About one-fourth of the opossums of Honduras showed trypanosomes in the blood. Bats of several species have been incriminated from California to Panama, and those that roost in both caves and trees showed a high incidence of parasitism in Panama. Other mammals that figure in the sylvatic reservoir include raccoon, fox, ferret, squirrel (*Leptosciurus*), some 15 species of Edentata, and five or more of Primata. Wood rats (*Neotoma*) and the house mouse may harbor the pathogen in southwestern United States. The most widely recognized domestic reservoir includes dog, cat, and domestic triatomine bugs. In some situations swine may become important. The guinea pig may well enter the reservoir in parts of South America. The role played by sheep and other domestic animals is not clear.

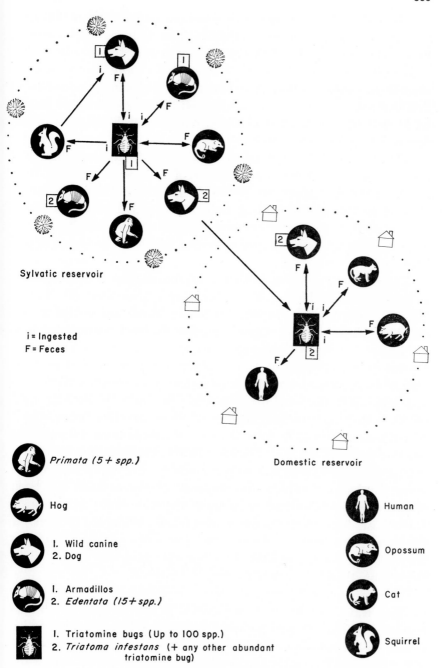

Sylvatic reservoir

i = Ingested
F = Feces

Domestic reservoir

Primata (5 + spp.)

Hog

1. Wild canine
2. Dog

1. Armadillos
2. Edentata (15+ spp.)

1. Triatomine bugs (Up to 100 spp.)
2. Triatoma infestans (+ any other abundant
                           triatomine bug)

Human

Opossum

Cat

Squirrel

Fig. 89. Sylvatic and domestic reservoirs for *Trypanosoma cruzi* in
South America.

The reduviid component of the reservoir includes about 100 species and subspecies of the subfamily Triatominae (Reduviidae). Presumably any species of this group may harbor the pathogen, but in domestic situations *Triatoma infestans* is far more important over most of the range. In Bolivia and Paraguay, for example, about two-thirds of a large series of bugs collected in houses harbored flagellates. Several records exist in which infection of 30–40 per cent of domestic bugs has been noted.

The parasite is so well adapted to life in triatomine bugs that they are often used for xenodiagnosis of a suspected human case where parasites cannot be observed directly. A clean insect is allowed to feed to repletion on the patient, and then it is cultured for several days to permit cyclopropagation of the parasite. Afterward the bug is dissected and examined for the presence of flagellates.

Trypanosoma cruzi completes a cyclopropagative development in bugs in a few days at 30° C but may require over 50 days at 22.5° C. This agent is ingested with the blood and completes its development in the gut. Upon ingestion the trypanosome assumes the leishmanial form in the anterior part of the gut. As it moves toward the rear of the gut, the crithidial form appears first as large cells, then smaller metacyclic or infective forms continue to appear and pass out in the fecal droplets while the bugs are feeding. Old adults harbor the greatest number of these infective forms which sometimes number 3500/cmm of feces. Presumably an infected bug remains infected for life. Francis (1938) reported that an earlier worker had maintained this trypanosome for five years in *Ornithodoros moubata*. Complete development of the parasite has been observed in the hemocoel of larvae of the wax moth, an obviously exotic host. This trypanosome is sometimes pathogenic to bugs. If the agent gains access to the coelom, it develops rapidly and causes disruption of tissues, possibly by stopping circulation or inhibiting respiration; thereby death of the bugs is hastened.

Transmission of this trypanosome to vertebrates is effected in one of three ways. (1) Either it is excreted in the feces or the bug is crushed and the released parasites are rubbed into the conjunctiva of the eye, the mucosa, or the abraded skin. (2) Rats and presumably other small animals may become contaminated by eating the bugs or by surface contamination. (3) Carnivores become contaminated by eating infected vertebrates.

TELOSPORASIDA: COCCIDIA

The order is represented by vertebrate parasites, some of which orbit in the vertebrates alone while several genera (see Table 24) have vertebrates and arthropods as serial hosts in their ontogeny. The six genera shown in Table 24 usually have acarines in their chains of hosts.

All representatives having arthropod-vertebrate reservoirs also have their schizogonous cycles in the blood, liver, or spleen of vertebrates and their sporogonous cycles in hematophagous acarines. Man, canines, cats, rabbits, rodents, and lizards may be hosts to various species of *Hepatozoon,* while ixodid ticks seem to be normal arthropodan components of reservoirs for most species. Argasid ticks are included in the reservoir of some species (Hoogstraal and Kaiser, 1957). Undoubtedly mites are significant, especially in the case of species that attack burrowing rodents (Clark, 1958). Species of *Haemogregarina* may live in many sorts of arthropods, and the schizogonous cycle occurs in man, cow, birds, and reptiles. Those of the genus *Karyolysus* are blood parasites of vertebrates and epithelial parasites in food tubes of mites, ticks, and insects. An organism of this group must be ingested by the arthropod, which must then be ingested by the vertebrate if infection of the vertebrate is to be accomplished. These parasites seem to have no deleterious effects on their arthropodan hosts (Garnham, 1955).

TELOSPORASIDA: HAEMOSPORIDIA

The four genera included are intracellular parasites of all cells in the blood stream, in the wall of the blood vessels, or in blood-forming tissues of vertebrates. Gametogenesis and sporogony occur in hematophagous arthropods, where the development is without cyst walls. Genera most commonly encountered by medical entomologists are listed in Table 24, and details of the ones best known follow.

Plasmodium

Of the arthropod-borne Protozoa, those in the genus *Plasmodium* have had the dubious distinction of containing the greatest number of known vertebrate pathogens as well as the pathogens causing the greatest misery to man. As a result of this duality, the genus has had the honor of eliciting the best efforts of some great men in medical entomology such as Ross, Manson, and Bignami, who did the pioneer work on plasmodia of human malaria. These workers and their followers accumulated a wealth of detail on the morphology, pathology, and bionomics of these parasites that has no equal in all other work on the parasites in the arthropod-borne group. The significance of these investigations is that man has been able to instigate campaigns that are stripping malaria of its strangle holds on vast areas of the world. Now for the first time, our expanding human population is pioneering tropical lands once deadly to a technological society. Indigenous peoples are awakening to their own potentialities, especially in Africa. For detailed accounts of malaria, see Boyd (1949) and Macdonald (1957).

Whereas the disease is basically tropical, it has had its periods of great pandemics over much of the earth. Presumably it spread from central Africa along the Nile Valley to cultures around the Mediterranean. Two millennia ago contacts to the east and to the west extended the range until malaria had much of the known world in its grip. Since then, the disease has gone through periods of explosion and recession. During the fourth decade of this century it receded dramatically from most of its temperate domain and from several of its tropical strongholds. Apparently this current trend is abetted by philanthropic, governmental, and world-wide organizations engaged in improving public health by the extensive application of knowledge of the chains of transmission.

Currently, malaria is a disease of man primarily in the tropics and in adjacent parts of the temperate zones, but it has been known to range to such extremes of latitudes as 60° North. It is more significant as a disease in an environment where water covers much of the land and supports an abundant flora of emergent stems and leaves. Thus in areas of warm climate, wherever marshes, swamps, fens, savannas, or man-made counterparts such as rice fields are abundant, the malaria potential is great. The fact that the disease is a concomitant of a high water table was well known to the early Greeks. Hippocrates mentions the fact, and Clearchus the Tyrant reputedly put this knowledge to practical use as he solved some of his problems in military morale by ordering recalcitrant units to engage in summer field maneuvers on an insalubrious plain. Malaria provided vacancies in all ranks.

The very name malaria comes to us from the ancients. To them the word meant "bad vapors" (the air and all that it carried), because the air seemed to bring the chills and fever from low ground heated in summer. In practice the belief was that because the noxious element was in the air, and particularly at night, it could be filtered out by placing a barrier of netting over sleeping persons. Even primitive Africans and other tribal groups have known the general relationship between bad air and the ague. One group is reported to have the same word for both malaria and mosquitoes. We now know that swamp air is bad only when it has blood-lusting anopheline mosquitoes that are bearing the noxious microbial specifics for malaria. These mosquitoes get their infective parasites from humans, and in time they may transmit some of them to other persons on whom they feed.

Malaria is a disease of many facets with symptoms that simulate most of the diseases of man. Since volumes have been written on diagnosis and symptomatology, little will be said here on this phase. Jeffery (1960) divides the parasitemia of man into four phases: (1) preclinical, (2) clinical, (3) terminal (asymptomatic), and (4) relapse (asymptomatic and symptomatic). Bray (1960) and others before him designate another phase prior to the preclinical as the pre-erythrocytic phase. This phase, which may last only 24 hours, is a period of cytoplasmic fission of a multinucleate mass. The preclinical period follows the appearance of the parasite in the peripheral blood, and it is the time when frank manifestations appear. Periods of chill alternating with longer febrile intervals are the classical manifestations. In an uncomplicated case, intervals between chills vary according to the species of parasite causing the disease. Actually, malaria is a collective name for any of four syndromes caused by the four different parasites, *Plasmodium vivax, falciparum, malariae,* and *ovale.* Terminal parasitemias are characteristic of infections with *P. falciparum.* This asymptomatic interval may extend from a hundred days to a year or slightly more. Relapse malaria is limited to infections with *P. vivax.* One to many recurrences of the clinical phase may be suffered by affected persons.

Plasmodia that cause human malaria live in human-*Anopheles* reservoirs which vary in composition according to locality, as Tables 25 and 26 indicate. All species are inoculated into the blood stream as sporozoites by an infected salivating anopheline during the feeding process. In the interval immediately following inoculation the parasite has a pre-erythrocytic period of development in the liver prior to its invasion into the red cells. Parasitic life in this phase is the subject of much of the present research on the disease because

Table 25. Reservoir for Plasmodia of Unstable Malaria.

Situation	Locality	Human Habitat	*Anopheles* Vector-Host
Sylvatic	Central U.S.	Pioneer	*punctipennis, quadri-maculatus*
	Sahara (oasis)	Nomadic	*sergenti*
	Sahara	Nomadic	*pharoensis*
	California (1850)	Indian villages near gold fields	*punctipennis*
	Krk (Adriatic Island)	Hayfield	*maculipennis*
	Brazil mts.	Cocoa grove	*bellator*
	Indonesia	Rubber plantation	*maculatus*
	Gallipoli (1918)	Army camp	*maculipennis*, etc.
Domestic	Central U. S. (to 1935)	Shanty	*quadrimaculatus*
	Mexico mts.	Adobe hut	*aztecus*
	Caribbean littoral	Villages	*darlingi*
	Brazil	Villages (near bromeliads)	*cruzii*
	Argentina (to 1940)	Shanty	*pseudopunctipennis*
	S. Amer. west coast	Shanty	*punctimacula*
	Holland (autumn)	Village	*maculipennis atroparvus*
	Hungary	Village or farm	*maculipennis messeae*
	Mediterranean littoral	Village or farm	*maculipennis labranchiae*
	Middle East	City (cisterns present)	*claviger*
	Middle East	Plains (summer)	*sacharovi*
	Middle East	Plains (late fall)	*superpictus*
	Iraq	Mountains	*maculipennis, superpictus*
	Iraq	Alluvial plains	*stephensi, sacharovi*
	Black to Caspian seas	Steppes	*maculipennis maculipennis, sacharovi*
	Afghanistan, Pakistan	Plains	*superpictus*
	India	Mountains	*lindesayi lindesayi, willmori*
	India	Central hills	*fluviatilis, varuna, minimus*
	India	Alluvial plains	*culicifacies*
	India	Western plains	*stephensi*
	Bengal, Assam	Plains	*philippinensis, annularis*
	Eastern Asia	Lowland rice fields	*hyrcanus*
		Terraced rice fields	*jeyporiensis candidiensis*
	S. Africa	Shanty	*gambiae*
	C. Africa	Mountains	*christyi*
	C. Africa	Flood plains	*moucheti, hancocki*

the form seems to be resistant to therapy. In time trophozoites reproduce repetitively, destroy the host cells, and then disperse to other cells at regular intervals that vary according to plasmodial species. Since the clinical manifestations coincide with cyclic activities of the pathogen, the clinician is enabled to recognize the probable cause. The repetitive cycle ends for some cells as they become gametocytes, or cells capable of producing either microgametes or macrogametes, when ingested by any mosquito. When gametes unite in an anopheline mosquito, they produce amoeboid zygotes and complete their development.

We must not accept complacently the position that the inter-human phase is the only one in the transmission chain for malaria parasites. Garnham (1958) reported that a sylvatic reservoir (chimpanzee-anopheline) exists in tropical Africa for *Plasmodium malariae*.

Table 26. Domestic Reservoir for Plasmodia of Stable Malaria.

Locality	Human Habitat	*Anopheles*
Caribbean littoral	Coast	*albimanus*
Malaya	Coast, riceland	*umbrosus, letifer*
	Riceland	*sinensis*
Indonesia	Riceland	*sinensis, aconitus*
	Coast	*sundaicus*
Philippines	Foothills	*minimus flavirostris*
Sarawak	Interior	*leucosphyrus leucosphyrus*
Borneo	Coast	*sundaicus, separatus, letifer* (?)
	Riceland	*sinensis*
	Woodland	*balabacensis*
Celebes	Woodland	*barbirostris*
New Guinea, Solomons	Coastal flood plains (sandy soil)	*farauti*
	Clay hills	*punctulatus, koliensis, karawi*
Queensland, Aus.	Coastal littoral	*amictus hilli*
Central Africa	Coastal littoral	*gambiae, melas*
	Plains	*gambiae* (?), *funestus, nili*
West Africa	Plains	*gambiae* (?), *funestus, rufipes ingrami*
Tanganyika	Swamp	*funestus*

Furthermore, *P. knowlesi* in a monkey-anopheline reservoir in Malaya may pass to people who live in an environment bridged by the anopheline host. *P. cynomologi* has induced infections in humans in the laboratory (Beye *et al.*, 1961).

Some historical examples suffice to show how malaria may afflict man under conditions where unrestricted chains of transmission exist. For a time during World War II, a site on eastern New Guinea had a case rate in excess of 4000 cases per 1000 men per year among allied troops. Between 1870 and 1874 one United States Army unit with a mean strength of 171 men reported 1229 cases of malaria while in a camp in Louisiana. Because of malaria, Illinois was known in its formative years as the "graveyard of the nation," according to Ackerknecht (1945).

A human population either in a warm climate or during a warm season, when associated with a sufficiently durable anopheline population, may constitute a complete reservoir for all species of *Plasmodium* affecting humans. The response to repeated infection or relapse is either one of becoming tolerant or, in some cases, one of becoming immune to the parasite. The tolerance that develops is normally only for the local strain of the parasite. When a new strain is introduced into the reservoir of another strain, it may find a fertile field for development. Human tolerance to any new strain will be established in time. The blood of the tolerant individual occasionally produces gametocytes, and these may inoculate the anopheline population. The survival time for the parasite in man is long enough to bridge any natural hiatus in the chain of transmission which could be caused by decimation of numbers or shortened longevity of mosquitoes. Gill (1921) noted in Ceylon that prior to the onset of an epidemic the incidence of relapses among tolerant persons showed a pronounced increase about one month before new cases appeared. Epidemic malaria in Jamaica began in one instance when the gametocyte rate in this group increased from 3 to 24 per cent.

The exact identity of the portions of a human population responsible for supplying gametocytes to most of the mosquitoes is only partially known. Apparently the majority of *Anopheles* often acquire the inoculum from human subjects before gametocytes become demonstrable (Jeffery, 1960). Muirhead-Thomson (1957) seemed to think that in western African villages the element of a group most frequently acting as host for *Anopheles* is the active adults and older children who have become tolerant to the plasmodium, but who have gametocytes in the peripheral blood. In Jamaica, where *A. albimanus* is involved, the youngsters are the prime donors of gametocytes. In both instances the individuals most often in contact with suitable mosquitoes supplied the inoculum. There is little or no chance for mosquitoes to become infected with *P. falciparum* at least during the preclinical period, according to Jeffery (1960). Shortly after onset of symptoms, rate of infection is maximal, but patients vary widely in their capacities as gametocyte donors. Even though the curve of donor efficiency drops off, some mosquitoes may be infected during the terminal period for about a year (Jeffery). Relapsed cases are prime donors of gametocytes, especially during the early stages and even 3–4 days before gametocytes are detectable.

Humans are the only vertebrates necessary for transmission of plasmodia that attack man. Since people vary widely in their contacts with the culicine component, the specific vector-host will vary accordingly. When an adequate anopheline population with anthropophilic tastes is available and has ready access to human hosts, we need only a human carrier to introduce the pathogen to the arena in order to instigate an epidemic. In extratropical, domestic situations the anopheline must invade dwellings and must feed on an infected person long enough or sufficiently often to acquire the parasite and then in time to transmit it (Fig. 90).

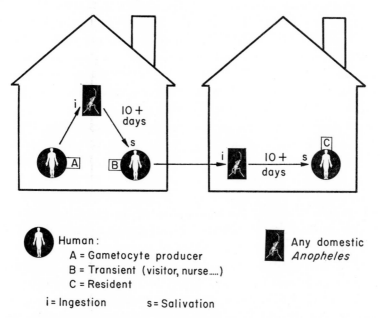

Fig. 90. Sites for transmission of *Plasmodium* spp. in typically unstable reservoirs of temperate regions.

The incidence of malaria is determined by the frequency of contact between man and infective anophelines. Barber (1929) noted that the incidence of malaria in rice-growing areas of Arkansas was relatively low even though the anopheline density was high. In a nearby cotton-growing economy the incidence of malaria was high and yet the anopheline density was vastly lower. The reason for this difference seemed to be that residents of the rice-growing area lived in well-screened homes and had less chance of repeated contact with vectors. Many persons of the cotton-producing zones lived in poorly screened houses, hence the rate of attack by vectors was high although the total number of mosquitoes was low.

Oasis malaria of Saudi Arabia has been found by Daggy (1959) to be instigated by only one of some six local species of *Anopheles*. *A. stephensi* is the key species because it is abundant, anthropophilic, and a product of man-made aquatic sites. Since an oasis is an intensively developed agricultural community with irrigation ditches, seeps, artesian wells and irrigated crops, abundant sites for development of this adaptable mosquito are provided.

The importation of new human carriers into an endemic area seems to have little or no effect on the incidence of malaria. Soldiers returning home from Cuba after the Spanish-American War caused no outbreaks in the United States. Immigrants have come to America in a steady stream from malarious Europe yet have caused no increase in incidence. The return of hundreds of thousands of British soldiers from Mediterranean encampments caused no epidemic wave after either of the World Wars.

Extensive disturbance of the topsoil in areas where the water table is high in the summer creates conditions conducive to a high incidence of vector anophelines. For example, the excavation required in construction of the Panama Canal produced a malaria problem long to be remembered. The excessive deforestation commonly practiced during the exploitation of the great forests of North America created the conditions for vast malaria epidemics. Late in the seventeenth century the culture of rice along the Carolina coast turned a malaria-free zone into one of devastating epidemics. Malaria raged from the Great Lakes to the Gulf of Mexico among the pioneer agriculturalists, as prairie and forest gave way to the plow. During World War II in New Guinea the shell holes and bomb craters, together with innumerable tracks in the mud, created conditions favorable to hordes of anophelines and attendant malaria where little had existed before.

Malaria is a disease that shows pandemic waves and both short-term and seasonal cycles. One of the pandemics advanced until about 1750. Another covered a 40-year span (1880–1920), during which time transmission was common as far north as Quebec in North America and almost reached the Arctic Circle in Russia. A recession has recently been in progress, and malaria has now retreated to its most restricted positions. On this continent none exists north of Mexico. The Balkan countries and parts of southern Russia still have malaria in the attack phase. In eastern Asia endemic foci extend northward into Korea. Southern Asia from the Pacific westward to the Mediterranean and much of the Indonesian archipelago, tropical Africa, and tropical South America still have endemic foci. Historically, decline of European pandemics was marked by exacerbations at intervals of about 20 years that have coincided with economic disruption.

Malaria has regressed to the point of no consequence in the United States, Crete, most of Russia, parts of the northern shores of South America, and Bermuda. Macdonald (1956) attributes this success to specific epidemiological attacks adapted to local situations. Eradication in Bermuda was accomplished about 1930, while Gambian malaria in Brazil was wiped out some 10 years later. Regression of the disease in Malaya during the past decade has been independent of the deliberate control activities of man. According to data in Alves and Blair (1955), malaria is less than one-eighth as common among Europeans in Southern Rhodesia as it was during the interval 1904–1908.

We must remember always that minor changes in the ecology may effect disproportionate changes in the complexion of an epidemic. Small differences in temperature may affect both longevity and susceptibility of anopheline hosts. Changes in human activity in relation to vector activity are important. Any modification in frequency of contact between vector and man may alter the course of an epidemic. These changes give rise to short-term cycles that seem to recur about every seven years in endemic foci of the Western Hemisphere. Martinique in the Caribbean showed peaks in 1935 and 1942 (Montestruc, 1955). The last peak in the United States was in 1935. All of this is not to say that malaria is definitely and permanently conquered. Disregard for the resurgent capability of the parasites could lead to future pandemics.

Climatic conditions cause seasonal peaks in incidence of malaria. In India transmission appears to be confined largely to those seasons when the mean monthly temperature is not less than $16°$ C and the monthly mean (8 A.M.) humidity is not less than 63 per cent (Gill, 1921). In Ethiopia the most important malaria season occurs immediately following the wet southwest monsoon (late September to mid-December). It comes to flood plains of streams after inundation caused by rains in the mountains. In Afghanistan, where hyperendemic foci are in river basins devoted to the culture of rice, seasons of transmission coincide with the flooding of rice fields. This interval is July to October for most of the country (Dhir and Rahim, 1957). Transmission in foci of northern Europe occurs coincidently with invasion of houses by vector species at the advent of cold weather. There is no material increase in mosquitoes, but the proximity of man and vectors assures more frequent contact than is the case in summer when mosquitoes are outside houses. Prehibernation flights in certain semiarid parts of California and the Middle East have caused a concentration of vectors near man which resulted in peak seasons of transmission.

Daggy (1959) related malaria transmission to mean temperatures in the area of the Persian Gulf as follows. No transmission occurs while a mean temperature of 10° C prevails because parasites cannot develop in mosquitoes. Transmission is possible at 15.5° C, and it increases in frequency as the temperature rises to about 30° C as long as humidity is favorable. Adult mosquitoes will live 33 days on the average at 19.6° C and only about 10 days at 32° C. Consequently *Plasmodium malariae* is transmitted more successfully at lower mean temperatures because of the lengthened life span for a large population of the culicine hosts.

The four species of *Plasmodium* that cause human malaria differ in range largely because they vary in their reactions to temperature while in the anopheline hosts. *Plasmodium vivax* may occur anywhere between 60° North and 30° South, wherever the summer isotherm is over 15° C, provided the anopheline host lives the requisite number of days (16 days at 20° C) and feeds on man at intervals thereafter. *Plasmodium malariae* may have nearly as wide a spread (53° North and 30° South) but is more spotted over the range because the mosquito bearing it requires a very long period (30–35 days at 20° C) between the time of its own infection and the time it may inject sporozoites. *P. falciparum* may occur wherever the summer isotherm is 20° C, at which temperature 22–23 days are required for sporogony. *P. ovale* seems to be largely an East African species, but it has been widely reported in the tropics. Its sporogonous cycle requires 16 days at 25° C. The season of transmission varies widely in different parts of its range. High temperatures kill the mosquito before development of the parasite is completed, and low temperatures prevent growth of the parasite in the mosquito.

Malaria varies in the stability of its rate of transmission (Macdonald, 1956a). Stability is greatest in areas where the following conditions are met: (1) climatic conditions permit rapid propagation of the parasite, (2) anopheline susceptibility is high, (3) anopheline longevity is increased, and (4) human hosts are dependably available. Much of tropical Africa provides these conditions, and malaria is universal. Instability of the transmission rate with its attendant epidemic expressions occurs under conditions (Fig. 90) where (1) rainfall is irregular (interrupted by prolonged drought), (2) weather is cold enough to cause feeding mosquitoes to seek protection in dwellings, while the temperature is warm enough to permit development of a parasite, and (3) anopheline zoophagy increases. In the first instance, the population of vector-hosts is erratic; and in the second, the climate is unfavorable much of the time. In the third condition, fewer mosquitoes acquire the parasite and still fewer feed sequentially on man. Unstable malaria exists in temperate, desert, and mountainous regions. These areas of instability have been the historical scenes of the great epidemics and are the places from which eradication is most likely. In regions of unstable malaria the disease will disappear when any combination of adverse factors continues to affect one or more of the elements of stability. The trend toward a disappearance of the disease is observable when the number of new cases continues to be less than the number of gametocyte donors. It is found that *P. vivax* persists more successfully in unstable conditions than does *P. falciparum*.

Any one of a hundred or more *Anopheles* may be hospitable to plasmodia of human malaria, but a much smaller number is actually important in the total reservoir (see Tables 25 and 26). Rarely is more than one species significant in any particular ecological situation. Changes in seasons or in habits of humans may bring additional species to bear, particularly if the primary species is strikingly successful in fomenting an epidemic. *Anopheles gambiae*, for instance, appears to become infected twice as readily as does *A. funestus* under the same conditions. One species may survive significantly longer and thereby have more frequent opportunities to inoculate more people or one species may feed on man more often than another.

To the biologist, malaria is the malignant residue that follows a wholesale exchange of gametocytes and sporozoites between man and mosquitoes. The gametocytes are terminal during the schizogonous cycle in the red blood cells of man, but if they are ingested by a mosquito, they become macrogametes and microgametes. If a hospitable mosquito has ingested them, these cells unite to form a mobile zygote which becomes the initial cell in the sporogonous cycle. The zygote passes between the cells of the intestinal epithelium and begins proliferation to form a multicellular oocyst between the epithelium and its basement membrane. Given enough time and favorable temperatures an oocyst will yield quantities of motile filaments, the sporozoites. These terminal cells swim about in the hemolymph, and some successfully lodge in the salivary glands, where they come to fill the ducts. A mosquito bearing sporozoites injects them with saliva into the blood of a new host while feeding. Those released into the capillaries of a human initiate the vertebrate cycle.

Oocysts tend to be situated toward the rear of the mid-gut, but exceptions do exist. Presumably the zygotes get to the epithelium by way of the caudal opening of the peritrophic membrane. If such is the case, zygotes would penetrate the epithelial layer in the caudal part of the mid-gut. Since peritrophic membranes are known to form sacks that vary in length, some might be short enough to permit lodgment of zygotes anywhere on the wall. A. gambiae of Liberia (Fox, 1957), when infected in the laboratory, supported only about 18 per cent of the parasites as cysts on the caudal third of the gut, while other infected parasites encysted all over the gut.

None of the plasmodia of human malaria seems to produce pathogenesis of an order that affects longevity or fecundity of anopheline hosts. Histological effects are (1) distortion of the intestinal wall and (2) stretching of the basement membrane of the epithelium.

Mosquitoes sometimes show observable resistant reactions. Exflagellation of the parasite is inhibited in some species. The peritrophic membrane of some mosquitoes blocks contact between the zygotes and the epithelium. The epithelium may resist penetration by the zygote. Sometimes sclerous walls are formed as capsules about oocysts and masses of sporozoites. These bodies have been called "black spores." Normally the older the mosquito at the time of ingestion of the pathogen, the less likely it is to become infected.

Much has been done toward elimination of malaria as a cause of misery and death. The coincidence of this effort with the reversal of the most recent pandemic wave has resulted in liberating many parts of the world from the grip of this dread disease. Even though it is not the purpose of this book to elaborate on suppressive efforts, the results have been so startling that some attention should be given to them. When the adult resting sites have been coated with residual deposits of durable toxicants, the domestic vectors have been either killed or driven from areas where frequent contact with humans was possible. In this process, marginal areas about sites of stable malaria first became sites of unstable malaria; then in time the sites supported no malaria. Widespread use of non-specific toxicants (as the agricultural insecticides) used on cotton and other crops growing in malarious areas have built extensive chemical walls that protect the residents. Nutrition, medication, and isolation have played important roles in keeping the malaria parasites off balance. Transmission is minimal much of the year in all but the most ingrained areas of stable malaria. Checking transmission during the minimal period has been the key to much eradication (Chapter 14).

PIROPLASMASIDA: PIROPLASMORIDA
Theileriidae

Some dozen or more species belong to this family. *Theileria* and *Gonderia* cause generalized febrile diseases called theileriases in ruminants. For greater detail see Neitz (1959). The parasites destroy the red corpuscles and may cause death of domestic cattle. Ixodid ticks of the genera *Rhipicephalus* and *Hyalomma* are variously essential in the reservoir. Larvae or nymphs of ticks ingest the parasite along with blood. During molting the intraepithelial forms divide into several motile ones. They enter the coelom and make their way to cells of the salivary glands and then become mulberry-shaped bodies. Within a few days after feeding begins, these forms proliferate into tiny cells that enter the salivary ducts and are discharged by salivation into the wound. These pathogens apparently must be transmitted by the individual that ingests them because they are not known to enter ovarian tissue or to infect offspring.

Theileria parva is the causative agent of East Coast fever in cow, buffalo, and wild ruminants in Africa. Presumably some wild ruminant, possibly the antelope, is the tolerant vertebrate in the reservoir. *Rhipicephalus appendiculatus* and *R. neavei* seem to be the more significant ticks in the reservoir, but both of them may occur in areas where there is no transmission. This indicates that either another tick is basic or the necessary ruminant is missing.

Larval or nymphal ticks normally acquire the pathogen in some five days after the onset of symptoms in the vertebrate. The parasites ingested by larvae develop, multiply and produce infective forms after ticks have molted, while those parasites ingested by nymphs become infective after the ticks reach maturity. The minimum time for development in larvae and nymphs is about 25 days. The pathogen may survive in a host for as much as a half year, but the ability to cause disease in vertebrates declines if the agent remains in the tick for a longer time.

Babesiidae

This is a family of parasites that infects the red blood cells of a number of vertebrates including ungulates, carnivores, rodents, primates, and birds. All species are spherical, ovoid, or pyriform, and all reproduce by binary fission or schizogony in the vertebrates as well as in the ixodid and argasid hosts. The best-known genus is *Babesia,* which is the cause of babesiosis, a group of important diseases of livestock. Other genera are *Echinozoon* and *Aegyptianella.*

Parasites of the genus *Babesia* (Table 27) develop in a similar manner in their ixodid hosts. They are ingested while feeding. Some become vermiform and penetrate the intestinal epithelium, where they develop into large amoeboid forms. Within a few days they multiply many fold and fill the invaded cells. Again each organism becomes vermiform and disperses in the hemocoel. By the time the ticks reach maturity, the parasites enter the ovarian tissue; then after a few divisions all development ceases. In the embryonic tick the parasite enters the salivary glands, where it lies dormant until the nymphal stage is reached. Binary fission then takes place in each infested cell. Ultimately the agent moves into the salivary ducts and, together with saliva, enters the circulatory system of a vertebrate host.

Babesia bigemina is the causative agent for cattle fever and is an intracellular parasite of red corpuscles of cow, water buffalo, and deer (*Mazama* sp. and *Dama* sp.). It is confined to the tropics and adjacent temperate regions up to the zone where the ground freezes during the winter. It is further restricted in the United States to occasional occurrences along the Mexican border and the type locality in southern Florida.

The reservoir is a combination of ungulates and ixodid ticks. The ticks are the one-host *Boophilus* (at least four spp.) and the three-host *Rhipicephalus* (three spp.) of Africa. In the United States the sylvatic reservoir may still exist in the white-tailed deer and *B. annulatus* in the southern tip of Florida. Early in the century the reservoir over most of the country was wholly a domestic one com-

Table 27. Reservoirs for Various Babesiidae.

Species	Region	Reservoir Arthropod	Vertebrate
Aegyptianella moshkovskii	S. Asia	—	House crow
A. pullorum	Africa	Argas sp.	Fowls
Babesia loxodontis	Cameroons	Dermacentor circumguttatus	Elephant
B. caballi	Russia	D. marginatus	Horse
	Greece	Hyalomma marginatum	Horse
	Africa	Rhipicephalus evertsi	Equines
	Russia	D. pictus	Equines
		D. silvarum	Equines
		H. volgense	Equines
	Bulgaria	R. bursa	Equines
	Greece	R. sanguineus	Equines
B. equi (Nuttallia)	Russia	D. marginatus	Equines
		R. bursa	Equines
		D. pictus	Equines
	N. Africa	H. dromedarii	Equines
		R. sanguineus	Equines
	S. Africa	R. evertsi	Equines
	Greece	H. marginatum	Equines
		H. anatolicum	Equines
B. canis	Europe	D. marginatus	Canines
	Russia	D. pictus	Canines
		H. marginatum	Canines
	S. Africa	Haemaphysalis leachi	Canines
	World	R. sanguineus	Canines
B. gibsoni	India	Haemaphysalis bispinosa	Canines
		R. sanguineus	Canines
B. bovis	Russia	Ixodes persulcatus	Bovines
	Europe	I. ricinus	Bovines
B. bigemina	Tropicopolitan	Boophilus spp.	Bovines
B. argentina	Argentina	Boophilus microplus	Bovines
		B. australis	Bovines
B. berbera (caucasica)	N. Africa	B. calcaratus	Cow
		R. bursa	—
B. ovis (motasi)	Roumania	R. bursa	Sheep, goat
B. felis	N. Africa	—	Cats, mt. lions, Sudanese lions, bobcats
B. trautmanni	Europe	B. decoloratus	Pigs
	E. Africa	Hyalomma dromedarii	—
Echinozoon hoogstraali	N. Africa	Argas brumpti	Hyraxes

posed of *Boophilus annulatus* and cow. Fortunately the cow was the only significant host of this tick, and since they were under human control, the ticks were eradicated. Without ticks no transmission of *Babesia* was possible.

In *Boophilus*, the agent causing cattle fever is normally transmitted by the succeeding generation, although the adult of the generation acquiring the agent could cycle it back through the same host from which an earlier instar acquired it. The reason for the delayed transmission is that *Boophilus* species are one-host ticks. In a three-host tick, *Rhipicephalus* and others, transmission is possible by the adult of the generation acquiring the pathogen. The reservoir is largely domestic, and the route of transmission is horizontal between tick and cow and vertical within the tick.

In the laboratory the piroplasm of *B. caballi* can persist and be infective in *Hyalomma marginatum* through at least seven generations (Abramov, 1955). The agent was demonstrated in all generations by examination of eggs and organs of the ticks. Transmission was effected by salivation.

At times *Babesia* spp. destroy or injure cells they invade, but the effect on the life of an active tick is mild. However, *B. caballi* may concentrate in eggs in such density as to prevent hatching. *Babesia canis* regularly passes through the egg, and final development takes place in the larva and nymph (Garnham, 1955). Host cells may be injured or even destroyed in the invasion process, but damage is inconsequential since the tick hatches and develops normally.

Babesioids of the genus *Aegyptianella* are parasites of birds and *Argas* ticks. *A. pullorum* is known from chicken, goose, turkey, and guinea fowl in Egypt.

ADDITIONAL READINGS

HALL (1953), KUDO (1954), and LEVINE (1961) discuss the speciation and systematics of Protozoa. The schemes of classification differ but are representative of divergent views on this controversial subject. Levine's book discusses the forms pathogenic to domestic animals.

MULLIGAN (1955) gives a detailed account of Gambian sleeping sickness and its current relation to the restless population of equatorial Africa. This reference, together with others listed in the text, should be consulted for details of ecology of the parasite.

MORRIS (1960) discusses the history and current state of Rhodesian sleeping sickness. Its relation to the return of land to its natural state is particularly well stated.

BOYD (1949) is a comprehensive account of malaria up to the close of the war of 1939–1945.

MACDONALD (1957) brings the discussion of malaria up to the current recession of the disease to its more stable foci.

CHAPTER 13

Platyhelminthes, Aschelminthes, Acanthocephala

GENERAL

Our knowledge of parasitic worms dates from ancient times, but their exact relation to arthropods has been known for only about a century. The early Egyptians recognized the presence of worms in the human body as an abnormality. Early Semites must have had ideas of ways in which intestinal worms invaded the body because their strict dietary taboos resulted in some degree of control of certain ones. Since "creeping things" were included in these taboos, it is reasonable to assume that they were suspected as being sources of parasitic worms.

PLATYHELMINTHES

Platyhelminthes are the flat worms, parasitic representatives of which belong to the classes Trematoda, or flukes, and Cestoda, or tapeworms. All of the Trematoda in the definitive stage are dorso-ventrally flattened, are usually hermaphroditic, lack a true coelom, are without a skeleton, and have no anal opening. Those that are parasitic bear hooks or suckers anteriorly. One or more "suckers" are present in an anterior-ventral region. Two or more larval forms are known from successively different hosts characteristic for each species. Cestoda as adults have "segmented" bodies that tend to be ribbon-like and may attain lengths of 12 or more meters. No food tube is present. Anteriorly there is a *scolex* bearing holdfast structures which attach the organism to the gut wall of some vertebrate.

Segments proliferate behind the scolex and gravid segments detach posteriorly. Each segment is bisexual. Larval forms are variable.

Trematoda

Trematoda, or flukes, have been divided into the subclass Monogenea (without alternation of generations) and Digenea (with alternation of generations). The latter group contains by far the greatest number of species. LaRue (1957) gives a catalogue of major categories of the Digenea, in which he lists five orders and a large number of families.

Members of the Monogenea are permanent parasites having one host for each species. Consequently they have no significance in medical entomology. Digenea have two or more serial hosts, some of which may be arthropods. Table 28 lists representatives of six families that have aquatic arthropods in their reservoirs. For further details one should consult references specifically devoted to helminthology.

Digenetic trematodes have a complex ontogeny involving 2–4 hosts and up to seven stages. The stages in order are *egg, miracidium, sporocyst, redia, cercaria, metacercaria,* and *adult.* The miracidium is a motile, aquatic stage with a life expectancy of less than 24 hours outside a suitable host. The sporocyst is mobile and parasitizes host No. 1. It gives rise by reproductive processes to other sporocysts or rediae. The redia is a mobile obligatory parasite in host No. 1, and it too is capable of reproduction as other rediae or cercariae. The cercaria is a motile stage that leaves host No. 1 and either invades host No. 2, is eaten by Host No. 2, or encysts on available inanimate substrates. This host may include medusae, turbellarians, annelids, crustaceans, mollusks, insects, or vertebrates (amphibians or fish). Ultimately this stage encysts inside host No. 2 as a stationary metacercaria. For further development, hosts bearing metacercariae must be ingested by host No. 3. Once inside the definitive host, the worm becomes an adult.

Trematodes of medical importance that have arthropod hosts in their ontogeny are the lung flukes, *Paragonimus* spp. These parasites in the definitive stage infest lungs of man, carnivores, and swine in Europe, central United States, South America, and the Orient including India. Sputum of man or feces of any host containing eggs contaminates the water in which certain operculate snails live. The parasite enters the snail and develops into sporocysts, rediae,

Table 28. Trematoda Whose Larval Stages Infest Arthropods.

| Family | Genus | Sequence of Hosts | | |
		Host 1	Host 2	Host 3
Plagiorchidae	*Prosthogonimus* spp.	Snail	Odonate nymph	Waterfowl, domestic fowl
	Haematoloechus	Snail	Odonate nymph	Frog
	Dolichosaccus sp.	Snail	Tricoptera larva	Frog
Troglotrematidae	*Paragonimus* spp.	Mollusk	Decapod	Man and carnivores
Halipegidae	*Halipegus* spp.	Snail	Copepod, Odonata	*Rana* spp.
Haplometridae	*Haplometra* sp.	Snail	Beetle (*Ilybius*)	Frog
Gorgoderidae	*Gorgodera* sp.	Snail	Odonate nymph	Frog
Allocreadiidae	*Allocreadium* sp.	Snail	Mayfly nymph	Fish
	Crepidostomum sp.	Bivalve mollusk	Mayfly nymph, amphipod, decapod, bivalve mollusk	Trout
	Hamacredium	Snail	None	Decapod, snail, fish

and cercariae. Cercariae crawl about in the water in the manner of leeches until they find crayfish and fresh-water crabs. They enter these crustaceans and encyst in their tissues. When a definitive host (host No. 3) swallows raw, infested crustaceans, the young flukes make their way progressively through the gut wall, diaphragm, and lung sacs to the lung tissue of the host, where fibrotic cysts form about them. Later these cysts rupture into the bronchioles.

The disease in man is called paragonimiasis or endemic hemoptysis. It manifests itself as a persistent cough and bloody sputum which bears multitudes of eggs. Patients are said to become seriously ill only rarely. Man contracts the disease after eating salted, pickled, or other uncooked crabs or crayfish. Since many small carnivores eat raw crustaceans, those inhabiting infected areas become the principal vertebrate hosts. When the worms (as eggs) are voided into ground pools from which the host drinks, a triangular reservoir (snail-crab-carnivore) is established. Man is an active component in the Oriental reservoir when he is careless with sputum, as workers in rice fields may often be.

Cestoda

General. The class Cestoda includes three orders, Proteocephala, Cyclophyllidea, and Pseudophyllidea, that have obligatory or facultative associations with arthropods (Table 29). So far as is known, all species of the first and third orders have some crustacean, especially Copepoda, as the first larval host. Some Cyclophyllidea require one of a variety of arthropodan hosts.

The layman usually recognizes tapeworms, the familiar parasites of the lumen of the gut, in their definitive forms. In general they are narrow bands of repetitive bisexual parts or *proglottids* that are joined to the knobby anterior *scolex* by a narrow *neck*. The scolex may be provided with holdfast structures as suckers or rows of recurved hooks that serve to attach the worm to the host tissue. The chain of flattened proglottids comprising a single worm may contain thousands of these bisexual bodies. Proglottids proliferate serially from the neck of the worm. They may break off at the terminal part singly or in groups as they mature. For variations and details of morphology and physiology see Hyman (1951) and Wardle and McLeod (1952).

Tapeworms of the groups mentioned above like the digenetic trematodes, require serial hosts. Most require two hosts, some re-

Table 29. Cestoda of Medical Importance Whose Larval Stages Infest Arthropods.

Family	Representative	Arthropodan Host	Vertebrate Host
Proteocephalidae	17 genera	Fresh-water copepods	Fish largely
Anoplocephalidae	*Moniezia* *Bertiella* *Cittotaenia* *Anoplocephala*	Oribatid mites (6 + families)	Ruminants Primates Rabbits Equines
Davaineidae	*Raillietina* (200 + spp.)	Carabidae, Formicidae, Muscidae	Birds, man (rarely), small mammals
Hymenolepidae	12 genera	Insects, millipedes, amphipods, ostracods, copepods	Birds, rodents
Dilepididae	51 genera 5 genera	Insects, earthworms (when known) Beetles, fleas, grasshoppers	Birds Mammals
Amabiliidae	3 genera	Odonate nymphs	Birds
Haplobothriidae	*Haplobothrium*	Copepod	Fish
Dibothriocephalidae	*Dibothriocephalus* *Spirometra*	Copepod Copepod	Mammals Dog, cat, man
Triaenophoridae	*Triaenophorus*	Copepod	Fish
Amphicotylidae	*Eubothrium*	Copepod	Fish
Bothriocephalidae	*Bothriocephalus*	Copepod	Amphibia

quire three, and only rarely does one suffice. Unlike the trematodes, however, all transmission is passive, that is, the infective stage must be swallowed by the suscept. The first larval stage is called the *oncosphere*, and it may or may not be surrounded by a cellular envelope bearing cilia. This stage in host No. 1 develops into one of several kinds of forms according to the kind of tapeworm and is designated *procercoid, cysticercoid*, or other (Wardle and McLeod, 1952). When this primary host bearing an infective larva is eaten by host No. 2, the larva is freed into the food tube. If this is the definitive host, the egg-producing adult is formed. If it is a species requiring yet another host, then a third larval stage develops, as for example, a *plerocercoid* of pseudophyllidean tapeworms. In this latter instance an additional host is required.

Proteocephala. This group hardly qualifies for a place in medical entomology because the species attack hosts other than man or his domestic animals. Snakes, fresh-water fish, and frogs are the usual hosts for definitive stages of these worms. Free eggs of the worms are ingested by copepods while they are actively grazing. Soon after ingestion, hatching is completed; then the oncospheres move to the body cavity through the gut wall. Within about 2 weeks the procercoids become infective, and further development ceases. Subsequent development as a plerocercoid usually takes place in some fish that has ingested the infected crustacean. The definitive adult finally develops in the same or a cannibalistic species of fish.

Infected copepods are affected by these worms. Essex (1927) noted that *Cyclops* bearing eight or more oncospheres did not always complete development. Any infestation retarded activity of these crustaceans and made them ready prey for minnows and other small fish. Some species of *Cyclops* are more prone to infection than others, presumably because of differences in activity or in sizes of mouth openings.

Cyclophyllidea. Among the Cyclophyllidea there are four families of some 100 genera that are known to have (or are suspected of having) arthropods as hosts. Each of these families contains representatives that are important to man because the definitive form of the worm lives in man or his domestic animals.

The Anoplocephalidae comprise some 36 genera and have an obligatory relationship with oribatid mites, a large group of pasture inhabitants. The best-known species is *Moniezia expansa,* a parasite of mites and both sheep and goats in North America and Europe. The mites become infected by feeding on fecal pellets of sheep and goats that contain eggs of the worms, and the vertebrates become infected by eating grass on which infected mites are resting. Larval worms hatch in the gut of the host mites and soon cut their way through the gut wall. After about 2–5 months the larva assumes a cysticercoid form capable of infesting sheep (Stunkard, 1939). The rate of infection in mites may run as high as 34 per cent, as was the case in a pasture heavily seeded with dung bearing eggs (Kates and Runkel, 1948). Examinations of several thousand mites taken from a permanent sheep pasture in Maryland showed infestations in nearly 4 per cent. A rough estimate indicated that during the summer this pasture provided a continuous supply of cysticercoids at a rate of about 400,000 to an acre.

The family Davaineidae is composed of about 12 genera usually parasitic in the definitive form in birds. Representatives of the genus *Raillietina,* of importance to man and domestic animals, live as larvae in insects. At least four species are known from Carabidae, and one scarab lives in animal droppings. The house fly may support larvae of at least two species. Muir (1954) reported that ants of three genera may also harbor a representative of this genus of worms.

Among the Hymenolepidae are about 12 genera which may have some association with a wide range of arthropods. Wardle and McLeod (1952) stated that infection of vertebrates by hymenolepids is usually accomplished by ingestion of an infected arthropod. *Hymenolepis nana,* that lives in man and rodents, may circumvent larval hosts and infect a mammal directly when eggs are swallowed; however, fleas and even mealworms will support cysticercoids that are capable of infecting a vertebrate host. *Hymenolepis diminuta* as a cysticercoid form may infest lepidopterous larvae such as those of the flour moth (*Asopia*) as well as other Pyralidae and Tineidae; it may infest a dermapteran (*Anisolabis*), dermestids, and other coleopterans; it may enter larval fleas and even cockroaches, and millipedes may be attacked. The dependable larval host, however, is the flour moth. Larvae of *H. brachycephala* have a bird-cyclops reservoir. Others attack ostracods or amphipods as larvae.

The family Dilepididae contains about 60 genera, the larvae of which attack insects or earthworms, as far as is known. In the definitive stage most species parasitize birds while others mature in mammals or reptiles. The genera *Dipylidium* and *Choanotaenia* are better known as economic parasites since some species include domestic animals and man in the sequences of hosts. *Dipylidium caninum* is ingested as eggs by either dog lice or larval fleas of any species associated with dogs. Eggs hatch in the gut of larval fleas, but the oncosphere quickly leaves it through slashes made in the gut wall. Oncospheres develop little in the larvae, but grow considerably in pupal and imaginal fleas. Transformation to the cysticercoid form takes place after a flea begins feeding on blood. To gain access to a dog, an infected adult flea must be swallowed. A child may swallow a flea, and when he does so, the worm finds lodgment in the human intestine, where it may mature. Hutchison *et al.* (1959) reported finding the ninth known human case from the United States. With one exception all victims were residents of the Gulf coastal states. Members of the genus *Choanotaenia* may use insects such as flies, grasshoppers, and beetles as larval hosts and domestic fowls as definitive hosts.

Chen (1934) in his work on *Dipylidium caninum* has reported on the effect cysticercoids may have on fleas. Pathogenesis in fleas occurs in varying degrees. In some instances mortality as high as 60 per cent has been observed within 24 hours after eggs were ingested. The first symptom is lethargy, and secondarily, just before death of larvae, there is a change in general body color from translucent white to reddish. This initial larval mortality is apparently caused by mechanical damage to the gut wall incident to passage of the oncosphere through it. A second series of developments may kill 20 per cent of larvae prior to pupation. Instead of spinning their cocoons immediately, some mature larvae may wander about or lie dormant for days before they die, while others spin their cocoons but delay pupation. During the pupal period a third series of reactions which end in death may cause an additional 10 per cent mortality. Infected pupae require at least two weeks longer for development than do uninfected ones. Symptoms in prepupae and pupae result from a depletion of reserve in the fat body caused by the rapidly developing juvenile worm. Displacement and distortion of organs in the host result when juvenile worms are numerous.

Histology of the blood of infected fleas shows changes, according to Chen. Macrocytes, normal only in larvae, persist through pupal and adult stages of infected fleas. The macrocytes form capsules about cysticercoids during larval life. As the cysticercoid grows, its capsule of macrocytes becomes thinner, as no new cells are added. By the time the flea reaches maturity, the capsule around each cysticercoid is a thin web. The capsule may actually kill cysticercoids in larval fleas but does not seem to do so in adults.

Pseudophyllidea. The Pseudophyllidea have three sequential hosts for representatives of the five families about which bionomic information is available. Eggs of this group hatch in water that supports populations of copepods. The free-swimming first larva or coracidium is ingested by the crustacean host. As is usual for first larvae, they rupture the gut wall and then lie in the hemocoel, where they develop into a procercoid form. If the infected copepod is swallowed by a potential second larval host, it yields its parasite for further growth in tissues of the new host as a plerocercoid. When the second larval host is eaten raw by a suscept, the definitive stage develops.

Spirometra spp. have a serial host range of cyclopid-amphibia-carnivore (snake and mammal). Cyclopids of paddy fields, ponds, and even streams become infective to a high degree in parts of the Orient where raw human feces are commonly used as fertilizer. Newly hatched oncospheres are readily caught by the faster-moving crustaceans. Sometimes this phase penetrates to the hemocoel within 25 minutes after ingestion. Heavily infected cyclopids are more sluggish than those not infected. Within three weeks at normal temperatures the procercoid is fully formed. When the infected arthropod is swallowed by a frog or snake, or even a rodent, the plerocercoid matures in the tissues of various internal organs. Transfer to man may be accomplished by ingestion of infected tissues of frog or snakes, or by use of "frog poultices" on open wounds, a medicinal practice common in the Orient.

Dibothriocephalus latus is a cosmopolitan parasite with a copepod-fish-mammal reservoir. It behaves very much as *Spirometra* and is more commonly a parasite of Europeans and Americans. The eating of raw fish is practiced by some Europeans as well as some Americans. The definitive hosts are so varied and so numerous that fecal contamination of ponds, streams, and lakes is commonplace. The cyclopid-fish portion of the reservoir is non-specific; hence several species of fishes may be infected. When man, dogs, cats, or wild carnivores eat the infected fish, the definitive stage may be completed.

ASCHELMINTHES

General

Aschelminthes is the phylum that includes, among other forms, the round worms. Numerically the speciation is enormous, rivaling that of Arthropoda. The free-living representatives are most numerous and are found in soil, water, and to some extent in plants and animals. Only a dozen or so afflict man, but one or the other of these manages to parasitize a great part of the world's population.

Nematoda

Nematoda constitute the only class of the six which is of significance to medical entomology. In all stages these worms are tubular, and they taper both anteriorly and posteriorly. The cuticula is clear or nearly so, is marked externally by minute striations, and may even have bristles, ridges, or flaps, but never jointed appendages. There is a distinct body cavity, or false coelom, in which the internal organs lie without attachment. The cavity is filled with fluid which bears nutriment to the cells and also acts as the hydraulic fluid in the manner characteristic of arthropods. The food tube opens ante-riorly and posteriorly. Sexes are for the most part separate. Eggs are encased in secreted shells of maternal origin.

Representatives of Nematoda have a relatively simple ontogeny. Embryos develop inside the egg and in some instances one or even two molts take place in the eggs. A total of four molts is normal for the larval worm (including any inside egg as well). The third larval stage is infective for species parasitic in arthropods. The first of these is very active. The second is at first sluggish as the "sausage" form in some arthropodan tissue.

Nematodes (Table 30) that have insects in their chain of hosts most often belong to the order Spirurida. Chitwood and Chitwood (1952) show 14 families in three superfamilies, species of which attack all sorts of mammals as adult worms. Larvae live as systemic parasites in arthropods. Insects and mites that feed subcutaneously may ingest larval worms. Usually the worms return to their adult hosts at the time the infected arthropod is feeding. Unfortunately little is known about the extrinsic bionomics of even the most im-portant species. The descriptive phase of our knowledge, however, is being supplemented more and more by new ecological informa-tion. The medically important representatives will be included herein.

Dracunculus medinensis. *Dracunculus medinensis* (guinea worm, medina worm, fiery serpent) is the cause of dracunculiasis (dra-contiasis) in man and other vertebrates. The parasite is tropico-politan. The disease is of concern to human welfare in those areas where persons wade in water which they later drink without treat-ment. It is one of the earliest known nematode diseases of man, as is shown by references in ancient Hebrew literature. Later, Alexan-der the Great considered it a major problem in his field armies. It was referred to by Galen in the second century A.D. The Arabians were concerned with it as a pest of livestock from time immemorial (Turkhud, 1920).

The worm, when fully grown, is a round, smooth creature that varies from about 30 to 120 cm in length and from about 1.0 to 1.7 mm in diameter. When mature the body is so packed with embryos from end to end that a million or more may be present.

Table 30. Nematoda That Have Both Vertebrates and Arthropods in Their Reservoirs.

Worm	Family	Arthropod Host	Vertebrate Host
Agamospirura parahormeticae	Spiruridae	Cockroach	Bird (?)
Ascarops strongylina	Thelaziidae	Coprophagous scarab	Pig
Brugia malayi	Dipetalonematidae	Mosquito	Primate, canine, Pholidota, cat
Cheilospirura hamulosa	Acuariidae	*Melanoplus* spp.	Bird
Chlamydonema sp.	Physalopteridae	—	Carnivore, monkey
Conspiculum sp.	Dipetalonematidae	Trombiculidae	Reptile
Dipetalonema grassi	Dipetalonematidae	*Rhipicephalus sanguineus*	Dog
D. reconditum	Dipetalonematidae	Tick, flea, louse, mosquito	Dog
D. perstans	Dipetalonematidae	*Culicoides*	Man
D. streptocerca	Dipetalonematidae	*Culicoides*	Man
D. vite	Dipetalonematidae	Tick	Burrowing rodent
Dirofilaria (many spp.)	Dipetalonematidae	Mosquito	Dog, primate
Dispharynx nasuta	Acuariidae	Isopod	Fowl
Dracunculus medinensis	Dracunculidae	Copepod	Man, dog, etc.
Dracunculus insignis	Dracunculidae	Copepod	Dog, racoon, mink, etc.
Echinuria uncinata	Acuariidae	*Daphnia*	Duck, goose
Filaria cypseli	Filariidae	Louse	African swift
Foleyella spp.	Dipetalonematidae	Mosquito	Frog
Gnathostoma spinigerum	Gnathostomatidae	Copepod to snake, fish, bird	Mink, feline, man
Gongylonema pulchrum	Thelaziidae	Coprophagus scarab, cockroach	Ruminant, equine, man
G. ingluvicola	Thelaziidae	Coprophagus scarab	Fowl
G. neoplasticum	Thelaziidae	Cockroach	Domestic rat
Habronema spp.	Spiruridae	Muscoid fly	Equine
Hartertia gallinarum	Gnathostomatidae	Termite	Fowl
Icosiella neglecta	Stephanofilariidae	Midge (*Forcipomyia*)	Frog
Litomosoides carinii	Dipetalonematidae	*Ornithonyssus* mite	Rat
Loa loa	Dipetalonematidae	*Chrysops, Haematopota*	Primate
Mansonella ozzardii	Dipetalonematidae	*Culicoides*	Man
Onchocerca volvulus	Dipetalonematidae	Simuliidae	Man
O. cervicalis	Dipetalonematidae	*Culicoides*	Equine
O. gibsoni	Dipetalonematidae	*Culicoides, Tabanus*	Bovine
Ornithofilaria fallisensis	Dipetalonematidae	Simuliidae	Duck
Oswaldofilaria chlamydosauri	Dipetalonematidae	*Culex*	Lizard
Oxyspirura sp.	Thelaziidae	Cockroach	Bird
Parabronema sp.	Acuariidae	Copepod	Bird
Physaloptera sp.	Physalopteridae	Cockroach, earwig	Primate
Rictularia sp.	Thelaziidae	Cockroach, beetle	Carnivore, rodent
Setaria sp.	Filariidae	*Stomoxys,* mosquito	Ungulate
Spirocerca	Thelaziidae	Scarab	Carnivore
Spirura sp.	Spiruridae	Scarab, tenebrionid, cockroach	Carnivore
Stephanofilaria assamensis	Stephanofilariidae	Fly (casual)	Bovine
Tetrameres sp.	Spiruridae	Grasshopper, amphipod	Bird
Thelazia rhodesii	Thelaziidae	Arthropod (?)	Bovine
Thelazia callipaedia	Thelaziidae	Arthropod (?)	Various mammals
Wuchereria bancrofti	Dipetalonematidae	Mosquito	Man

The embryos are about 0.5 mm long and somewhat flattened, and when discharged by the female they are in such a mass that the surrounding water may appear to be almost milky.

Dracunculiasis occurs about a year after infection by the worms. Symptoms may appear without warning as the victim vomits, feels giddy, or even collapses. The painful swelling of a limb may be noted, or there may be a local reaction, usually on an ankle or foot, but the symptoms are by no means so wholly limited. Seldom does a patient have more than one female worm present, and local reactions are seen along the position of the worm. A blister will form on an ankle or foot and may attain a diameter of 5 cm or more. Eventually the blister ruptures and exposes the anterior end of the worm. Sometimes the worm dies or is killed in place by efforts to extract it from its tortuous path along the subcutaneous tissues. In such cases cellulitis occurs along the route of the worm. Abscesses may form at intervals along the path, and sometimes they develop to serious and even fatal proportions.

The worm has a copepod-vertebrate reservoir, which becomes active wherever susceptible and carrier vertebrates wade in and drink water that bears crustaceans of the family Cyclopidae. When a vertebrate host bearing gravid worms wades into a pool, the uterus of the worm ejects quantities of embryos into the water. The embryos are motile and swim about actively. Those that are ingested by a cyclopid complete their larval instars internally. A susceptible vertebrate becomes infected after drinking raw water containing cyclopids which bear infective forms of the worm.

It would appear that any canine or primate (especially man) may constitute the basic vertebrate in the reservoir of this parasite, provided the animal regularly wades into a permanent ground pool and drinks. In the Old World, prolific sources for human infections are shallow open ponds and wells. Mirza (1938) stated that at one time a town in India had some 95 per cent of its population infected. Jackal and wolf are known to be in the reservoir in Egypt.

Larvae of the medina worms are pathogenic to *Cyclops*. The majority of the hosts die soon after the worms mature and after the appearance of a series of histological symptoms. Ovisacs cease to be formed after infection in *Mesocyclops*, according to Moorthy (1938). Female cyclopids are more often infected than are males or juvenile stages; possibly this is because they remain closer to the bottom of the pool, where nematodes are more likely to be abundant.

Loa loa. This is the eye worm that causes loaiasis of man in tropical Africa from the Congo Basin eastward and northward into Sudan. Symptoms may not develop, but when they do appear the conspicuous one is the "calabar swelling," a transient, painful enlargement of the surface that may be as large as a hen's egg. The swellings disappear as quickly as they appear. Sometimes urticaria, hydrocoel, and edema of the lymphatics accompany an infection.

Specifically, this is a disease of villagers in and near rain forests. It affects all ages and both sexes where residences are in the forest proper. Also, it affects those who may range into the woods for food, firewood, or other activities. Lastly, it is often a disease of those who tap rubber trees. This close connection with forests suggests a basic sylvatic reservoir and such seems to be the case in part.

The known reservoir is one involving primates and forest tabanids of the genus *Chrysops* (Kershaw, 1955, among others). Man and other primates are hospitable vertebrates. Possibly any *Chrysops* is a suitable host, but only those that frequent the haunts of primates are normally in the reservoir. Historically, it appears that the parasite has been long established in wild primates. Transmission is currently at a high level where humans live in small villages in unbroken rain forests that are inhabited by abundant arboreal primates. The relation between forest and the rate of infection may be seen and compared most easily at an abrupt interface between forest and mountain grasslands. All ages of the villagers inside the forest show a high incidence of the filariid. Villages in the grasslands within a space of 2–3 miles from a forest show a sharp decline in incidence. Infection is virtually absent in persons living in remote grasslands and in mangrove swamps, neither of which has wild primates. Transmission of the pathogen at the site is apparently absent in villages that become urbanized incidentally to commercial development.

The relations between infections with *Loa* sp. found in man and in wild primates are important. Wild tabanids become infected while feeding on either. It seems that those flies near and in rubber plantations, together with the workers who tap the trees, form a horizontal chain of transmission involving only these two components. Both hosts and suscepts are human and come to the flies for exchange of the pathogen. Flies in the forest may derive their infection from primates and then impart the agent to some other wild vertebrate. Just as freely do they inoculate persons who invade their haunts. Exchange of this parasite from wild primates to humans takes place most consistently in villages at the edges of great forests. The primates most likely to be important in the reservoir for *Loa loa* are human, drill (*Mandrillus* spp.), monkeys (*Cercopithecus* spp.), *Papio* sp., and *Cercocebus* sp. because all are tolerant toward the parasite. Horizontal *Chrysops*-human transmission may be continuous and unlimited in conditions permitting unlimited contact. Circuitous *Chrysops*-primate transmission likewise is continuous in the intersylvatic phase. Adult worms infest primates, and larvae live in flies.

Duke and Wijers (1958) postulate that under natural conditions in Cameroons transmission of the human strain of *Loa loa* to monkeys takes place on such an insignificant scale that the monkey population constitutes no effective host in the chain. For practical purposes consideration of monkeys may be ignored in any control program in that country.

The only known insects in the reservoir are species of *Chrysops*. According to Gordon (1955) many species of the genus are probably hospitable to larvae of this filariid, but only those that feed repeatedly on primates are significant in the reservoir. Some seem to be restricted to the high canopy and feed on wild primates; others feed both in the canopy and near the ground; still others generally feed on the ground. *Chrysops silacea* must be significant in the sylvatic-human phase. It feeds any time during the day in the canopy, but it may be attracted to the forest floor when groups of persons are present and if cooking fires are burning. The fly is readily attracted from the canopy to persons near the fires. This tabanid has been seen following troops of monkeys in the canopy as well as troops of the terrestrial drills as they move about in the forest. *Chrysops distinctipennis* is considered to be the important species in the Sudan.

Larvae of *Loa loa* develop in tissues of the hemocoel of *Chrysops*. Within 24 hours or less the microfilariae may penetrate the gut wall and become intracellular parasites in the oenocyte-like cells of the fat body (Lavoipierre, 1958). Most settle in the abdomen, but some are in the thorax and even the head. By the third day a larva has outgrown its host cell, but it continues to stay in the tissue of the fat body. Disorganization of the cytoplasm and loss of cell membranes are pathological results of larval development. Larvae begin to move toward the head after about 10 days. Should they not leave the host, they disperse throughout the body.

Worms that mature fully seem to cause some cellular pathology but no symptoms of major injury (Lavoipierre, 1958a). Cells of the fat body occupied by larvae may show disorganization, but no observable injurious effects are caused as the larvae migrate to the head. If the worms do not vacate the fly immediately, but wander in the body instead, they may cause damage to some organs which had not been invaded during their development. For example, some of the thoracic muscles show considerable lysis and disruption of the bundles. Exit of the larvae from the body of the host may shorten the life of the fly.

Details of larval emergence from a host fly are poorly known. When mature, they do escape by rupturing the labiohypopharyngeal membrane at the time of the kinking of the labium incident to feeding (Gordon and Crewe, 1953). Neither heat nor moisture stimulates the exodus, as larvae will emerge when host flies have been induced to feed on cold, dry surfaces of mammalian tissue.

Larvae penetrate intact skin at the site of a feeding puncture (Gordon, 1950). Once through the *stratum corneum,* they enter the hemorrhaged area. From the deeply situated hemorrhage, filariae make their way into the connective tissue of the underlying muscle layer.

Dirofilaria. Worms of the genus *Dirofilaria* cause heartworm disease of canines, rodents, felines, and primates. Symptoms appear when a number of adult worms lie in the cardiac portion of the circulatory system. In some parts of the world, notably in Pacific Oceania, incidence of disease in dogs may be very high. Where such is the case, both felines and humans may become infected. Only *D. immitis* seems to be common in temperate regions.

Dirofilaria immitis has a reservoir involving canines and mosquitoes. Microfilariae released into the blood by adult filariids are ingested from peripheral capillaries by the culicine hosts. Because infections in mosquitoes may be mixed with other species, including those that infest humans, the group is included in this account. The domestic *Culex annulirostris* on Tahiti is readily infected naturally, and other domestic species may become infected. Only *Aedes polynesiensis* and this *Culex* showed mature larvae in wild mosquitoes (Rosen, 1954). In the laboratory, worms may reach maturity in other members of the subgenus *Culex* as well as in species of *Anopheles* (s. gen. *Anopheles*), but some are better vector-hosts than others. Kartman (1954) found that *Anopheles quadrimaculatus* and *Aedes albopictus* were excellent hosts for larvae after 15 days of filariid development, while other mosquitoes were not. Steuben (1954) considered fleas the important arthropods in the reservoir, but he may have been dealing with a *Dipetalonema.*

Progress of larval development of mosquitoes was noted as early as 1900 by Grassi and Noe in Rome. Bancroft (1901) reported that larvae leave the gut and lodge in the malpighian tubules, where they develop through the sausage stage. Mature larvae move about in the hemocoel of the body and all appendages. The sausage form may be reached in 90 hours, and maturity may be attained in 144 hours.

Mature larval filariids escape from the hemocoel by passing through the membranous cuticula of the mouth parts of their culicine hosts while they are taking a blood meal. Intercoelomic blood pressure created by the expanding stomach of the host insect is said to aid in the escape of the worms in some way. Once free of the culicine host, larval filariids are able to make their way through unbroken skin, but they may enter by way of the channel of a feeding puncture. Infective larvae may be freed when the host is crushed on the skin, and may survive the episode to penetrate unbroken skin.

Pathogenesis in mosquitoes is often severe and results in the death of many. In the case of *Aedes aegypti*, the mortality rate is many times that for uninfected ones. The greatest injury results when the filariids penetrate the epithelium of the mid-gut. Lavoipierre (1958b) stated in his literature review of filariid pathogenesis that worms in the malpighian tubules caused degeneration of the cytoplasm of the excretory cells but left the nuclei intact at first. Walls of infested tubules were composed of distorted polynucleate cells. By the time a filariid had reached its infective form, total disintegration of the cells of the tubules had taken place, and the worms were enclosed in translucent bags of basement membrane. Development in an unfertilized culicine host is said to cause much less injury to the tissues than is the case with fertilized mosquitoes.

When dissecting mosquitoes, fleas, mites, and possibly ticks, the observer is cautioned of the possibility of finding filariids of several species. *Dirofilaria scapiceps, D. aethiops,* and *D. repens* are known to be associated with mosquitoes and presumably some might be in fleas. *D. scapiceps* has been found in the lumen of the gut of a rabbit tick. Since little is known about the reservoirs of these and other filariids, care is advised in assigning the filariids to species.

Onchocerca volvulus. This is the cause of onchocerciasis, a disease estimated to involve millions of humans, mostly in tropical Africa. The only area affected outside Africa is a region on the Pacific slope of Guatemala and adjacent Mexico. Blindness caused by this worm may be conservatively placed at 2 per cent or higher in Guatemala and Sudan. In addition to damaging the eyes, larvae in the dermal areas cause fibrous tumors that become painful and even incapacitating. Symptoms have been variously called lichenification, craw-craw, keratodermia, elephant skin, and presbydermia. It may be deduced that larvae in man have a predilection for cutaneous regions of the body. This filariid persists in a human population for years after all means for transfer have been removed (Garnham, 1954). Microfilariae may continue to be produced seven years after the last infection. Clinically, the disease retrogresses after four years.

Onchocerciasis is associated with life in shady situations along turbulent streams. Browne (1960) gives a description of sites in the Republic of Congo. In Ghana and other centers in western Africa, the disease is rife among populations who live near swift streams and rivers (Fig. 91). In Guatemala the afflicted zone is a band some 75 miles long on the Pacific side of the Sierra Madre Mountains (Dalmat, 1955), where residents acquire the pathogen during the rainy season between late October and February. Non-resident or migratory workers on coffee plantations and other transients in Guatemala may become infected during this interval. In Kenya transients seem to be more often infected at major fords across streams. Migrants who become infected may serve as porters of the pathogen to other areas.

The arthropodan component of the reservoir is composed solely of flies of the genus *Simulium*. In Kenya, S. *neavei* is important; in Ghana and elsewhere on the West Coast of Africa, it is S. *damnosum*, and in Guatemala the vector-hosts are S. *ochraceum*, S. *metallicum*, and S. *callidum*. Intensity of infection in flies is inversely proportional to the number of flies, while incidence in humans is directly proportional to the frequency of contact with infected flies. In Nigeria, Crosskey (1954) showed that no decline in incidence of disease was observable within seven miles of a major river, but beyond this limit the decline was rapid.

Flies become infected while feeding on or near nodular lesions on the skin. Microfilariae move from the subdermal connective tissue into the area lacerated by the mandibles and torn by the maxillae (Gibbons, 1938). When capillaries are cut, filariids are ingested with blood from the hemorrhage. Flies fed on skin free of nodules were only occasionally infected; about 60 per cent of those fed in a nodular area, and about 80 per cent of those fed directly on nodules may become infected. Fibrosed nodules have few or no larvae in surface layers; hence rate of infection drops in flies that feed on them (Kershaw, 1958).

Microfilariae ingested by black flies penetrate their gut walls and move through the hemocoel. It seems that the African pathogen matures in the thoracic muscles within about seven days (Edwards,

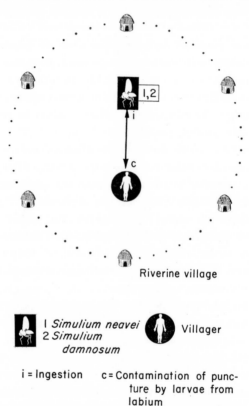

Riverine village

I *Simulium neavei*   Villager
2 *Simulium*
  damnosum

i = Ingestion   c = Contamination of puncture by larvae from
labium

Fig. 91. A domestic reservoir for *Onchocerca volvulus* in a riverine village in hill regions of central Africa.

1956). The onchocercan in Guatemala invades the malpighian tubules, where it remains until ready to leave the insect (Léon, 1957). Larvae emerge by way of ruptures of a labial membrane while the fly is feeding. Mature larvae enter the skin of man through feeding punctures made by the flies.

Individual flies vary in their ability to survive infestation by this filariid. Edwards (1956) noted that *Simulium damnosum* cannot survive a heavy invasion. Mortality is high in *S. ochraceum* and *S. callidum* (Dalmat, 1955). In one series, all infested flies of these two species were dead within four days. *S. metallicum* was somewhat more resistant so that about 16 per cent were still infested on the eighth day. Lavoipierre (1958a) called attention to the degeneration of cells of the thoracic muscles of *S. damnosum* in the vicinity of growing larvae. Earlier they interfere in some way with the formation of the peritrophic membrane.

Dipetalonema perstans. Dipetalonema perstans (syn. *Acanthocheilonema*) is the cause of a common form of benign filariasis in man and chimpanzees in rain forests of central Africa. Presumably the reservoir involves man and ceratopogonid flies of the genus *Culicoides*, and chimpanzees may be involved secondarily. Man is tolerant toward the parasite, but he seldom shows immune reactions even after repeated infections.

The only known vector-host in the reservoir is *Culicoides milnei* (syn. *austeni*), but *C. grahamii* may be a secondary one. The former species is more hospitable to larvae and permits more of them to mature in each individual than is the case with *C. grahamii*. In transmission an abundance of flies may be more significant than the degree of infection in individuals. Fallis and Bennett (1961) have reviewed past work with this species.

The incidence of filariids in humans is proportional to the extent of contact with rain forests (Kershaw *et al.*, 1953). Within the forests, infection is present in both sexes and begins to appear in the very young. Near the fringe of a forest, where trees are more obviously deciduous, the incidence of infection declines, and the age group of persons showing total infection is older. In areas of grasslands, infection occurs only in a small percentage of adult residents, while in villages remote from the flies only transient humans are infected. Significant infection of an individual requires time for development. A person new in an area of hyperendemicity may remain one or two years before becoming heavily infected.

The companion species, *D. streptocerca*, is unlike *D. perstans* in that it seems to be specific for *Culicoides grahamii* (Duke, 1954). Sharp (1927 and 1928), who probably worked with this worm instead of *D. perstans*, was the first to incriminate *Culicoides* as the larval host. He noted that the worm underwent metamorphosis up to the sausage stage in the thoracic muscles. Infective larvae rupture the labium and escape onto the skin of the host.

Litomosoides carinii. This agent is the cause of a filariasis in rodents and has no direct medical significance. It is of interest more for the arthropodan component in the reservoir than for its vertebrate one. Here we have a filariid that develops in a mite, specifically *Ornithonyssus bacoti*. The definitive form lives in the pleural cavity of the cotton rat (*Sigmodon*) as well as in *Sciurus, Mus, Holochilus*, and *Nectomys*.

Mites ingest the microfilariae along with the blood of the rat. The worms penetrate the gut wall of a mite within 24 hours after ingestion. They complete their development generally in the parenchyma surrounding the gut in the anterior part of the hemocoel. Some two weeks later larvae are mature and escape at the time the mites are feeding, in the manner of other filariids (Wagner, 1956).

Wuchereria bancrofti. *Wuchereria bancrofti* (syn. *Filaria sanguinea hominis* and *F. nocturna*) is the cause of bancroftian filariasis in areas where a warm, moist climate prevails most of the year. The moist tropics provide ideal conditions for propagation of this agent. The parasite will range out of such foci into temperate climates wherever the summers are comparable to those of the moist tropics and wherever the bridge to a basic focus is continuous. Thus the range of this worm extends from Malaya northward into China as far as 42° North. From the focus in the Ethiopian Region, southward extensions are known to reach 30° South. It is well established that symptoms may abate and even disappear in persons afflicted with filariasis after their removal to a cold climate; therefore, whenever a tenuous bridge between a tropical focus and a distant temperate one is broken, the pathogen dies out. This is thought to be the course of this pathogen in the focus that once existed along the Atlantic Coast in southeastern United States. During the early days of importations of slaves from central Africa, repeated introductions of the worms were made into the region. When this traffic ceased, introduction of the agent ceased, and in time filariasis disappeared from North America. The disease still deserves attention because even now there are an estimated 200,000,000 sufferers from it.

Adult humans are normally the only ones that show clinical manifestations of filariasis because symptoms develop slowly. Repeated inoculations are required to cause symptoms within five years or advanced symptoms such as elephantiasis within ten or more years. Observers have reported that an incidence of worms great enough to yield 60 microfilariae in 20 cmm of blood will usually lead to formation of hydrocoels in males in five years. Enlargements of axillary, inguinal, and other lymph nodes result in gigantism of scrotum, arms, legs, and breasts. Males are much more commonly infected than females. Cooray (1960) found that adult worms infest the spermatic cord, lymphatic glands, and female breast. They cause endolymphangitis with lymphatic occlusions of calcium salts followed by the formation of new ducts. Granulomatous tissue resembling tuberculous follicles and characterized by epithelioid cells and giant cells develop around dead parasites. Eosinophilic leucocytes are typically present. Microfilariae that migrate into lymphatic glands cause hyperplasia and giant-cell reaction in the sinuses.

The parasite exists as four variants according to habits. In the islands of the tropics it is more frequently found in persons or groups active in the bush or away from their homes. In the Philippines, those most often attacked are the workers in hemp fields. In Samoa transmission is most common to those on the trail or at work on the plantations. Populations in villages in the bush are much more heavily infested than are others from villages in clearings. In India and in Brazil the disease is more common in urban situations. Raghavan (1957) quoted observers to the effect that the rate of infection declines from the centers of towns to their outskirts in India. The degree of maximum infection was always inversely proportional to the degree of sanitation, irrespective of the section of the town. Besides the urban and rural forms there also exist periodic and non-periodic variants. The periodic form occurs throughout the greater part of the parasite's range, but in Polynesia and Fiji a non-periodic one releases microfilariae largely during the daylight hours. Both forms tend to be restricted to flat coastal areas, but numerous exceptions exist, especially in the Fiji Islands.

Presumably reservoirs for *W. bancrofti* involve only man as the vertebrate and selected groups of mosquitoes, which may vary according to locality. Over the range of the pathogen, at least 40 species of mosquitoes may play some part in perpetuating it. Apparently any anthropophilic mosquito that can withstand the invasion of the larval filariids may enter the reservoir of this worm. The species most widely effective in urban areas at least is *Culex pipiens fatigans,* the one probably used by Manson in his experiments nearly a century ago. It is certainly responsible for maintaining the parasite in urban foci in continental areas where the non-periodic form occurs. Various species of *Mansonia* are significant in the reservoir of the rural form in both India and Africa, while many *Anopheles* species enter the reservoir in Asia, South America, Africa, and tropical islands. *Anopheles farauti* and *bancrofti* together with *M. uniformis* are the common vector-hosts in the western part of the South Pacific. *Aedes* of the *scutellaris* group are particularly significant in the transmission of the non-periodic rural form in Pacific Oceania.

Mosquitoes become infected while feeding on a person who has microfilariae circulating in the peripheral blood. The threshold incidence of worms in the peripheral blood necessary for infection of *Aedes* (*Stegomyia*) seems to be about 10 worms per 20 cmm of blood. Muirhead-Thomson (1954) reported that an incidence between 16 and 100 worms per 20 cmm of blood brought about a similar rate of infection in mosquitoes. When incidence of worms was between 120 and 189 per 20 cmm of blood, the rate of infection rose from 18 to 60 per cent. The highest rate of infection for *Anopheles gambiae* occurred when the incidence of worms was 200 to 300 per 20 cmm of blood.

Regardless of the species of susceptible mosquitoes, the development of the worms in them has been found to be similar. Climate or time of year when infection of the mosquito is accomplished is more significant. No larval development takes place at 10° C, for in fact the larvae die. In Shanghai some 23 days were required for development at room temperature in April, while the time was shortened to 12 days in June. The worms molt twice during their development. Within a few hours the ingested worms penetrate the gut wall and lodge in the thoracic muscles. A few days later they are in the "sausage" form, and within 10 days they may be as long as 1.3 mm. At this time the worms swim free in the coelom and may be found in all parts of the body.

Subsequent fate of mature larvae has been a subject for investigation for a long time. In 1878, Sir Patrick Manson thought they remained in the host until its death, at which time they ruptured the cuticula and escaped from those mosquitoes that lay on the surface of the water. Some 20 years later, Bancroft dissected larvae taken from live and dead mosquitoes and found that none survived when put into water. He then proposed that the larvae reentered the food tube and made their exits through the labral gutter. First Dutton, then others, showed that the worms remained in the coelom until they ruptured the cuticula in the vicinity of the labella. It is now known that the site of the rupture is the tip of the labella and that it is made while the mosquito is in the act of feeding. The exit is definitely an active effort on the part of the worms, furthermore, the act of entering a human is an active effort. When a worm escapes from the proboscis of the culicine host and then is lodged on moist human skin (Flu, 1921), it quickly burrows through the intact skin and makes its way to a blood vessel. The significance of a moist warm climate is that the human skin is more likely to be moist from perspiration when the infective stage of the worm is on the skin.

Mosquitoes vary widely in their ability to serve as suitable hosts for this filariid. Those of the subgenus *Culex* may support large populations. Likewise some *Anopheles* and *Mansonia* are suitable hosts, while other species such as *Aedes aegypti* are unsuitable. Either the worms fail to complete development or they prove fatal to an inhospitable mosquito. Other species of mosquitoes ingest few or no worms during their feeding because of differences in degree of capillary feeding or possibly differences in content and secretion of saliva.

Brugia malayi. This is the cause of Malayan filariasis in eastern Asia; the range extends from southern India to China, Japan, Formosa, Malaya, and Indonesia. Reports from an island off the east coast of Kenya indicate the occurrence of a "malayi-like" form. It is restricted to foci in areas of permanent water and, in India at least, it is particularly attracted to those situations that encourage the growth of the aquatic plant, *Pistia stratiotes*. Sasa *et al.* (1952) reported a focus of this worm unmixed with *W. bancrofti* in an island about 130 km south of Tokyo. The climate of this Japanese site is said to be subtropical but devoid of water supporting floating plants.

Two forms of this parasite are now recognized based on the regularity with which the microfilariae appear in the peripheral blood of man. One, the periodic form, occurs regularly sometime after the host goes to bed. It tends to be restricted to human hosts. The so-called semi-periodic form shows little host specificity. Laing (1960) stated that it is a natural parasite of the leaf monkey (*Presbytis*) in Malaya. Other hosts include man, the domestic cat, the long-tailed macaque monkey, the civet cat, and others. Since both forms may occur together and often in conjunction with other *Brugia* species, care must be exercised in assigning a species name to larval filariids dissected from mosquitoes.

According to Laing *et al.* (1960) both periodic and semi-periodic forms are known from Malaya. The periodic form showing a pronounced nocturnal periodicity occurs in areas of open rice fields in northwestern Malaya. The semi-periodic form is indigenous to villages on the banks of major rivers and near swamp forests. Mosquitoes in the reservoir include certain species that are general feeders. Indian foci are maintained largely by one or the other of two species, *Mansonia annulifera* and *M. longipalpis,* although others of the subgenus Mansonioides are hospitable to the worm. In Malaya the periodic form has both *Anopheles* and *Mansonia* species as hosts for its juvenile stages while the semi-periodic one has only members of the genus *Mansonia* (Laing *et al.*). In China *Anopheles sinensis* and *M. uniformis* may be most significant. In Japan *Aedes togoi,* a domestic species, seems to be solely responsible for transmission. Once worms are ingested by a hospitable host, development is similar to that of *W. bancrofti* (Iyengar, 1956). Probably members of the subgenus *Culex* are refractive to this worm and do not comprise a part of the reservoir as they do for the bancroftian form. Some mosquitoes void many of the ingested larvae whereas others retain them. After feeding, *Mansonioides* species, the chief Indian hosts, void clear straw-colored liquid free of larvae. *Anopheles barbirostris* voids whole blood that teems with live worms.

Transmission occurs both indoors and outside; hence humans of all ages from infants to adults may bear the Malayan form. In India this parasite is both rural and urban. In Malaya it may be transmitted in the forest, where *M. longipalpis* feeds readily any time of the day. In the Japanese focus, transmission is domestic, where *Aedes togoi* develops in domestic containers.

ACANTHOCEPHALA

Acanthocephala comprise a phylum of worms all of which require arthropods as host animals in their ontogeny. They have elongate, unsegmented bodies devoid of a food tube. Anteriorly they are provided with a crown of recurved sclerous hooks in the adult stage at least. Adults are in the gut of vertebrates of all classes while the juvenile forms are tissue or coelomic parasites in arthropods. Optional, secondary juvenile hosts may include vertebates. The stages in order of succession are *egg, acanthor, acanthella, cystacanth,* and *adult.* All transfers from host to host are by ingestion. Van Cleave (1953) gives a general account of the phylogeny of this little-known group.

Present information about juvenile hosts indicates that species of insects and Crustacea having wide distribution and varied feeding habits may be suitable hosts for some acanthocephalid. Most fish, aquatic birds, and aquatic mammals are liable to infection by feeding, directly or indirectly, on Crustacea. Even subaquatic isopods may harbor some of these worms. Among the insects most subject to infection are grubs in soil, granary insects, and cockroaches.

The acanthor hatches in the gut of its arthropod host and soon afterward it literally claws its way through the gut wall. Once in the hemocoel the worm attaches to the outer surface of the intestine. The second stage, or acanthella, comes to lie free in the hemocoel. This form gradually becomes a cystacanth. When the initial host is swallowed by a suitable later host, the last juvenile form attaches to the gut of the new host. Should an arthropod bearing an incompletely developed acanthocephalan be swallowed by a potential host, the worm may remain a juvenile in the new host until it in turn is eaten by a suitable definitive host.

The worms whose juvenile hosts are best known are *Macracanthorhynchus hirudinaceus*, the thorny-headed worm, and *Moniliformis moniliformis*. The former has a reservoir of swine and some 25 species of soil-inhabiting coleopterous larvae. Pigs allowed to feed in sod land infested by white grubs provide a closed reservoir sufficient to maintain an infestation. Eggs pass out in the swine feces, and may then be eaten by scarabaeid larvae particularly. All juvenile stages are completed in the hemocoel of a larva. When a grub containing an encysted worm is eaten by a pig, the worm is freed from its cyst and matures in the gut of the pig. *Moniliformis moniliformis*, a cosmopolitan species, lives as an adult in the gut of a rodent. The juveniles develop in the coelom of grain beetles or cockroaches. Other terrestrial species occur in canines, felines, opossums, skunks, and even anteaters. Little is known of their development.

A developing acanthocephalan (*Leptorhynchoides*) within an amphipod (*Hyalella*) is pathogenic to the crustacean (DeGuisti, 1949). A mass of epithelial cells is proliferated at the site where the worm passed through the gut wall. The coelomic side of the developing cyst is covered by motile blood cells. When the cyst wall ruptures, host cells respond as to a foreign body and the worm is coated by a layer of amoeboid cells which form an enveloping protoplasmic syncytium. An effective syncytium will check growth of the parasite. A dead parasite is walled off by a brown sclerous membrane. Similarly walled larvae of *M. hirudinaceus* have been found in larvae of the Japanese beetle. Parasites are more often walled off at lower rather than higher temperatures.

ADDITIONAL READINGS

WARDLE and McLEOD (1952) discuss the morphology and physiology of tape-worms. Readers seeking specific information about a representative of the group are referred to the bibliography of this work and that of HYMAN (1951).

CHITWOOD and CHITWOOD (1952) is a good reference to nematode worms. It, to-gether with its bibliography, will provide the student an extensive insight into the group.

MIRZA (1938) should be examined for details about the worm that causes dracun-culiasis.

KERSHAW (1955) discusses the ecology of *Loa loa*. This paper and those in the bibliography should be read by persons likely to be involved with diseases of tropical Africa.

DALMAT (1955) and papers in his bibliography are source materials for details about onchocerciasis and flies in the transmission chains.

CHAPTER 14

Abatement and Suppression

GENERAL

The medical entomologist is often called upon to devise and apply measures for (1) abating annoyances from populations of arthropods and (2) suppression or eradication of those pests responsible for propagation of some pathogen. He may work toward these ends in league with others in local, national, international, or philanthropic agencies concerned with public health; he may be responsible for abatement in the military establishment; or he may advise business organizations on measures for suppressing pests.

Information in the preceding chapters forms a background for understanding concepts of abatement and suppression. Obviously much more detail is needed about any one arthropod before measures designed to regulate it may be applied to a particular situation. The chief reason for this statement is that every specific problem requires its own ecological appraisal and therefore its own solution by readjustment of the environment. Equally obvious is the observation that no single chapter can do more than suggest the strategic approaches to the area. Here again, the reason is that specific solutions to problems must be regulated by innumerable details peculiar to the situation at hand.

Strategic concepts for abatement and suppression of arthropods, when mastered, permit a practitioner to apply the most reasonable tactical measure to a specific situation. It is in the planning stages of regulatory procedures that sound knowledge of strategy pays the greatest dividends. The practitioner who knows the problem thoroughly and who knows the weaknesses of the noxious arthropod can plan effectively to apply the tactical measure or combination of them

377

to cause the pest to yield. Equally important is the fact that thorough knowledge of strategy will enable the planner to sift objectively the false from the valid claims of promoters of proposals for tactical solutions to particular arthropodan nuisances.

The means to desired ends for subjugating noxious arthropods, while simple in retrospect, are seldom so in the planning stage. To the degree that an entomologist has mastered the fundamentals of strategic concepts, the clearer are the objectives ahead. The brief discussion of strategy that follows is more to highlight a need for this approach than to complete one's understanding. The road to a life relatively free from annoying arthropods and their vectored pathogens is one of many lanes of traffic. The lane free of roadblocks is the one cleared by signals based on a comprehension of the problem in light of its time and place.

ABATEMENT OF NUISANCES

General

Abatement practices may have to be applied to persons, groups, areas, and regions. The individual may be at home or ranging into haunts of arthropods or pathogens borne by them. Groups of persons may be in camp sites, at outdoor gatherings, on playgrounds, or in domestic situations either rural or urban. Abatement measures may be applied over areas as small as a yard or over those the size of a city, county, a whole river valley or a coastal marsh. Usually each person fights his own problem at the individual and intradomestic level, while professional workers are directly responsible for controls when large areas are involved. Tactics employed by the non-professional individual must be chosen by rule of thumb, must be simple in form, and must be easy to apply because the average layman seldom knows the reasons for his procedures. He is as the soldier in the front line who knows only to use the weapon at hand on the target assigned. When the enemy presents itself as a new target, the novice is at a loss until some new tactic is provided. The professional, on the other hand, must know the possible problems so well that he can immediately call on reserves for the correct tactic to meet the particular situation.

Personal Abatement

Personal abatement involves avoiding attack (1) out of doors and in the range of insects and (2) in buildings where insects may be invaders. There are many variations included in these extreme situations. Exposure out of doors may be short or prolonged to the point that the individual is permanently in the range of noxious insects. Exposure indoors may be to resident insect parasites or to transient ones in search of a meal. Examination of a few situations will illustrate the kinds of protection which may be used by any person.

The simplest problem that must be solved for human protection is one in which the pest invades a permanent dwelling in temperate regions. Tight walls, doors, windows, and screens solve these problems in most instances. The doors and windows must be protected by screens where invaders may fly into a house. Cracks in walls, around the foundations and in the eaves of the building should be sealed to avoid the creeping forms. Lastly, domestic articles or hosts that could bear noxious pests such as lice, fleas, ticks, bed bugs, and cockroaches must be prohibited from entry into the dwelling. These potential harborers of pests include clothing, laundry, and containers for groceries as well as pets. Once the pests become established in a building, eradication may call for drastic measures which involve the services of a professional pest-control operator. Entrenched resident pests as certain cockroaches, bed bugs, and the brown dog tick may require fumigation or other treatment of the premises. Fleas can be eliminated more easily since they are dependent on some pet and its bedding if they are to remain long.

Measures for eradication of a pest from a household in temperate regions are effective in proportion to the chances for re-entry of that pest. Fleas may be eliminated by evicting the domestic host animal and all of its bedding and then thoroughly scrubbing the area where the animal bedded. In time the remaining fleas will starve or leave the premises. It is only when the pets are not evicted from the building that a nuisance becomes chronic. Bed bugs can be eradicated by liberal use of residual toxicants on all resting places of the bugs. DDT is the toxicant of choice unless one is cursed by a resistant strain of the bugs. The brown dog tick, the usual domiciliary tick in temperate regions, is difficult to eradicate unless the dog responsible for the infestation is kept away from the house; there is no problem when the pet stays permanently out of doors. If a house dog is kept, the pests can be eliminated most reliably by hand-picking the engorged adult ticks daily from the animal until no more appear. In the meantime the dog must be prevented from entering other infested situations. In enlightened parts of the world, human lice occasionally enter a household by way of heads and clothing of children. They can be eradicated by heat treatment of clothing to kill the nits and lice and by scrubbing the hair and scalp with soap and water every second day until all lice are gone. When any of these household problems become chronic, the services of competent professional help are required.

The most variable results from efforts at personal abatement are experienced when persons frequent areas infested with active arthropods. The best protection is obviously to keep the pests away from the skin. This means keeping the body fully covered from head to foot with the clothing as the barrier to the arthropodan attack. The necessarily exposed parts of the body as face and hands may be protected for limited periods by surface chemical repellents, used as lotions or salves. Among the many effective repellents are ethyl hexanediol, dimethyl phthalate, and indalone. Efficiency of surface applications is reduced when (1) the rate of perspiration is high, (2) activity rubs the material from the skin, or (3) the abundance of insects is great.

Creeping pests such as chiggers and ticks can be easily avoided in the field by following three simple rules. (1) Wear boots or high shoes, heavy socks, and trousers, and then tuck the trousers into the socks. (2) Treat the socks with dimethyl phthalate before entering the infected area. (3) Refrain from sitting or lying on the ground; and keep on the move or rest only on bare ground, preferably at a place in direct sunlight.

Spiders, scorpions, centipedes, and other creeping arthropods will bite humans, but rarely do so unless they are disturbed. Avoidance then requires one to be on guard when in an infested area. These animals are normally secreted in some site which has not been disturbed for some time. Piles of wood, stones, or trash may harbor them. Little-used clothing, especially that kept in outbuildings may be a hiding place. Even a shoe left overnight may attract scorpions, spiders, or centipedes in some situations. One should be alert when entering little-used outbuildings, crawl spaces beneath dwellings, and attics. Clothing should be inspected before being worn if it is likely to be infested. Since spiders lurk beneath the seats of privies, one should be cautious. Certainly all efforts should be redoubled by the camper who is occupying an infested area.

The individual can often keep biting flies, especially mosquitoes, away from his yard or even camp sites, in temperate areas at least, by using area repellents in the vegetation and over the grass. These repellents are on the market as dusts. They can be expected to yield temporary protection where mosquitoes invade from a distance. Resident populations of mosquitoes seldom respond favorably to the treatment.

Area Abatement

Area abatement is in the province of trained personnel who work under competent professional directors. Most of these programs are carried out by incorporated abatement districts operating under laws of the particular state. Organizations such as World Health Organization, Rockefeller Foundation, Tennessee Valley Authority, Pan American Sanitary Bureau, institutes for control of arthropod-borne diseases as those in India, Argentina, Brazil, and British possessions, and many others perform special services in the suppression of disease. The military organizations of the United States engage in abating arthropod nuisances and in controlling associated diseases. Business establishments often maintain their own control units for the protection of personnel, buildings, and equipment.

The general strategy employed by all abatement agencies is one of defense in depth. The object is to keep pests away from people within a protected area. Most tactics are employed at the source and are designed to (1) remove sites for pest development, (2) decrease efficiency of sites as sources, (3) keep arthropods that begin development from reaching maturity, and (4) prevent those that reach maturity from moving to places where they will be a nuisance.

Site removal (which involves "change" as well as elimination) is commonly employed in the control of mosquitoes, house flies, stable flies, horse flies, and wood ticks. Larvae of the first four groups of arthropods live in specialized situations which are often at a distance from centers of human populations. These sites may be drained, filled, or impounded to remove the sources of certain mosquitoes and horse flies. Piles of refuse may be burned, buried, scattered, or even prohibited as a means for avoiding house flies and stable flies. Wood ticks originating on vacant lots, ditch banks, and margins of woods may be eliminated by selective planting and cutting or burning as circumstances dictate. All these tactics involve adaptation to each problem. Procedures are not universally applicable, even when apparently desirable. For example, in some instances, site removal may be such an enormous task that it can be accomplished only on a progressive basis and over a long period of time.

In situations in which progressive site removal is desired, interim tactics are obviously required. Many expedients may be employed to make the normal sites less productive of pests. Tidal marshes may be ditched to channel and exchange water without temporary impounding. Inland marshes can be stabilized during the mosquito season by dikes and tidegates. It is possible to drain seeps by use of tiles or surface ditches. Water levels in reservoirs should be fluctuated in order to strand flotage and keep margins unacceptable for the production of massive populations. Accumulations of organic waste may be piled so that they will become too dry to attract ovipositing flies. Impoundments should be cleared of vegetation to discourage oviposition.

After insect development has begun, immature forms may be killed by mechanical or chemical means so that the numbers that survive are markedly reduced. Toxicants may be floated on, suspended in, or allowed to settle to the bottom of, ground pools and streams to kill gnats, midges, mosquitoes, and black flies. Timing of treatments and placement of materials are the variables that determine the degree of control. Piles of waste may be completely eliminated or so thinly spread that the immature stages of the pests will be killed. Sometimes surfaces of waste piles may be covered by residual toxicants that penetrate the insect body either through its cuticula or food tube.

After insects mature, expedients are still available to reduce the number that may reach the human population. Aerosols containing toxicants generated by heat and by fans may then be projected under high velocity into the air. Tiny droplets of the materials settle out of the air onto surfaces in collection sites for flies, gnats, and mosquitoes with telling effect. Timing the applications of aerosols is critical and requires much experience if the tactic is to be effectively employed. Bands of residual toxicants dispersed over vegetation as a barrier between the sources of the pests and their potential destinations have been successfully used when the insects are known to walk over, or rest on, the treated area.

SUPPRESSION OF ARTHROPOD-BORNE DISEASES

Man has tended to become urbanized during his cultural evolution. One of the dividends reaped from this change is that he has left some pathogens in the wild that could be detrimental to his health. The concentration of his dwelling places has removed him from many former animal associates and transient parasites. He has by no means avoided all arthropod-borne parasites by urbanization, for he has intensified some of these problems. Furthermore, man presently lives in varying degrees of urbanization as well as in isolated situations which completely lack vestiges of community living. Over half of the world's population still remains either in small community units or in isolated rural and sylvatic environments.

In sylvatic and rural surroundings people acquire most of their arthropod-borne diseases from other animals. Villagers and inhabitants of small communities may be subjected to the gamut of these diseases. Urbanites in temperate regions where winters are moderate to severe are practically free of any of these diseases except those having pathogens adapted as man's closest personal parasites. Those in mild to tropical climates may suffer from a few additional arthropod-borne diseases because the arthropods are able to live in the cities. Agencies engaged in guarding the public health must consider the differences in conditions that predispose a community to epidemics of this category of diseases.

For the purpose of studying principles for suppression of arthropod-borne diseases, we may consider them according to whether their agents come to man primarily from (1) wild animals (sylvatic-human transmission), (2) domestic animals (domestic-human transmission), or (3) other humans (interhuman transmission). Even though the pathogens reach man in the manner indicated, it is to be recalled that many pathogens exist in benign states in complexes of wild and domestic situations and break out as epidemics in man only occasionally. Sometimes suppression should be directed at hosts in the reservoir rather than at a pathogen while an epidemic is in progress. Suppressive principles used to break or control these three transmission chains will be illustrated by examples from the long list mentioned elsewhere in this text.

Sylvatic-Human Transmission

Sylvatic-human transmission is controlled largely through avoidance of contact between humans and vectors. Persons whose work, travel, or recreation requires them to enter environments likely to provide inoculum should know the hazards to be encountered in order to avoid them. Precautions prescribed for protection from flies, gnats, chiggers, and ticks should be followed. The lower the attack rate of possible vectors, the greater the individual's chance of avoiding inoculation. One should assume that all potential vectors are actual ones and thus avoid any contact while in a zone of likely inoculation.

Rickettsia rickettsii, the cause of *Rocky Mountain spotted fever*, and similar tick-borne agents are borne to suscepts by salivary contamination from wood ticks. These ticks must have contact with the skin for attachment, and the interval of time between boarding and injection of inoculum into the victim is usually a matter of hours. To avoid contamination (1) wear clothing which does not permit the tick access to skin, (2) stay on the move while in heavily infested areas, (3) after leaving an infested area examine the body surface carefully and remove all ticks, and (4) wash hands thoroughly after handling ticks in order to avoid contamination of conjunctiva and mucosa. Urban areas of possible contamination should be sanitized in the manner discussed under area abatement.

Tsutsugamushi is the result of salivary contamination by a few species of chiggers. Chiggers must crawl to get to an attachment site, but unlike ticks they are tiny and are not easily seen once they are on the skin. When a person is in an area of likely contamination, chiggers must be kept off the skin. This can be done as outlined previously in this chapter. While chiggers cannot be easily seen, they can be washed from the skin by liberal use of soap and water. The body should be lathered and scrubbed well with a soft brush, and then soap should be allowed to stay on the skin for several minutes before being rinsed away. If this is done immediately after leaving an infested area, few or no chiggers will become attached. Community-wide measures of suppression involve clearing the interfacial areas discussed in the chapter on wild hosts for vectors of this agent.

Tularemia in man is the result of an epizootic in a complicated reservoir. In areas of likely transmission the best protection is (1) covering the body with fly-proof clothing when work or other activities require exposure to the vectors, (2) avoid contamination while skinning or handling infected vertebrates by wearing rubber gloves, and (3) refrain from drinking any raw, surface, or ground water. Fortunately medication and therapy have relieved many of the more serious aspects of infection, but prevention of contamination may avoid a period of illness.

Rhodesian sleeping sickness in man occurs in persons who have been bitten by infected tsetse in the big-game country in parts of eastern Africa. Exposure of body surface must be reduced to a minimum, and tsetse must be kept away from exposed parts. Persons should avoid the interfacial zones where the flies congregate to feed to reduce the possibility of attack. Chances are excellent that tsetse will break through any guard when the flies are abundant.

Loaiasis is a concomitant of the fringes of the great forests of tropical Africa and strikes transient visitors as well as village inhabitants at the forest edges. Tabanid flies of the genus *Chrysops* are the vector-hosts of the pathogen. Little can be done about sources of the flies, and little is actually done by indigenous peoples to cover themselves for protection against the bites of the vector flies. As a public health measure, villages may be built away from the forest at such a distance that (1) flies in the settlements cannot become infected by feeding on wild primates or (2) flies that have become infected will not range to the villages. Workers whose duties require them to be in forests should be encouraged to ward off attacking flies or enter the woods only when the flies are least active. Incidence of this disease is likely to continue high among indigenous people, but the visitor can avoid infection very easily by properly covering the body.

Paragonimiasis or lung-fluke disease is actually a disease of well-populated areas rather than remote ones. It can be easily avoided by individuals, but control at a level of public health involves changing some well-established habits of the masses. Since eating raw, fresh-water crabs bearing infective worms is the means of becoming infected, avoidance of uncooked crabs as food will prevent infection. Refusing this food will be difficult for people who have long enjoyed raw crabs. Expectorating in water furthers the chances of this worm, hence controlled disposal of sputum would greatly lessen the chances of initiating the extrinsic cycle of this worm. Enlightenment is the key to success for persons who may become infected.

Domestic-Human Transmission

Domestic-human diseases borne by arthropods are best controlled by (1) eradicating the vector-hosts from the domestic environments, (2) exterminating or greatly suppressing the vector-hosts, and (3) housing or pasturing domestic animals away from human dwellings. Sometimes a change in the construction of dwellings will make eradication of vector-hosts possible or will discourage undesirable domestic vertebrates as rats and mice. Toxicants of a wide variety may prove useful when properly applied.

Chagas' disease in its domestic aspects is a result of contamination of mucosa, conjunctiva, and abraded skin with feces of triatomine bugs living as domestic pests. Houses providing ample hideaways for the bugs set up the favorable conditions for transmission. The bugs must be eradicated and conditions must be changed so that their re-entry is prevented. The use of screens, plastered walls devoid of cracks, and the erection of buildings off the ground help in avoidance of the bugs. Residual toxicants, rigid inspections, and vigorous efforts are required to eliminate these bugs. Such changes come slowly where family incomes are low. The disease is likely to remain a problem in public health for a long time in much of Central and South America.

Rickettsialpox is a domestic disease that is passed to the human population from domestic mice when conditions allow mites to have ready access to both mice and humans. This is a disease of apartment dwellers in suburban America. Buildings that have chutes to carry garbage from various apartments to a central incinerator (which is usually located in the basement) are the usual setting for an outbreak of the disease in man. The elimination of murine hosts is essential. Provisions for better means of garbage disposal could avoid the direct mite runways from mice to man.

Murine or flea typhus, another disease of rodents in warm parts of the world, breaks over into the human population in rural situations. It has been a problem on farms in the southeastern United States. A vigorous campaign against rodents and their fleas has caused a dramatic reduction in the incidence of the disease. The killing of the mice and rats must be accompanied by modifications in structural designs of buildings for storage of farm products if permanent reduction of the disease is to be achieved. The success of any effort to control flea typhus will always be determined by vigilance in maintenance of rodent-free farms.

Plague as a domestic disease is present only where man and domestic rats live together in crowded conditions. For the most part it is a disease found where there are extensive, poorly managed warehouses located near a teeming human population. Such situations have been numerous historically, and they are currently common along waterfronts of port cities. When transient rats bearing the bacillus leave a ship or other transport and then, in turn, become hosts for the fleas of local rats, conditions necessary for rodent plague are met. If the disease is virulent and decimates the rat population, the fleas move to the human population and thereby make possible an epidemic of plague in humans. Here again the remedy is constant effort to reduce the number of rats and thereby reduce their populations of fleas. Residual toxicants forced into rodent burrows help in reducing fleas. Improved living quarters for the populace reduce the likelihood of intimate association between rats and humans.

In parts of the world where the human flea, *Pulex irritans,* is the domestic vector of plague bacilli, efforts must be made to eradicate this flea. Generally a change in residential construction coupled with a separation of living quarters of man from those of his livestock will eliminate the flea. When domestic animals have stables removed from human dwellings and people sleep on clean surfaces other than straw, this flea ceases to be a problem. In any campaign to eliminate these insects from a building, residual toxicants should be used initially. To rid an area of plague that is associated with the human flea is largely a matter of enlightenment as well as, to some degree, of economic stability for the population. These changes usually come slowly.

Plague will always be a potential hazard to impoverished peoples, and control demands eternal vigilance. Agencies responsible for the public health have done much during the past two centuries to keep the disease in check and to prevent the devastation of urban man.

Viral encephalitides (WEE, EEE, SLE, etc.) in domestic environments are difficult to manage and call for the best efforts of all control agencies in those parts of the world where outbreaks recur. Efforts are currently being directed toward abatement of primary culicine hosts. In irrigated regions where *Culex tarsalis* is the primary vector-host, the problem is a growing one. Persons are advised to practice individual protection from mosquitoes as indicated earlier in this chapter. Since the virus invades domestic situations from wild birds, some of which are migrants, it is most difficult to suppress. In agricultural economies based on irrigated crops, the sources of the mosquitoes are very likely extensive. Efforts to regulate the mosquito population require continuous and careful execution of control programs. Avoidance of transmission of these viruses in areas subject to sporadic outbreaks is still one of individual attention to abatement procedures before the virus is introduced by some migrant bird.

Other viral encephalitides (JBE, MVE, VEE, etc.) present similar problems of control. Mosquitoes of the subgenus *Culex* that feed on both birds and man are the responsible vector-hosts. All efforts to minimize the diseases these viruses cause should be directed toward breaking the contacts between man and the mosquitoes. Success in these efforts has been variable.

Interhuman Transmission

Interhuman diseases (those caused by pathogens that have a man-arthropod reservoir) may result when (1) man lives in the habitat of the arthropod or (2) conditions are created that encourage an arthropod to live with man. The arthropod may develop (1) in the general vicinity of human living quarters, (2) in the quarters, or (3) on a person. In all cases pathogens are acquired from a human and are transferred to another human by the vector-host. Diseases in this category are those most devastating to man.

Malaria has a complex relationship with many species of mosquitoes and many different situations, as may be seen in Tables 25 and 26 of the discussion on *Plasmodium*. Obviously no short discussion can do more than state the broadest of principles applying to adequate suppression where the transmission chain is domestic. It must also be remembered that malaria of extra-domestic transmission is known.

Unstable malaria of domestic origin may be suppressed wherever the vector-host can be (1) kept outside the domicile by adequate construction of the dwelling, (2) caused to vacate the domestic unit before taking a blood meal, (3) discouraged from occupying dwellings as resting sites (or hibernating sites in some cases), (4) reduced in numbers at their source so that fewer are present to enter houses, (5) killed outright before feeding, and (6) killed by residual toxicants applied to walls of dwellings and other buildings where persons sleep. Tactics are available for use in accomplishing all these aims. The degree of effectiveness will vary according to the habits of the people involved, the species of mosquito, the proximity of the people to the sources of mosquitoes, the technique of toxicant application, and the climate.

Actually, remarkable success with suppression of unstable malaria has been attained (see discussion under *Plasmodium*). Wherever the chain of transmission has involved a vector with a low capability (as has *Anopheles quadrimaculatus* in the Mississippi Valley of central United States), the chain has been broken to such a degree that few or no new cases occur each year. Observers seem to think that the sum of a number of measures has almost completely prevented the occurrence of new cases.

We must be aware that malaria is an insidious disease in that the parasite may lie dormant in human tissues for years, if not for a lifetime. This means that all transmission among resident populations must be prohibited for an entire generation in order to insure eradication. If transient carriers enter any area, the time required for eradication must be extended. Vigilance is the essence of preventive practices.

Stable malaria presents a wholly different picture, and this form bids fair to remain a problem for generations. Eradication seems to be unlikely under present ecological conditions. Far less malaria is possible even now, and it is actually being suppressed in many parts of the tropics. In order to break contact between vector-hosts and man, chief reliance is put on (1) reduction in incidence of mosquitoes in and around the protected area and (2) use of bed nets over sleeping persons. A great deal has been done to prevent vector-hosts from ingesting plasmodia by the use of the several therapeutic and suppressive drugs now available (Burgess and Bray, 1961). As tropical cultures become more technological, extensive and orderly urbanization will do much to further the retardation of stable malaria.

Yellow fever in its heyday was known as an urban disease particularly of ports and of the hinterland in communication with the ports. It was dependent on the one mosquito, *Aedes aegypti*, in these situations. Man is the only host in domestic situations. Since the disease is so very dangerous, eradication was greatly desired and was attained in most places. The principle involved required that diseased persons and infective mosquitoes on ships be prevented from coming ashore. Diseased persons were kept out by quarantine, and ships coming from ports where epidemics were in progress were denied entry. Infected mosquitoes were ultimately eliminated by changes in shipping vessels from sail to motor. Once an epidemic ran its course in a city, it died out and could be reintroduced only when susceptibles were abundant. Yellow fever is no longer present in port cities anywhere in the world. This fact provides us with the best example of eradication of a devastating arthropod-borne disease around the coasts of the tropical world.

Dengue was once a disease of tropical port cities. It, too, was dependent on a domestic Stegomyia-human reservoir in ports. It traveled aboard ships to the ports of the world in the days of sailing ships. It is no longer the disease of prominence, because it is no longer shipped about so much. Its sylvatic reservoir seems to permit it to invade ports more easily than yellow fever; consequently the disease still occurs in tropical cities.

Louse typhus is present in malnourished populations living in unhygienic conditions where lice are almost universally present. It is rife where facilities for bathing and laundering are inadequate for a period of time. Suppression and eradication may be accomplished when conditions allow people to keep themselves and their clothing clean. Those few persons who persist in living in filth can be induced to improve cleanliness through social pressures. The principle involved in maintaining a clean body and clean clothing is that the vector-host of typhus rickettsiae, the body louse, is eradicated in proportion to the percentage of louse-free persons in the population. In a population in which it has been well seeded, typhus will remain latent for the duration of an infected generation. Heavily infested areas cannot be considered free of carriers in less time. Should conditions of economic chaos with attendant infestation return to a free area, typhus would recur. This has been the history of the vast endemic area mentioned in the discussion of the pathogen.

Typhus was once stopped dramatically during the war of 1939–1945 by the mass delousing of the whole population of a large city in Italy. Delousing was total and was accomplished within the span of a few weeks. Spread of the disease was stopped during the winter which is the normal time for maximum transmission. Never before had there been a record of turning back typhus when an obvious epidemic was in the making.

Fortunately individual protection of a high order is obtained by immunization. Complete vaccination of allied troops during World War II and consistent campaigns to maintain louse-free soldiers made typhus a disease of virtually no consequence for the first time in any army engaged in a long war.

Gambian sleeping sickness is a chronic disease of tropical Africa wherever man and certain tsetse come into repeated contact. Reference to the section on *Trypanosoma gambiense* will show that contact may be made in many different situations, each of which requires a different tactic for suppression. Transmission is mainly effected on the trail at interfaces where tsetse vector-hosts abound. One should consult Buxton (1955) for details of specific tactics. In summary the measures for suppression hinge on forcing the tsetse away from routes followed by travelers. Motorized vehicles may transport people past haunts of tsetse with no exposure. Until the infested belts are better developed and the land is more fully utilized, Gambian sleeping sickness will persist in its well-entrenched situations.

Examples of abatement of annoyance from arthropods and suppression or eradication of arthropod-borne diseases given herewith are intended to encourage the inquiring student to seek answers to specific problems in the field. The information contained herein may help shape strategy in combating problems, but the tactics used must always be dictated by local conditions.

ADDITIONAL READINGS

Because no comprehensive treatise covering the area of abatement and suppression of arthropods and their associated diseases now exists, no citations will be made to authors. Furthermore, choice and application of measures to effect these ends is regulated by local situations. The reader, therefore, is referred to serials most likely to contain articles that may shed light on a particular problem. Arrangement below is arbitrary and does not imply relative importance, neither does it attempt to include all significant journals.

Bibliography

Bibliography of Agriculture (1942 to date). (Washington, D. C.: U. S. Department of Agriculture Library.) World literature on agricultural subjects with a section on entomology containing references to applied aspects.

Abstract

Abstracts of World Medicine (1947 to date). (London: British Medical Association.) Deals with applied aspects of medical entomology as well as with other matters affecting health.
Bulletin de l'Institute Pasteur (1903 to date). (Paris: Masson et Cie.) World literature on diseases with excellent coverage on those borne by arthropods.
Excerpta Medica, Sec. XIII (1947 to date). (London, Amsterdam, and New York: Excerpta Medica Foundation.) World literature on dermatology and venerology including suppression of arthropods and diseases related to them.
Review of Applied Entomology, Ser. B (1913 to date). (London: Commonwealth Institute of Entomology.) World literature on arthropods of medical and veterinary importance with emphasis on the applied aspects.
Tropical Diseases Bulletin (1912 to date). (London: Bureau of Hygiene and Tropical Diseases.) World literature on medical entomology including the applied aspects. Reviews of arthropod-borne diseases are included in nearly all numbers.
Veterinary Bulletin (1931 to date). (Farnham Royal, England: Commonwealth Agricultural Bureaux.) Veterinary parasitology with portions dealing especially with applied aspects of medical entomology.

Reports

American Journal of Tropical Medicine and Hygiene (1952 to date) (successor to *American Journal of Tropical Medicine* and *Journal of the National Malaria Society*). (Baltimore: Williams & Wilkins Co.) Includes papers on results of control work in different parts of the world.

Bulletin of the World Health Organization (1947 to date). (Geneva: World Health Organization.) Includes lengthy papers on aspects of control work.

Indian Journal of Malariology (1947 to date) (successor to *Journal of the Malaria Institutes of India*). (Kanpur, India: Indian Council of Medical Research.) Includes papers on control of arthropods and diseases in India and elsewhere. Contains much on insecticides and their use.

Journal of Tropical Medicine and Hygiene (1899 to date). (London: Staples Holdings Ltd.) Contains papers on the applied aspects of medical entomology.

Pest Control (1933 to date). (Cleveland: Trade Magazines, Inc.) Contains many papers on insecticides, their use, and means for applying.

Transactions of the Society of Tropical Medicine and Hygiene (1907 to date). (London: Royal Society of Tropical Medicine and Hygiene.) Includes papers on control of tropical diseases related to arthropods.

Appendix

Recognition of insects is one of the important functions of entomologists, and it is often necessary for the physician, the sanitarian, and others to be able to make identifications. While it is not the purpose of this book to provide the keys and descriptions necessary to this end, it is thought desirable to provide important references by which insects of medical importance may be determined. The listing is by no means complete, but it should provide clues to the literature whereby any insect may be identified. Arrangement of citations is by author and date, with a comment on the extent of contents. The complete citation appears in the general bibliography of the book.

CHAPTER 2

General

Ross, H. H. 1956. This is a general text, touching on all aspects of entomology and including keys to larger categories of arthropods.
Schröder, C. (ed.). 1925–1929. (4037 pp. in 3 vol.) Includes all aspects of entomology, including keys and bionomics; world-wide.

Diplopoda

Attems, C. G. 1926–1930. A complete account of all aspects including phylogenetic arrangement.
Verhoeff, K. W. 1928 and 1932. An extensive coverage of all aspects of the class, together with material on classification.

Chilopoda

Attems, C. G. 1926–1930a. A complete account of all aspects, including phylogeny.

Crustacea

Edmondson, W. T. 1959. (Pp. 558–901.) Mostly keys and line drawings of fresh-water forms. Very useful.
Pennak, R. W. 1953. Restricted to fresh-water forms present in the United States, but very useful.

Arachnida, General

Petrunkevitch, A. 1952. Principles of classification used in the class.

Scorpionida

Millot, J., and M. Vachon. 1949. General and phylogenetic.

Araneae

Levi, H. W. 1958. Species of the genus *Latrodectus.*
Millot, J. 1949. All aspects of the order, including phylogeny.

CHAPTER 3

Acarina: Mites

Audy, J. R. 1957. A check list of trombiculid mites in the Oriental and Australasian regions.
Baker, E. W., *et al.* 1956. Recognition features of mites of medical importance.
Brennan, J. M., and E. K. Jones. 1959. Key to North American species.
Radford, C. D. 1950. Systematic check list of genera and species with literature.
Womersley, C. D. 1952. Trombiculid mites of the Asiatic-Pacific region.
Womersley, H. 1954. Species of Laelaptidae, subfamily Phytoseiinae of Australia.
Yunker, C. E. 1955. Classification of Acaridiae of the suborder Sarcoptiformes.

Acarina: Ticks

Cooley, R. A. 1946. Keys to *Boophilus, Rhipicephalus,* and *Haemaphysalis* of the New World.
Cooley, R. A., and G. M. Kohls. 1944. Keys to the genus *Amblyomma* of the United States.
Cooley, R. A., and G. M. Kohls. 1944a. Key to the Argasidae of North America, Central America and Cuba.
Cooley, R. A., and G. M. Kohls. 1945. Key to the genus *Ixodes* of North America.
Floch, H., and P. Fauran. 1958. *Ixodes* of French Guiana.
Gregson, J. D. 1956. Ticks of Canada.
Hoogstraal, H. 1956. Ticks of the Sudan, with descriptions.
Hoogstraal, H., and M. N. Kaiser. 1958a. Ticks of Iraq.
Hoogstraal, H., and G. Theiler. 1959. Ixodid ticks from lower primates in Africa and Madagascar.

CHAPTER 4

Hexapoda, General

Brues, C. T., *et. al.* 1954. (917 pp.) Keys to families of insects with some discussion of the orders.
Imms, A. D. 1957. (886 pp.) A general text but particularly good for classification of insects to family.
Jeannel, R. 1949. Classification, evolution, and phylogeny.
Séguy, E. 1944. (684 pp.) Insect ectoparasites. Good descriptions of many different forms.

Cursoria

Rehn, J. W. H. 1951. Classification.

Dermaptera

Beier, M. 1933. Classification and bionomics.

Trichoptera

BARNARD, K. H. 1934. South African forms.

Ephemeroptera

BURKS, B. D. 1953. (216 pp.) Classification of species in central United States.
NEEDHAM, J. G., and J. R. TRAVER. 1935. Biology of the group, including keys and descriptions.

Phthiraptera

FARENHOLZ, H. 1936. Classification of Anoplura.
FERRIS, G. F. 1951. (320 pp.) Classification of Anoplura.
HOPKINS, G. H. E., and T. CLAY. 1952. A check list of genera and species of chewing lice.

Cimicidae

KASSIANOFF, L. 1937. General and speciation of family.

Reduviidae

NEIVA, A., and H. LENT. 1941. A synopsis of triatomine bugs.
USINGER, R. L. 1944. Cone-nosed bugs of North America and the West Indies.

Siphonaptera

HOPKINS, G. H. E., and M. ROTHSCHILD. 1953 and 1956. (806 pp. in 2 vol.) On fleas in the Rothschild collection in the British Museum.
HUBBARD, C. A. 1947. (533 pp.) Fleas of western North America.
JOHNSON, P. T. 1957. (299 pp.) Fleas of South America.

CHAPTER 5

Diptera, General

CURRAN, C. H. 1934. Families and genera of North America.
HENNIG, W. 1948–1953. (3 vol.) Larval forms of Diptera with general discussion of classification.

Psychodidae

FAIRCHILD, G. B. 1955. Relationships and classification of Phlebotominae.

Culicidae

STONE, A., et. al. 1959. A synoptic catalogue to species of the world with references to regional keys.

Ceratopogonidae: *Culicoides*

ARNAUD, P. 1956. Keys to species in Japan, Korea, etc.

Simuliidae

CROSSKEY, R. W. 1957. Species in Nigeria.
SMART, J. 1945. A classification for the family.

Tabanidae

CROSSKEY, R. W., and M. E. CROSSKEY. 1955. Classification of species in Nigeria and British Cameroons.
HAYS, K. L. 1956. A synopsis of Michigan species.
MIDDLEKAUFF, W. 1950. Californian species.
OLDROYD, H. 1952–1957. (927 pp. in 3 vol.) Descriptions and classification of species in the Ethiopian region.

Bibliography[*]

ABONNENC, E., M. LARIVIÈRE, and M. L. YVINEC. 1957. Observations sur la biologie de quelques phlébotomes de la région Éthiopienne en milieu expérimental. *Ann. Parasit. hum. comp. 32:* 173–184.

ABRAMOV, I. V. 1955. A new type of transmission by vector ticks of the casual agent of nuttalliasis of horses (*Nuttallia equi* Laveran, 1901). In Russian. *Veterinariya 32:* 43–45.

ACKERKNECHT, E. H. 1945. Malaria in the upper Mississippi Valley, 1760–1900. *Supp. to Bull. History Med. No. 4.* Baltimore: Johns Hopkins Press. 142 pp.

AESCHLIMANN, A. 1958. Développement embryonnaire d'*Ornithodorus moubata* (Murray) et transmission transovarienne de *Borrelia duttoni. Acta trop.* (Basel) *15:* 15–64.

ALEXANDER, A. J. 1956. Mating in scorpions. *Nature* (London) *178:* 867–868.

ALLINGTON, H. V., and R. R. ALLINGTON. 1954. Insect bites. *J. Amer. med. Ass. 155:* 240–247.

ALLRED, D. M. 1960. *Medical arthropodology.* Laboratory guide. Minneapolis: Burgess. 84 pp.

ALVES, W., and D. M. BLAIR. 1955. Malaria control in Southern Rhodesia. *J. trop. Med.* (*Hyg.*) *58:* 273–280.

AMES, C. T., S. F. QUAN, and R. E. RYCKMAN. 1954. Triatominae in experimental transmission of plague. *Amer. J. trop. Med. Hyg. 3:* 890–896.

ANDERSON, C. R., L. P. SPENCE, W. G. DOWNS, and T. H. G. AITKEN. 1960. Manzanilla virus: A new virus isolated from the blood of a howler monkey in Trinidad, W. I. *Amer. J. trop. Med. Hyg. 9:* 78–80.

ANDREWES, C. H., R. C. MUIRHEAD-THOMSON, and J. P. STEVENSON. 1956. Laboratory studies of *Anopheles atroparvus* in relation to myxomatosis. *J. Hyg.* (Cambridge) *54:* 478–486.

ARAGAO, H. DE B. 1939. Mosquitoes and yellow fever virus. *Mem. Inst. Osw. Cruz. 34:* 565–581.

AREÁN, V. M., and I. FOX. 1955. Dermal alterations in severe reactions to the bite of the sand fly, *Culicoides furens. Amer. J. clin. Path. 25:* 1359–1365.

ARNAUD, P. 1956. The heleid genus *Culicoides* in Japan, Korea and Ryukyu Islands (Insecta: Diptera). *Microentomology 21:* 85–156 + Figs. 44–94.

ARTHUR, D. R. 1951. The capitulum and feeding mechanism of *Ixodes hexagonus* Leach. *Parasitology 41:* 66–81.

ARTHUR, D. R. 1953. The capitulum and feeding mechanism of *Ixodes hexagonus* Leach. II. *Parasitology 42:* 187–191.

[*] For abbreviations of journals, see *World List of Scientific Periodicals* (London: Butterworth Scientific Publications, 1951).

ARTHUR, D. R. 1960. *Ticks: A monograph of the Ixodoidea.* Part V. On the genera *Dermacentor, Anocentor, Cosmiomma, Boophilus* and *Margaropus.* Cambridge: Cambridge University Press. xvii + 251 pp. + 4 pls.

ATKINS, J. A. 1957. Probable cause of necrotic spider bite in the Midwest. *Science* 126: 73.

ATTEMS, C. G. 1926–1930. Dritte Klasse der Progoneata . . . Diplopoda. *Handb. Zool. Berl. 4:* 29–238.

ATTEMS, C. G. 1926–1930a. Dritte Klasse der Progoneata . . . Chilopoda. *Handb. Zool. Berl. 4:* 239–402.

AUDY, J. R. 1957. A checklist of trombiculid mites of the oriental and Australasian regions. *Parasitology 47:* 217–294.

AUSTEN, E. E. 1911. *A handbook of the tsetse flies [genus Glossina].* London: Brit. Mus. x + 110 pp. + 10 pls.

AUSTEN, E. E., and E. HEGH. 1922. *Tsetse flies, their characteristics, distribution and bionomics. Imp. Bur. Ent.* (London). 188 pp.

BABUDIERI, B. 1957. Relapsing fever in Jordan. *Bull. Wld Hlth Org. 16:* 911–928.

BABUDIERI, B. 1959. Q fever: a zoonosis. *Advanc. vet. Sci. 5:* 82–182.

BACOT, A. 1914. A study of the bionomics of the common rat fleas and other species associated with human habitations, with special reference to the influence of temperature and humidity at various periods of the life history of the insect. *J. Hyg.* (Cambridge) 13 *(Plague Sup. 3):* 447–654 + 8 pls.

BACOT, A., and C. J. MARTIN. 1924. The respective influences of temperature and moisture upon the survival of the rat flea (*Xenopsylla cheopis*) away from its host. *J. Hyg.* (Cambridge) *23:* 98–105.

BACOT, A. W., and C. J. MARTIN. 1914. Observations on the mechanism of the transmission of plague by fleas. *J. Hyg.* (Cambridge) 13 *(Plague Sup. 3):* 423–439.

BAERG, W. J. 1954. Regarding the biology of the common Jamaican scorpion. *Ann. ent. Soc. Amer. 47:* 272–276.

BAKER, A. C. 1943. The typical epidemic series. *Amer. J. trop. Med. 23:* 559–566.

BAKER, E. W., T. M. EVANS, D. J. GOULD, W. B. HULL, and H. L. KEGAN. 1956. *A manual of parasitic mites of medical or economic importance.* New York: National Pest Control Association, Inc. iii + 170 pp.

BAKER, E. W., and G. W. WHARTON. 1952. *An introduction to acarology.* New York: The Macmillan Company. xiv + 565 pp.

BALFOUR, A. 1914. The wild monkey as a reservoir for the virus of yellow fever. *Lancet 1:* 1176–1178.

BALOZET, L. 1956. Scorpion venoms and antiscorpion serum. *In* papers on venoms. *Publ. Amer. Ass. Advanc. Sci. 44:* 141–144.

BALTAZARD, M., M. BAHMANYAR, A. HABIBI, C. MOFIDI, and B. SEYDIAN. 1950. Fièvres récurrentes humaines, leur transmissibilité par le pou. *Bull. Soc. Path. exot. 43:* 309–317.

BALTAZARD, M., M. BAHMANYAR, and C. MOFIDI. 1950. *Ornithodorus erraticus* et fièvres récurrentes. *Bull. Soc. Path. exot. 43:* 595–601.

BALTAZARD, M., M. BAHMANYAR, R. POURNAKI, and C. MOFIDI. 1952. *Ornithodorus tartakovskyi* Olenov 1931 et *Borrelia (Spirochaeta) latychevi* Sofiev 1941. Note préliminaire. *Ann. Parasit. hum. comp. 27:* 311–328.

BALTAZARD, M., M. BAHMANYAR, C. MOFIDI, and B. SEYDIAN. 1954. Le foyer de peste du Kurdistan. *Bull. Wld Hlth Org. 5:* 441.

BALTAZARD, M., R. POURNAKI, M. BAHMANYAR, and M. CHAMSA. 1955. *Ornithodorus tartakovskyi* Oleney 1931 et *Borrelia (Spirochaeta) latychevii* Sofiev 1941. *Ann. Parasit. hum. comp. 30:* 225–242.

BANCROFT, T. L. 1901. Preliminary notes on the intermediary host of *Filaria immitis* Leidy. *J. roy. Soc. N. S. W. 35:* 41–46.

BARANOV, N. 1939. Stand der Kolumbatscher Mückenforschung in Jugoslawien. *Z. Parasitenk. 11:* 215–234.

BARBER, G. W., and E. B. STARNES. 1949. The activities of house flies. *J. N. Y. Ent. Soc. 57:* 203–214.

BARBER, M. A. 1929. The history of malaria in the United States. *U. S. Publ. Hlth Rept.* 44: 2575–2587.

BARDOS, V. 1957. Natural foci of the western type of North American equine encephalomyelitis (WEE) in Czechoslovakia. *Acta virologica* 1: 198–202.

BARNARD, C. C. 1952. Yaws and flies. *J. trop. Med.* (*Hyg.*) 55: 100–114, 135–141.

BARNARD, K. H. 1934. South African caddis flies (Trichoptera). *Trans. roy. Soc. S. Afr.* 21: 291–394.

BARNETT, H. C. 1956. The transmission of western equine encephalitis virus by the mosquito *Culex tarsalis*. Coq. *Amer. J. trop Med. Hyg.* 5: 86–98.

BEACHLEY, R. G., and F. C. BISHOPP. 1942. Report of a case of nasal myiasis due to a bot fly larva. *Va. med. Month.* 69: 41–42.

BECK, D. E. 1955. Distributional studies of parasitic arthropods in Utah, determined as actual and potential vectors of Rocky Mountain spotted fever and plague with notes on vector-host relationships. *Brigham Young Univ. Sci. Bull.* (*Biol. ser.*) 1: 1–14.

BEDSON, S. P., A. W. DOWNIE, F. D. MacCALLUM, and C. H. STUART-HARRIS. 1955. *Virus and rickettsial diseases.* Baltimore: Williams & Wilkins Company. viii + 407 pp.

BEIER, M. 1933. Orthopteroidea, Dermaptera. *In* SCHULZE, *Biologie Tiere Deutschlands.* Vol. 36, Part 26: pp. 169–231.

BELL, E. J., and C. B. PHILIP. 1952. The human rickettsiosis. *Annu. Rev. Microbiol.* 6: 91–118.

BENNETT, G. F. 1955. Studies on *Cuterebra emasculator* Fitch 1856 (Diptera: Cuterebridae) and a discussion of the status of the genus *Cephenemyia* Ltr. 1818. *Canad. J. Res.* (*Zool. Sci.*) 33: 75–98.

BEQUAERT, J. C. 1942. Monograph of Melophaginae. *Ent. Amer.* 22: 1–220.

BEQUAERT, J. C. 1954 and 1955. The Hippoboscidae or louse-flies (Diptera) of mammals and birds. Part II. Taxonomy, evolution and revision of American genera and species. *Ent. Amer.* 34: 1–232; 35: 233–416.

BEQUAERT, J. C. 1957. The Hippoboscidae or louse-flies. (Diptera) of mammals and birds. Part II. Taxonomy, evolution and revision of American genera and species. *Ent. Amer.* 36: 417–578.

BERLAND, L. 1932. *Les arachnides.* Paris: Paul Lechevalier et Fils. 485 pp.

BERLESE, A. 1884. *Acari, Myriopoda et scorpiones hucusque in italia reperta.* Vol. 55: *Hyalomma marginatum* (plate). Padua: Fratelli Salmin.

BERTRAND, H. 1954. *Les insectes aquatiques d'Europe.* Paris: Paul Lechevalier et Fils. Vol. 1, 556 pp. Vol. 2, 547 pp.

BEYE, H. K., M. E. GETZ, G. R. COATNEY, H. A. ELDER, and D. E. EYLES. 1961. Simian malaria in man. *Amer. J. trop. Med. Hyg.* 10: 311–316.

BINGHAM, M. L. 1941. A note on the bionomics of *Ixodes ricinus. Parasitology* 33: 316–319.

BISHOPP, F. C., and H. L. TREMBLEY. 1945. Distribution and hosts of certain North American ticks. *J. Parasit.* 31: 1–54.

BITTER, R. S., and O. B. WILLIAMS. 1949. Enteric organisms from the American cockroach. *J. infect. Dis.* 85: 87–90.

BLACKLOCK, B., and M. G. THOMPSON. 1923. A study of the tumbu-fly, *Cordylobia anthropophaga* Grünberg, in Sierra Leone. *Ann. trop. Med. Parasit.* 17: 443–502.

BLANC, G., and J. CAMINOPETROS. 1930. Recherches expérimentales sur la dengue. *Ann. Inst. Pasteur* 44: 367–436.

BLASKOVIC, D. 1960. On the problem of the epidemiology of tick-borne encephalitis. *J. Hyg. Epidemiol. Microbiol. Immunol.* 4: 278–281.

BLATTNER, R. J., and F. M. HEYS. 1941. Experimental transmission of St. Louis encephalitis to white Swiss mice by *Dermacentor variabilis. Proc. Soc. exp. Biol.* (New York) 48: 707.

BLUM, M. S., J. R. WALKER, P. S. CALLAHAN, and A. F. NOVAK. 1958. Chemical, insecticidal, and antibiotic properties of fire ant venom. *Science* 128: 306–307.

BONÉ, G. J. 1943. Recherches sur les glandes coxales et la régulation du milieu interne chez l'*Ornithodorus moubata* Murray. *Ann. Soc. zool. Belg.* 74: 16–31.

BOORMAN, J. P. T. 1958. Transmission of Uganda S virus by *Aedes* (*Stegomyia*) *aegypti* Linn. *Trans. R. Soc. trop. Med. Hyg.* 52: 383–388.

BOORMAN, J. P. T. 1960. Observations on the amount of virus present in the haemolymph of *Aedes aegypti* infected with Uganda S, yellow fever and Semliki Forest viruses. *Trans. R. Soc. trop. Med. Hyg.* 54: 362–365.

BOOTH, B. N., and R. W. JONES. 1954. Mites in industry. *Arch. Derm. Syph.* (New York) 69: 531–542.

BORN, W. 1956. Ein neuartiger Parasitenfund aus dem Formenkreis der Tarsonemini als Beitrag zur medizinischen Entomologie. *Z. Tropenmed. u. Parasit.* 7: 241–243.

BORROR, D. J., and D. M. DELONG. 1954. *An introduction to the study of insects.* New York: Rinehart & Co. ix + 1030 pp.

BOSHELL, J. M., and G. A. BEVIER. 1958. Yellow fever in the lower Montagua Valley, Guatemala. *Amer. J. trop. Med. Hyg.* 7: 25–35.

BOURGAIN, M. 1950. Sur certains faits expérimentaux concernant l'epidémiologie de la fièvre récurrente à *Spirochaeta persica. Bull. Soc. Path. exot.* 43: 689–691.

BOYD, M. F. (ed.). 1949. *Malariology; a comprehensive survey of all aspects of this group of diseases from a global standpoint.* Philadelphia: W. B. Saunders Co. 2 vols. xxi + 1643 pp.

BRAY, R. S. 1960. Observations on the cytology and morphology of the mammalian malaria parasites. I. A process of apparent plasmotomy in the preërythrocytic phase of *Laverania falciparum. Riv. Parassit.* 21: 267–276 + 2 col. pls.

BREED, R. S. 1956. The relationships of the bacteria and viruses to other living things. *Canad. J. Microbiol.* 2: 201–211.

BREMNER, K. C. 1959. Observations on the biology of *Haemaphysalis bispinosa* Neumann (Acarina: Ixodidae) with particular reference to its mode of reproduction by parthenogenesis. *Aust. J. Zool.* 7: 7–12.

BRENNAN, J. M., and E. K. JONES. 1959. Keys to the chiggers of North America with synonymic notes and descriptions of two new genera (Acarina: Trombiculidae). *Ann. ent. Soc. Amer.* 52: 7–16.

BRIGHAM, G. D. 1937. Strain of endemic typhus fever isolated from field mouse. *U.S. Publ. Hlth Rept.* 52: 659–660.

BRISTOWE, W. S. 1946. Man's reaction to mosquito bites. *Nature* (London) 158: 750.

BRODIE, R. C. E. 1952. Rosacea: the role of *Demodex folliculorum. Aust. J. Dermat.* 1: 149–152.

BROWN, A. W. A. 1958. Factors which attract *Aedes* mosquitoes to humans. *Proc. 10th int. Congr. Ent.* 3: 757–763.

BROWN, A. W. A. 1958a. Insecticide resistance in arthropods. *Wld Hlth Org. Monog.* Ser 38. 240 pp.

BROWN, A. W. A., D. S. SARKARIA, and R. P. THOMPSON. 1951. Studies on the responses of the female *Aedes* mosquito. Part I. The search for attractant vapours. *Bull. ent. Res.* 42: 105–114.

BROWN, J. H. 1955. Colorado tick fever in Alberta. *Canad. J. Res.* (*Zool. Sci.*) 33: 389–390.

BROWNE, S. G. 1960. Observations on *Simulium neavei* Roubaud, with special reference to a focus of onchocerciasis in the Belgian Congo. *Bull. ent. Res.* 51: 9–15 + 1 pl.

BRUCE, W. G. 1938. Soil moisture and its relation to the mortality of *Hypoderma* pupae. *J. econ. Ent.* 31: 639–642.

BRUCE, W. G. 1942. The horn fly. *U. S. Dept. Agr. Yearbook 1942:* 626–630.

BRUCE, W. N. 1948. Studies on the biological requirements of the cat flea. *Ann. ent. Soc. Amer.* 41: 346–352.

BRUCE, W. N., and G. C. DECKER. 1958. The relationship of stable fly abundance to milk production in dairy cattle. *J. econ. Ent.* 51: 269–274.

BRUES, C. T., A. L. MELANDER, and F. M. CARPENTER. 1954. *Classification of insects.* 2nd ed. Cambridge: Harvard Museum. v + 917 pp.

BRUMPT, E. 1936. Réceptivité de divers oiseaux domestiques et sauvages au parasite (*Plasmodium gallinaceum*) du paludisme de la poule domestique. Transmission de cet hematocaire par le moustique *Stegomyia fasciata*. *C. R. Acad. Sci.* (Paris) *203:* 750–751.

BRUMPT, E. 1936a. Le virus de la fièvre pourprée des montagnes rocheuses peut se conserver plus de 600 jours dans le corps de l'*Ornithodorus turicata*, mais n'est pas transmis par la piqûre de cet acarien. *Ann. Parasitol. 14:* 629–631.

BRUMPT, E. 1937. Facteurs qui agissent sur la transmission des infections par les Arthropodes hématophages. *Ann. Parasit. hum. comp. 15:* 75–85.

BRUMPT, E. 1949. *Précis de parasitologie.* Paris: *Masson et Cie.* xii + 1042 + 4 pls.

BUCK, A. DE. 1937. Some observations on the salivary and stomach secretion of *Anopheles* and other mosquitoes. *Proc. Acad. Sci. Amst. 40:* 217–223.

BURGDORFER, W. 1951. Analyse des Infektionsverlaufes bei *Ornithodorus moubata* (Murray) und der natürlichen Übertragung von *Spirochaeta duttoni. Acta trop.* (Basel) *8:* 193–262.

BURGDORFER, W. 1956. The possible role of ticks as vectors of Leptospirae. I. Transmission of *Leptospira pomona* by the argasid tick, *Ornithodoros turicata,* and the persistence of this organism in its tissues. *Exp. Parasit. 5:* 571–579.

BURGDORFER, W., and C. M. EKLUND. 1959. Studies on the ecology of Colorado-tick-fever virus in Western Montana. *Amer. J. Hyg. 69:* 127–137.

BURGESS, R. W. 1951. The life history and breeding habits of the eye gnat, *Hippelates pusio* Loew, in the Coachella Valley, Riverside County, California. *Amer. J. Hyg. 53:* 164–177.

BURKS, B. D. 1953. The mayflies, or Ephemeroptera, of Illinois. *Ill. nat. Hist. Surv. Bull. 26:* 1–216.

BURROUGHS, A. L. 1947. Sylvatic plague studies. The vector efficiency of nine species of fleas compared with *Xenopsylla cheopis. J. Hyg.* (Cambridge) *45:* 371–396.

BURROUGHS, A. L. 1953. Sylvatic plague studies. X. Survival of rodent fleas in the laboratory. *Parasitology 43:* 35–48.

BURTT, E. 1947. Exudate from millipedes with particular reference to its injurious effects. *Trop. Dis. Bull. 44:* 7–12.

BUTTON, J. A. 1952. The insect vectors in relation to myxomatosis in Australia. *J. Dept. Agr. W. Aust. 1:* 819–823, 825, 827–829.

BUXTON, P. A. 1932. Terrestrial insects and the humidity of the environment. *Biol. Rev. 7:* 275–320.

BUXTON, P. A. 1940. The biology of the body louse (*Pediculus humanus corporis:* Anoplura) under experimental conditions. *Parasitology 32:* 303–312.

BUXTON, P. A. 1941. Studies on populations of head-lice (*Pediculus humanus capitis:* Anoplura). IV. The composition of populations. *Parasitology 33:* 224–242.

BUXTON, P. A. 1947. *The louse. An account of the lice which infest man, their medical importance and control.* 2nd ed. London: Edward Arnold & Co. viii + 164 pp.

BUXTON, P. A. 1955. *The natural history of tsetse flies: An account of the biology of the genus Glossina* (Diptera). London: H. K. Lewis & Co., London Sch. trop. Med. Mem. 10. xviii + 816 pp. + 47 pls.

CAPUTO, C. 1957. Contributo all'epidemiologia delle febbri dermotifosimili. La Febbre bottonosa Provinci di Savona durante gli anni 1942–1954. *Igiena moderna 50:* 45–56.

CARAYON, J. 1954. Fécondation hémocoelienne chez un Hémiptère Cimicidé dépourvu d'organe de Ribaga. *C. R. Acad. Sci.* (Paris) *239:* 1542–1544.

CARLÉ, R. 1951. Das ökologische Mosaik der Infektketten bei einigen Seuchen in Südrussland (Tularämie, Pest, Malaria, Pappatacifieber). *Z. Tropenmed. u. Parasit. 2:* 558–602.

CARO, M. R., V. J. DERBES, and R. JUNG. 1957. Skin responses to the sting of the imported fire ant (*Solenopsis saevissima*). *Arch. Derm. Syph.* (New York) *75:* 475–488.

CARPENTER, S. J., and W. J. LACASSE. 1955. *Mosquitoes of North America north of Mexico.* Berkeley: University of California Press. vii + 360 pp. + 127 pl.

CARTER, H., G. WEDD, and V. ST. E. D'ABRERA. 1944. The occurrence of mites (Acarina) in human sputum and their possible significance. *Indian med. Gaz.* 79: 163–168.

CARTER, H. F. 1919. New West African Ceratopogonidae. *Ann. trop. Med. Parasit.* 12: 289–302 + 1 pl.

CARTER, H. R. 1900. A note on the interval between infecting and secondary cases of yellow fever from the records of the yellow fever at Orwood and Taylor, Mississippi, in 1898. *Med. surg. J. New Orleans* 52: 617–636.

CASALS, J. 1957. Viruses: the versatile parasites. I. The arthropod-borne group of animal viruses. *Trans. N. Y. Acad. Sci. (Ser. II)* 19: 219–235.

CASALS, J. 1961. Procedures for identification of arthropod-borne viruses. *Bull. Wld Hlth Org.* 24: 723–734.

CASALS, J., and L. WHITING. 1957. Mayaro virus: A new human disease agent. I. Relationship to other arbor viruses. *Amer. J. trop. Med. Hyg.* 6: 1004–1011.

CHABAUD, A. G., and M. T. CHOQUET. 1953. Allométrie des variants sexuels chez les Ixodidae. *Arch. Zool. exp. gen.* 89: 139–146.

CHAMBERLAIN, R. W., E. C. CORRISTAN, and R. K. SIKES. 1954. Studies on the North American arthropod-borne encephalitides. V. The extrinsic incubation of eastern and western equine encephalitis in mosquitoes. *Amer. J. Hyg.* 60: 269–277.

CHAO, P., and H. CHUNG. 1951. Chinese estivo-autumnal encephalitis (endemic encephalitis). *Chin. med. J.* 69: 522–560. (*Rev. appl. Ent.* 41: 127.)

CHEN, H. T. 1934. Reactions of *Ctenocephalides felis* to *Dipylidium caninum*. *Z. Parasitenk.* 6: 603–637 + 1 pl.

CHITWOOD, B. G., and M. B. CHITWOOD. 1950. *An introduction to nematology.* Section I. Anatomy. Baltimore: B. G. Chitwood. viii + 213 pp.

CHRISTOPHERS, S. R., H. E. SHORTT, and P. J. BARRAUD. 1925. Further observations on the feeding of sandflies, *Phlebotomus argentipes,* on cases of Indian kala-azar. *Indian J. med. Res.* 13: 159–165.

CHUNG, H. L., and Y. L. WEI. 1938. Studies on the transmission of relapsing fever in north China. II. Observations on the mechanism of transmission of relapsing fever in man. *Amer. J. trop. Med.* 18: 661–674.

CIUREA, T., and G. DINULESCU. 1924. Ravages causés par la mouche de Goloubatz en Roumanie; ses attaques contre les animaux et contre l'homme. *Ann. trop. Med. Parasit.* 18: 323–334.

CLARK, G. M. 1958. *Hepatozoon griseisciuri* n. sp.: A new species of *Hepatozoon* from the grey squirrel (*Sciurus carolinensis* Gmelin, 1788), with studies on the life cycle. *J. Parasit.* 44: 52–59 + 5 pls.

CLARK, H. C., and L. H. DUNN. 1932. Experimental studies on Chagas' disease in Panama. *Amer. J. trop. Med.* 12: 49–77.

CLAY, T. 1949. Piercing mouth-parts in the biting lice (Mallophaga). *Nature* (London) 164: 617.

CLOUDSLEY-THOMPSON, J. L. 1949. The significance of migration in Myriapods. *Ann. Mag. nat. Hist. (12th ser.)* 2: 947–962.

CLOUDSLEY-THOMPSON, J. L. 1955. On the function of pectines in scorpions. *Ann. Mag. nat. Hist. (12th ser.)* 8: 556–560.

CLOUDSLEY-THOMPSON, J. L. 1955a. Some aspects of the biology of centipedes and scorpions. *Naturalist* (London) 1955: 147–153.

COLAS-BELCOUR, J., and P. NICOLLE. 1938. Sur le parasitisme du cobaye par un mallophage sud-americain, *Trimenopon jenningsi* K. et P. Présence de sang et de rickettsies dans le tube digestif de l'insecte. *Bull. Soc. Path. exot.* 31: 635–640.

COLAS-BELCOUR, J. and G. VERVENT. 1955. Transmission de divers spirochètes de la fièvre récurrente par une souche soudanaise de l'*Ornithodoros erraticus* Lucas (= *O. e.* var. *sonrai.* J. Sautet, H. Marneffe et M. Witkowsky, 1944). *Bull. Soc. Path. exot.* 48: 747–757.

COLYER, C. O., and C. O. HAMMOND. 1951. *Flies of the British Isles.* London: Frederick Warne & Co., Ltd., 383 pp. + 103 pls.

COMSTOCK, J. H. 1912. *The spider book.* Garden City, N. Y.: Doubleday. xi + 721 pp.

COMSTOCK, J. H. 1948. *The spider book*. Rev. and ed. by W. J. Gertsch. Ithaca, N. Y.: Comstock Publishing Co., Inc. xi + 729 pp.

COOK, T. W. 1953. *The ants of California*. Palo Alto, Calif.: Pacific Books. xiii + 462 pp.

COOLEY, R. A. 1946. The genera *Boophilus, Rhipicephalus* and *Haemaphysalis* (Ixodidae) of the New World. *U. S. Nat. Inst. Hlth Bull. 187.* 54 pp.

COOLEY, R. A., and G. M. KOHLS. 1944. The genus *Amblyomma* (Ixodidae) in the United States. *J. Parasit. 30:* 77–111.

COOLEY, R. A., and G. M. KOHLS. 1944a. The argasidae of North America, Central America and Cuba. *Amer. Mid. Nat. Monograph No. 1.* 152 pp.

COOLEY, R. A., and G. M. KOHLS. 1945. The genus Ixodes in North America. *U. S. Nat. Inst. Hlth Bull. 184.* 246 pp.

COORAY, G. H. 1960. Some observations on filarial infection in Ceylon with special reference to its histopathology. *Indian J. Malar. 14:* 617–632.

COSTA, O. G. 1945. An extensive case of chigoe infestation (dermatophyliasis). *J. trop. Med. (Hyg.) 48:* 121–122.

COWDRY, E. V. 1922. The distribution of *Rickettsia* in the tissues of insects and arachnids. *J. exp. Med. 37:* 431–456 + 3 pls.

COWDRY, E. V., and W. B. C. DANKS. 1933. Studies on East Coast Fever, II. Behaviour of the parasite and the development of distinctive lesions in susceptible animals. *Parasitology 25:* 1–63 + 10 pls.

COWDRY, E. V., and A. W. HAM. 1930. The life cycle of the parasite of East Coast fever in ticks transmitting the disease (preliminary note). *Science 72:* 461–462.

CRAGG, F. W. 1912. The structure of *Haematopota pluvialis* (Meigen). *Sci. Mem. med. sanit. Dep. India 55:* 36 pp. + 7 pls.

CRAGG, F. W. 1913. Studies on the mouth parts and sucking apparatus of the bloodsucking Diptera No. 4. The comparative anatomy of the proboscis in the bloodsucking Muscidae. *Sci. Mem. med. sanit. Dep. India 60:* 56 pp. + 5 pls.

CRAGG, J. B., and J. HOBART. 1955. A study of a field population of the blowflies *Lucilia caesar* (L.) and *L. sericata* (Mg.). *Ann. appl. Biol. 43:* 645–663.

CRISP, G. 1956. *Simulium and onochocerciasis in the Northern Territories of the Gold Coast*. London: H. K. Lewis & Co., Ltd. 171 pp.

CROSSKEY, R. W. 1954. Infection of *Simulium damnosum* with *Onchocerca volvulus* during the wet season in northern Nigeria. *Ann. trop. Med. Parasit. 48:* 152–159.

CROSSKEY, R. W. 1957. The Simuliidae (Diptera) of northern Nigeria. *Bull. ent. Res. 48:* 59–74.

CROSSKEY, R. W. 1959. Aspects of black-fly control and entomology in the New World in relation to the *Simulium* problem in Nigeria. *Bull. Wld Hlth Org. 21:* 727–736.

CROSSKEY, R. W., and M. E. CROSSKEY. 1955. The horse-flies (Diptera: Tabanidae) of Nigeria and the British Cameroons. *Trans. R. ent. Soc. Lond. 106:* 341–374.

CRUTCHFIELD, C. M., and H. HIXSON. 1943. Food habits of several species of poultry lice with special reference to blood consumption. *Fla. Ent. 26:* 63–66.

CULWICK, A. T., H. FAIRBAIRN, and R. E. CULWICK. 1951. The genetic relationship of the polymorphic trypanosomes and its practical implications. *Ann. trop. Med. Parasit. 45:* 11–29.

CURRAN, C. H. 1934. *The families and genera of the North American Diptera*. New York: The Ballou Press. 512 pp.

CUTKOMP, L. K., and A. L. HARVEY. 1958. The weight responses of beef cattle in relation to control of horn and stable flies. *J. econ. Ent. 51:* 72–75.

DAGGY, R. H. 1959. Malaria in oases of eastern Saudi Arabia. *Amer. J. trop. Med. Hyg. 8:* 223–291.

DAITER, A. B. 1960. The bed bug as a possible reservoir of *Rickettsia burneti* (experimental and epidemiological findings). *Problems of Virology. 5:* 644–652.

DAKSHINAMURTY, S. 1948. The common house-fly, *Musca domestica*, L., and its behavior to temperature and humidity. *Bull. ent. Res. 39:* 339–357.

DALMAT, H. T. 1943. A contribution to the knowledge of the rodent warble flies (Cuterebridae). *J. Parasit. 29:* 311–318.

Dalmat, H. T. 1955. The black flies (Diptera: Simuliidae) of Guatemala and their role as vectors of onchocerciasis. *Smithson. misc. Coll. 125 (1):* 1–425 + 43 pls. + 1 tbl.

Daniel, M., and J. Slais. 1957. Intradermal parasitism by larvae of the chigger *Euschöngastia ulcerofaciens* (Acari, Trombiculidae) and its histological evaluation. In Hungarian. *C. S. Biol. 6:* 365–371.

Daubney, R., and J. R. Hudson. 1933. Rift Valley Fever. *E. Afr. med. J. 10:* 2–19.

Daubney, R., and E. A. Mahlav. 1957. Near-eastern equine encephalomyelitis. *Nature* (London) *179:* 584–585.

Davey, J. T., and F. J. O'Rourke. 1951. Observations on *Chrysops silacea* and *C. dimidiata* at Benin, Southern Nigeria. Part III. *Ann. trop. Med. Parasit. 45:* 101–109.

Davies, A. M., and Y. Yoshpe-Purer. 1953. *Aedes aegypti* as a vector of West Nile virus. *Bull. Res. Council Israel 3:* 127–128. (*Abs. Rev. appl. Ent. 43:* 65).

Davis, D. H. S. 1953. Plague in South Africa: A study of the epizootic cycle in gerbils (*Tatera brantsi*) in the Northern Orange Free State. *J. Hyg.* (Cambridge) *51:* 427–449.

Davis, G. E. 1940. *Bacterium tularense:* its persistence in the tissues of the argasid ticks *Ornithodoros turicata and O. parkeri. U. S. Publ. Hlth Rept. 55:* 676–680.

Davis, G. E. 1941. *Ornithodoros turicata:* the male, feeding and copulation habits, fertility, span of life, and the transmission of relapsing fever spirochetes. *U. S. Publ. Hlth Rept. 56:* 1799–1802.

Davis, G. E. 1941a. Tick vectors and life cycles of ticks. In A symposium on relapsing fever in the Americas. *Amer. Ass. Advanc. Sci. Publ. 18:* 67–76.

Davis, G. E. 1942. Species unity or plurality of the relapsing fever spirochetes. In A symposium on relapsing fever in the Americas. *Amer. Ass. Advanc. Sci. Publ. 18:* 41–47.

Davis, G. E. 1943. Relapsing fever; the tick *Ornithodoros turicata* as a spirochetal reservoir. *U. S. Publ. Hlth Rept. 58:* 839–842.

Davis, G. E. 1952. Biology as an aid to the identification of two closely related species of ticks of the genus *Ornithodoros. J. Parasit. 38:* 477–480.

Davis, G. E. 1956. A relapsing fever spirochete *Borrelia mazzottii* (sp. nov.) from *Ornithodoros talaje* from Mexico. *Amer. J. Hyg. 63:* 13–17.

Davis, G. E., and H. Hoogstraal. 1956. Étude sur la biologie du spirochète *Borrelia persica,* trouvé chez la tique *Ornithodoros tholozani* (Argasinae) récoltée dans le govenorate du desert occidental égyptien. *Ann. Parasit. hum. comp. 30:* 147–159.

Davis, G. E., and A. J. Mavros. 1955. Observations on the biology of *Ornithodoros d. delanoei,* Roubaud and Colas-Belcour, 1931 (Ixodoidea, Argasidae). *Bull. Soc. Path. exot. 48:* 698–704.

Davis, N. C., M. Frosbisher, Jr., and W. Lloyd. 1933. The titration of yellow fever virus in *Stegomyia* mosquitoes. *J. exp. Med. 58:* 211–226.

Davis, N. C., and R. C. Shannon. 1929. Studies on yellow fever in South America. IV. Transmission experiments with *Aedes aegypti. J. exp. Med. 50:* 793–801.

Deane, L. M. 1958. Epidemiologia *E. profilaxia* do calazar Americano. *Rev. bras. Malariol. 10:* 431–449.

Deane, L. M. 1958a. Novo hospedeiro de tripanossomos dos tipos *cruzi e rangeli* encontrado no estado do Pará: o marsupial *Metachirops opossum opossum. Rev. bras. Malariol. 10:* 531–538.

DeGuisti, D. L. 1949. The life cycle of *Leptorhynchoides thecatus* (Linton), an acanthocephalan of fish. *J. Parasit. 35:* 437–460.

Deoras, P. J. 1941. Structure of *Hemimerus deceptus* Rehn, var. *ovatus:* an external parasite of *Cricetomys gambiense. Parasitology 33:* 172–185.

Deoras, P. J., and A. K. Joshee. 1959. Proventricular teeth in some rat fleas. *Ind. J. med. Res. 47:* 261–265 + 2 pls.

De Oreo, G. A. 1958. Pigeons acting as vector in acariasis caused by *Dermanyssus gallinae* (De Geer, 1778). *Arch. Derm. Syph.* (New York) *77:* 422–429.

DERRICK, E. H., D. SMITH, H. BROWN, and M. FREEMAN. 1939. The role of the
bandicoot in the epidemiology of "Q" fever: a preliminary study. *Med. J. Aust.*
1: 150–155.
DHIR, S. L., and A. RAHIM. 1957. Malaria and its control in Afghanistan (1950–
1954). *Indian J. Malar.* 11: 73–125.
DIAS, E., and R. ZELEDÓN. 1955. Infestaçao domiciliária em grau extremo por
Triatoma infestans. Mem. Inst. Osw. Cruz. 53: 473–486.
DICK, G. W. A. 1953. Epidemiological notes on some viruses isolated in Uganda.
Trans. R. Soc. trop. Med. Hyg. 47: 13–43.
DICK, G. W. A. 1957. The transmission of viruses to the vertebrates by arthropods.
In HORTON-SMITH, *Biological aspects of the transmission of disease.* Edinburgh:
Oliver & Boyd, Ltd. pp. 65–72.
DICKERSON, G., and M. M. J. LAVOIPIERRE. 1959. Studies on the methods of feeding
of blood-sucking arthropods. II. The method of feeding adopted by the bed bug
(*Cimex lectularius*) when obtaining a blood meal from the mammalian host.
Ann. trop. Med. Parasit. 53: 347–357.
DOWNES, J. A. 1958. The genus *Culicoides* (Diptera: Ceratopogonidae) in Canada;
an introductory review. *Proc. 10th int. Congr. Ent.* 3: 801–808.
DOWNS, W. G., C. R. ANDERSON, and J. CASALS. 1957. The isolation of St. Louis
virus from a nestling bird in Trinidad, British West Indies. *Amer. J. trop. Med.
Hyg.* 6: 693–696.
DOWNS, W. G., T. H. G. AITKEN, and L. SPENCE. 1959. Eastern equine encepha-
litis virus isolated from *Culex nigripalpus* in Trinidad. *Science 130:* 1471.
DUKE, B. O. L. 1954. The uptake of the microfilariae of *Acanthocheilonema strepto-
cerca* by *Culicoides grahamii* and their subsequent development. *Ann. trop. Med.
Parasit.* 48: 416–433.
DUKE, B. O. L. 1955. Studies on the biting habits of *Chrysops.* II. The effect of
wood fires on the biting density of *Chrysops silacea* in the rain-forest at Dumba,
British Cameroons. *Ann. trop. Med. Parasit.* 49: 260–272.
DUKE, B. O. L., and D. J. B. WIJERS. 1958. Studies on loaiasis in monkeys. I. The
relationship between human and simian *Loa* in the rain-forest zone of the British
Cameroons. *Ann. trop. Med. Parasit.* 52: 158–175.
DUKE, H. L. 1933. Studies on the factors that may influence the transmission of the
polymorphic trypanosomes by tsetse. I. A review of existing knowledge on this
subject, with some general observations. *Ann. trop. Med. Parasit.* 27: 99–118.
DUTOIT, R. M. 1944. The transmission of blue tongue and horse sickness by *Culi-
coides* Onderstepoort. *J. vet. Sci.* 19 (1–2): 7–16.
EDMONDSON, W. T. 1959. *Fresh-water biology.* 2nd ed. New York: John Wiley &
Sons, Inc. xx + 1248 pp.
EDWARDS, E. E. 1956. Human onchocerciasis in West Africa with special reference
to the Gold Coast. *J. W. Afr. Sci. Ass.* 2: 1–35.
EDWARDS, F. W. 1932. Diptera, family Culicidae. In *Genera insectorum,* Fasc. 194.
258 pp. + 5 pls.
EDWARDS, F. W., H. OLDROYD, and J. SMART. 1939. *British blood-sucking flies.*
London: British Museum. viii + 156 pp. + 45 pls.
EICHLER, W. 1940. Untersuchungen zur Epidemiologie der Aussenparasiten. II.
Masseninvasionen von Ektoparasiten. *Arch. wiss. Prakt. Tierheilk.* 75: 212–221.
EPSHTEIN, G. V., I. L. SIL'VERS, and E. V. EKZEMPLYARSKAYA. 1935. Rat fleas as
carriers of experimental pneumonococcus infection. *In Russian. Rec. Trav. 25th
anniv. sci. Pavlovsky 14:* 1099–1111 *(Rev. appl. Ent. [B] 24:* 177).
ESKEY, C. R., F. M. PRINCE, and F. B. FULLER. 1951. Double infection of the rat
fleas X. cheopis and N. fasciatus with *Pasteurella* and *Salmonella. U.S. Publ.
Hlth Rept.* 66: 1318–1326.
ESSEX, H. E. 1927. The structure and development of *Corallobothrium* with descriptions of two new fish tapeworms. *Ill. Biol. Monogr.* 11 (3): 7–74.
EWING, H. E. 1924. On the taxonomy, biology and distribution of the biting lice of
the family Gyropidae. *Proc. U. S. Nat. Mus.* 63 (20): 1–42 + 1 pl.

EWING, H. E., and I. FOX. 1943. The fleas of North America. *U. S. Dept. Agr. misc. Pub. 500.* 142 pp.

FAHLANDER, K. 1938. Beiträge zur Anatomie und systematischen Einteilung der Chilopoden. *Zool. Bidr. Uppsala, 17:* 1–148 + 18 pls.

FAHRENHOLZ, H. 1936. Zur Systematik der Anopluren. *Z. Parasitenk. 9:* 50–56.

FAIRBAIRN, H. 1954. The animal reservoirs of *Trypanosoma rhodesiense* and *Trypanosoma gambiense. Ann. Soc. belge Méd. trop. 34:* 663–669.

FAIRBAIRN, H., and E. BURTT. 1946. The infectivity to man of a strain of *Trypanosoma rhodesiense* transmitted cyclically by *Glossina morsitans* through sheep and antelope: evidence that man requires a minimum infective dose of metacyclic trypanosomes. *Ann. trop. Med. Parasit. 40:* 270–313 + 2 charts.

FAIRBAIRN, H., and J. WILLIAMSON. 1956. The composition of tsetse-fly saliva. I. A histochemical analysis. *Ann. trop. Med. Parasit. 50:* 322–333.

FAIRCHILD, G. B. 1955. The relationships and classification of the Phlebotominae (Diptera, Psychodidae). *Ann. ent. Soc. Amer. 48:* 182–196.

FALLIS, A. M., and G. F. BENNETT. 1958. Transmission of *Leucocytozoon bonasae* Clark to ruffed grouse (*Bonasa umbellus* L.) by the black flies *Simulium latipes* Mg. and *Simulium aureum* Fries. *Canad. J. Zool. 36:* 533–539 + 1 pl.

FAY, R. W. 1939. A control for the larvae of house flies in manure piles. *J. econ. Ent. 32:* 851–854.

FEDER, I. A. 1944. Tick bite pyrexia. *J. Amer. med. Ass. 126:* 293–294.

FEINBERG, A. R., S. M. FEINBERG, and C. BENAIM-PINTO. 1956. Asthma and rhinitis from insect allergens. I. Clinical importance. *J. Allergy 27:* 437–444.

FENG, L. C., and H. L. CHUNG. 1939. The transmission of *Spirochaeta duttoni* by *Ornithodorus moubata. Acta Conventus terti Tropics atque Malariae Morbis, Part 1:* 438–443.

FENNER, F., and G. M. WOODROOFE. 1953. The pathogenesis of infectious myxomatosis: The mechanism of infection and the immunological response in the European rabbit. *Brit. J. exp. Path. 34:* 400–411.

FERRIS, G. F. 1951. *The sucking lice.* San Francisco: Pacific Coast Entomological Society. ix + 320 pp.

FIGLEY, K. D. 1940. Mayfly (Ephemerida) hypersensitivity. *J. Allergy 11:* 376–387.

FINDLAY, G. M. 1941. Yellow fever and the Anglo-Egyptian Sudan: Historical. *Ann. trop. Med. Parasit. 34:* 59–65.

FITZPATRICK, F. K. 1948. Susceptibility to typhus of rats on deficient diet. *Amer. J. Publ. Hlth, 38:* 676–681.

FLOCH, H., and P. FAURAN. 1954. Les vecteurs de la myiase furonculeuse en Guyane Francaise. *Bull. Soc. Path. exot. 49:* 652–656.

FLOCH, H., and P. FAURAN. 1958. *Ixodides de la Guyane et des Antilles Francaises.* Cahors: Imprimerie A. Coueslant. 94 pp.

FLU, P. C. 1921. Some notes on an inquiry on the spread of *Filaria bancrofti* among the native inhabitants of Weltevreden. *Meded. burgerl. geneesk. Dienst. Ned.-Ind. 9:* 330–363.

FOGGIE, A. 1959. Studies on the relationship of tick-bite to tick pyaemia of lambs. *Ann. trop. Med. Parasit. 53:* 27–34 + 1 pl.

FOX, C. 1925. *Insects and Disease of Man.* Philadelphia: P. Blakiston's Son & Co. xii + 349 pp.

FOX, I. 1955. A catalogue of the blood-sucking midges of the Americas (*Culicoides, Leptoconops* and *Lasiohelea*) with keys to the subgenera and Nearctic species, a geographic index, and bibliography. *J. Agric. Univ. P. R. 39:* 214–285.

FOX, I. 1957. *Ornithonyssus bursa* (Berlese) attacking man in Puerto Rico. *J. econ. Ent. 50:* 838.

FRANCIS, E. 1938. Longevity of the tick *Ornithodoros turicata* and of *Spirochaeta recurrentis* within this tick. *U. S. Publ. Hlth Rept. 53:* 2220–2241.

FRANCIS, E. 1941. The longevity of fasting and non-fasting *Ornithodoros turicata* and the survival of *Spirochaeta obermeiri* within them. In a symposium on relapsing fever in the Americas. *Publ. Amer. Ass. Adv. Sci. 18:* 85–88.

FRIEDLAENDER, M., D. H. MOORE, R. LOVE, R. BROWN, and H. KOPROWSKI. 1955. Studies with the electron microscope of virus-host relationship in Ehrlich-ascites tumor cells. I. The identification and structure of Anopheles A virus. *J. exp. Med. 102:* 361–370 + 6 pls.

FROHNE, W. C. 1959. Observations on Alaskan snipe-fly pests. *Mosquito News 19:* 172–178.

FYODOROV, V. N. 1960. The question of the existence of natural foci of plague in Europe in the past. *J. Hyg. Epidemiol. Microbiol. Immunol. 4:* 135–141.

GALINDO, P., E. DE RODANICHE, and C. M. JOHNSON. 1959. St. Louis encephalitis in Panama. *Amer. J. trop. Med. Hyg. 8:* 557–560.

GALOUZO, I. G. 1957. Argasid ticks and their epizootological significance. *In Russian.* Alma-Ata: Acad. Sci. Kazakh SSR. 131 pp. (Trans. U. S. Nav. Med. Unit #3.)

GALOUZO, I. G., and M. M. REMENTSOVA. 1956. Les réservoirs et les vecteurs de l'infection brucellique dans la nature. *In Russian. Entomol. Obozrenie 35:* 560–569. *(Bull. Inst. Past. 55.)*

GARNHAM, P. C. C. 1954. Final results of an experiment on the control of onchocerciasis by eradication of the vector. *Bull. ent. Res. 45:* 175–176.

GARNHAM, P. C. C. 1955. The comparative pathogenicity of protozoa in their vertebrate and invertebrate hosts. No. 5. Mechanisms of microbial pathogenicity. *Sympos. Soc. gen. Microbiol.* 191–206.

GARNHAM, P. C. C. 1958. Zoonoses or infections common to man and animals. *J. trop. Med. (Hyg.) 61:* 92–94.

GEAR, J. 1954. The rickettsial diseases of southern Africa: A review of recent studies. *S. Afr. J. clin. Sci. 5:* 158–175.

GEAR, J., B. WOLSTENHOLME, R. HARWIN and F. S. STAKES. 1952. Brill's disease (recrudescent epidemic typhus fever): Its occurrence in South Africa. *S. Afr. med. J. 26:* 566–569.

GEIGY, R., and A. AESCHLIMANN. 1957. Ratten als Reservoir von *Borrelia duttoni. Z. Tropenmed. u. Parasit. 8:* 96–108.

GEIGY, R., and A. HERBIG. 1955. Erreger und überträger tropischer Krankheiten. *Acta trop.* (Basel) *Supp. 6:* 1–472.

GEIGY, R., and H. MOOSER. 1955. Studies on the epidemiology of African relapsing fever in Tanganyika. *J. trop. Med. (Hyg.) 58:* 199–201.

GEIGY, R., H. MOOSER, and F. WEYER. 1956. Untersuchungen an Stämmen von afrikanischem Rückfall fieber aus Tanganyika. *Acta trop.* (Basel) *13:* 193–224.

GERBERICH, J. B. 1952. The house fly (*Musca domestica* Linn.), as a vector of *Salmonella pullorum* (Retteger) Bergy, the agent of white diarrhea of chickens. *Ohio J. Sci. 52:* 287–290.

GERHARDT, U., and A. KÄSTNER. 1938. Araneae. *Handb. Zool. Berl. 3:* 390–656.

GERRY, B. E., and N. S. BAILEY. 1948. Control of the greenhead fly (*Tabanus nigrovittatus*) in Massachusetts. *Mass. Legis. Rept. s 429.* (Abs. *Mosq. News 8* (1): 37).

GERTSCH, W. J. 1949. *American spiders.* New York: D. Van Nostrand Co. xiii + 285 pp.

GIBBINS, E. G. 1938. The mouth parts of the female in *Simulium damnosum* Theobald, with special reference to the transmission of *Onchocerca volvulus* Leuckart. *Ann. trop. Med. Parasit. 32:* 9–20.

GILL, C. A. 1921. Malaria in England, with special reference to the role of temperature and humidity. *J. Hyg.* (Cambridge) *19:* 320–332.

GILLETT, J. D., and C. A. C. MIMS. 1955. Relation between the virus and its mosquito host. *E. African Virus Research Inst. Rept. 1955:* 7–8.

GIRARD, G. 1943. Les ectoparasites de l'homme dans l'épidémiologie de la peste. *Bull. Soc. Path. exot. 36:* 4–43.

GLASER, R. W. 1930. The intracellular "symbionts" and the "rickettsiae." *Arch. Path. 9:* 71–96 and 557–576.

GLUCHOVA, V. M. 1958. Types of attack in *Culicoides* Latr. (Diptera, Heleidae.) *Trans. from Russian. Ent. Rev. 37:* 277–281.

GODFREY, D. G. 1961. Types of *Trypanosoma congolense*. II. Differences in the courses of infection. *Ann. trop. Med. Parasit. 55:* 154–166.

GOLDMAN, L. 1952. Local effect of compound F on reactions to mosquito bites. *J. Amer. med. Ass. 149:* 265.

GOLDMAN, L., E. ROCKWELL, and D. F. RICHFIELD. 1952. Histopathological studies on cutaneous reactions to bites of various arthropods. *Amer. J. trop. Med. (Hyg.) 1:* 514–525.

GOLDMAN, L., F. SAWYER, A. LEVINE, J. GOLDMAN, S. GOLDMAN, and J. SPINANGER. 1960. Investigative studies of skin irritations from caterpillars. *J. investig. Derm. 34:* 67–79.

GORDON, R. M. 1950. Reactions produced by arthropods directly injurious to the skin of man. *Brit. med. J. 1950:* 316–318.

GORDON, R. M. 1955. A brief review of recent advances in our knowledge of loaiasis and of some of the still outstanding problems. *Trans. R. Soc. trop. Med. Hyg. 49:* 98–105.

GORDON, R. M., and W. CREWE. 1948. The mechanisms by which mosquitoes and tsetse-flies obtain their blood-meal, the histology of the lesions produced, and the subsequent reactions of the mammalian host; together with some observations on the feeding of *Chrysops* and *Cimex*. *Ann. trop. Med. Parasit. 42:* 334–356.

GORDON, R. M., and W. CREWE. 1953. The deposition of the infective stage of *Loa loa* by *Chrysops silacea* and the early stages of its migration to the deeper tissues of the mammalian host. *Ann. trop. Med. Parasit. 47:* 74–84.

GORDON, R. M., W. CREWE, and K. C. WILLETT. 1956. Studies on the deposition, migration and development to the blood forms of trypanosomes belonging to the *Trypanosoma brucei* group. I. An account of the process of feeding adopted by the tsetse-fly when obtaining a blood-meal from the mammalian host, with special reference to the ejection of saliva and the relationship of the feeding process to the deposition of the metacyclic trypanosomes. *Ann. trop. Med. Parasit. 50:* 426–437 + 3 pls.

GRASSÉ, P. P. 1949. *Traité de zoologie; anatomie, systématique biologie.* Paris: Masson et Cie. Vol. 9. 1117 pp.

GREEN, R. G., C. A. EVANS, and C. L. LARSON. 1943. A ten-year population study of the rabbit tick *Haemaphysalis leporis-palustris*. *Amer. J. Hyg. 38:* 260–281.

GREGSON, J. D. 1952. Further studies on tick paralysis. *Proc. ent. Soc. B. C. 48:* 54–58.

GREGSON, J. D. 1956. The Ixodoidea of Canada. *Canad. Dept. Agr. Pub. 930:* 1–92 pp.

GREGSON, J. D. 1960. Morphology and functioning of the mouth parts of *Dermacentor andersoni* Stiles. *Acta. trop.* (Basel). *17:* 48–79.

GRESSER, I., J. L. HARDY, S. M. K. HU, and W. F. SCHERER. 1958. Factors influencing transmission of Japanese B encephalitis virus by a colonized strain of *Culex tritaeniorhynchus* Giles, from infected pigs and chicks to susceptible pigs and birds. *Amer. J. trop. Med. Hyg. 7:* 365–373.

GREWAL, M. S. 1956. *Trypanosoma rangeli* Tejera, 1920, in its vertebrate and invertebrate hosts. *Trans. R. Soc. trop. Med. Hyg. 50:* 301–302.

GROOT, H., A. OYA, C. BERNAL, and P. BARRETO-REYES. 1959. Guaroa virus, a new agent isolated in Colombia, South America. *Amer. J. trop. Med. Hyg. 8:* 604–609.

GUDGEL, E. F., and F. H. GRAUER. 1954. Acute and chronic reactions to black-fly bites. *Arch. Derm. Syph.* (New York) *70:* 609–615.

GUELMINO, D. J., and M. JEVTIC. 1953. The epidemic of sandfly fever in country Vojvodina in 1951. *In Serbian. Glas Srpske Akad. Nauk; Odeljenje med. Nauk 209:* 1–11. (Abs. *Trop. Dis. Bull. 51:* 912.)

HAAS, G. E., and R. J. DICKE. 1958. On *Cuterebra horripilum* Clark (Diptera: Cuterebridae) parasitizing cottontail rabbits in Wisconsin. *J. Parasit. 44:* 527–540.

HACKETT, C. J. 1957. The transmission of yaws in nature. *J. trop. Med. (Hyg.) 60:* 159–168.

HADDOW, A. J. 1956. Observations on the biting habits of African mosquitoes in the genus *Eretmapodites* Theobald. *Bull. ent. Res. 46:* 761–772.

HADDOW, A. J. 1956a. *East African Virus Research Institute, Entebbe. Report No. 6, July 1955–June 1956.* Nairobi: Govt. Printer. 52 pp., 1 fig.

HALE, J. H., D. H. COLLESS, and K. A. LIM. 1957. Investigation of the Malaysian form of *Culex tritaeniorhynchus* as a potential vector of Japanese B encephalitis virus on Singapore Island. *Ann. trop. Med. Parasit. 51:* 17–25.

HALFF, L. A. 1956. Untersuchungen über die Abhängigkeit der Entwicklung der Reduviidae *Triatoma infestans* Klug von ihrem Darmsymbionten. *Acta trop.* (Basel) *13:* 225–253.

HALL, D. G. 1948. *The blow flies of North America.* Washington, D. C.: Ent. Soc. Amer. iv. + 477 pp. + 5 col. pls.

HALL, M. C. 1937. The bed bug. *U. S. Publ. Hlth Rept., Suppl. 129:* 1–7.

HALL, R. P. 1953. *Protozoology.* Englewood Cliffs, N. J.: Prentice-Hall, Inc. 682 pp.

HANEC, W. 1956. A study of the environmental factors affecting the dispersion of house flies (*Musca domestica* L.) in a dairy community near Fort Whyte, Manitoba. *Canad. Ent. 88:* 270–272.

HARANT, H., and J. THÉODORIDÈS. 1950. Note sur les cas d'infestation accidentelle par des coléoptères chez l'homme. *Bull. Soc. Path. exot. 43:* 54–55.

HARRISON, J. L., and J. R. AUDY. 1951. Hosts of the mite vector of scrub typhus. I. A check-list of the recorded hosts. *Ann. trop. Med. Parasit. 45:* 171–185.

HARRISON, L. 1916. A preliminary account of the structure of the mouth-parts in the body-louse. *Proc. Camb. phil. Soc. 18:* 207–226 + 1 pl.

HARWOOD, R. F., and W. R. HORSFALL. 1959. Development, structure and function of coverings of eggs of floodwater mosquitoes. III. Functions of coverings. *Ann. ent. Soc. Amer. 52:* 113–116.

HASE, A. 1930. Über die Lebensgewohnheiten einer Fledermausfliege in Venezuela; *Basilia bellardii* (Fam. Nycteribiidae-Diptera Pupipara). *Z. Parasitenk. 3:* 220–257.

HAYS, K. L. 1956. A synopsis of the Tabanidae (Diptera) of Michigan. *Misc. Pub. Mus. Zool. Univ. Mich. No. 98.* 79 pp.

HECHT, O. 1930. Die Hautreaktionen auf Insektenstiche als allergische Erscheinungen. I, II, III. *Zool. Anz. 87:* 94–109, 145–157, 231–246.

HEILESEN, B. 1946. *Studies on Acarus scabei and scabies.* Copenhagen: Rosenkilde and Bagger. 370 pp.

HEISCH, R. B. 1950. On *Spirochaeta dipodilli* sp. nov., a parasite of pygmy gerbils (*Dipodillus* sp.). *Ann. trop. Med. Parasit. 44:* 260–272 + 1 pl.

HEISCH, R. B. 1950a. Studies on East African relapsing fever. *E. Afr. med. J. 27:* 1–58.

HEISCH, R. B. 1955. Do spirochaetes have a negative phase in lice? *Bull. Soc. Path. exot. 48:* 322–325.

HEISCH, R. B. 1955a. On the presence of intracellular granules in lice infected with *Spirochaeta duttoni. Trans. R. Soc. trop. Med. Hyg. 49:* 92–93.

HEISCH, R. B. 1956. Zoonoses as a study in ecology with special reference to plague, relapsing fever, and leishmaniasis. *Brit. med. J. 1956 (2):* 669–673.

HEISCH, R. B. 1957. The isolation of *Leishmania* from a ground squirrel in Kenya. *East Afr. med. J. 34:* 183.

HEISCH, R. B., R. McPHEE, and L. R. RICKMAN. 1957. The epidemiology of tick-typhus in Nairobi. *E. Afr. med. J. 9:* 459–477.

HENNIG, W. 1948, 1950, and 1953. *Die Larvenformen der Dipteren.* Berlin: Akademie-Verlag. Part 1: 1–186; Part 2: viii + 460 pp.; Part 3: viii + 628 pp.

HERMS, W. B. 1916. The Pajaroella tick (*Ornithodorus coriaceus* Koch) with special reference to life history and biting habits. *J. Parasit. 2:* 137–142.

HERMS, W. B. 1923. *Medical and veterinary entomology.* New York: The Macmillan Co. 462 pp.

HERMS, W. B., and C. M. WHEELER. 1936. *Ornithodoros hermsi* Wheeler as a vector of relapsing fever in California. *J. Parasit. 22:* 276–282.

HERRER, A. 1953. Carrión's disease. III. Experimental infection of squirrels. *Amer. J. trop. Med. Hyg. 2:* 650–654.

HERTIG, M. 1939. *Phlebotomus* and Carrión's disease. *Proc. 6th Pacific sci. Congr.* 5: 775–779.

HERTIG, M. 1942. Phlebotomus and Carrion's disease I–IV. *Amer. J. trop. Med.* 22 (*Supp.*): 1–81.

HINDLE, E. 1912. The transmission of *Spirochaeta duttoni. Parasitology* 6: 133–149.

HIRST, L. F. 1953. *The conquest of plague. A study of the evolution of epidemiology.* London: Geoffrey Cumberlege, Oxford University Press. xvi + 478 pp.

HIRST, S. 1919. *The genus* Demodex Owen. *In his studies on Acari.* London: British Museum (Nat. Hist.). No. 1. vi + 44 pp. + 13 pls.

HIXSON, H. 1940. Field biology and environmental relationships of the gulf coast tick in southern Georgia. *J. econ. Ent.* 33: 179–189.

HOARE, C. A. 1955. The epidemiological role of animal reservoirs in human leishmaniasis and trypanosomiasis. *Vet. Rev. Annotations* 1: 62–68.

HOEPPLI, R., and L. C. FENG. 1931. Histological reactions in the skin due to ecto-parasites. *Dermacentor sinicus* P. Schulze from hedgehog, *Haemaphysalis campanulata hoeppliana* P. Schulze from dog, *Cimex lectularius* and *Pediculus vestimenti* from man. *Nat. med. J. China* 17: 541–556 + 4 pls.

HOLDEN, P., and A. D. HESS. 1959. Cache Valley virus, a previously undescribed mosquito-borne agent. *Science* 130: 1187–1188.

HOLDENRIED, R. 1952. Sylvatic plague studies. VIII. Notes on the alimentary and reproductive tracts of fleas, made during experimental studies of plague. *J. Parasit.* 38: 289–292.

HOLDENRIED, R., and S. F. QUAN. 1956. Susceptibility of New Mexico rodents to experimental plague. *U. S. Publ. Hlth Rept.* 71: 979–984.

HOLLAND, G. P. 1949. The Siphonaptera of Canada. *Dom. Canad. Dept. Agr. Tech. Bull.* 70. 306 pp.

HOOGSTRAAL, H. 1952. Biological factors of ticks (Ixodoidea) of the Ethiopian faunal region in relation to human injury and disease. *Trans. 9th int. Congr. Ent. Amsterdam* 1: 959–963.

HOOGSTRAAL, H. 1953. *Ornithodoros arenicolous* sp. nov. (Ixodoidea, Argasidae) from Egyptian desert-mammal burrows. *J. Parasit.* 39: 505–516.

HOOGSTRAAL, H. 1956. Notes on African *Haemaphysalis* ticks. III. The hyrax parasites, *H. bequaerti* sp. nov., *H. orientalis* N. and W., 1915 (new combination), and *H. cooleyi* Bedford, 1929 (Ixodoidea, Ixodidae). *J. Parasit.* 42: 156–172.

HOOGSTRAAL, H. 1956a. African Ixodoidea. I. Ticks of the Sudan (with special reference to Equatoria Province and with preliminary reviews of the genera *Boophilus, Margaropus* and *Hyalomma*). *U. S. Dept. Navy Res. Rept. NM 005050.2 9.07.* 1101 pp.

HOOGSTRAAL, H. 1958. The elephant louse, *Haematomyzus elephantis* Piaget, 1869, on wild African elephants and wart hogs. *Proc. ent. Soc. Wash.* 60: 232–233.

HOOGSTRAAL, H. 1959. On *Allophysalis*, a new subgenus of *Haemaphysalis* (Ixodoidea, Ixodidae). *J. Egypt publ. Hlth Ass.* 34: 37–42.

HOOGSTRAAL, H. 1959a. Biological observations on certain Turkish *Haemaphysalis* ticks (Ixodoidea, Ixodidae). *J. Parasit.* 45: 227–232.

HOOGSTRAAL, H., and M. N. KAISER. 1957. Results of the Namru-3 Southeastern Egypt expedition, 1954. 3. *Argas brumpti* Neumann, 1907, and *Ornithodoros foleyi* Parrot, 1928 (Ixodoidea, Argasidae) in Egypt. *Bull. zool. Soc. Egypt* 13: 29–37 + 3 pls.

HOOGSTRAAL, H., and M. N. KAISER. 1958. Observations on Egyptian *Hyalomma* ticks (Ixodoidea, Ixodidae). 2. Parasitism of migrating birds by immature *H. rufipes* Koch. *Ann. ent. Soc. Amer.* 51: 12–16.

HOOGSTRAAL, H., and M. N. KAISER. 1958a. The ticks (Ixodoidea) of Iraq; keys, hosts, and distribution. *J. Iraqi Med. Prof.* 6: 1–22 + 1 pl.

HOOGSTRAAL, H., and M. N. KAISER. 1959. Observations on Egyptian *Hyalomma* ticks (Ixodoidea, Ixodidae). 5. Biological notes and differences in identity of *H. anatolicum* and its subspecies *anatolicum* Koch and *excavatum* Koch among Russian and other workers. Identity of *H. lusitanicum* Koch. *Ann. ent. Soc. Amer.* 52: 243–261.

HOOGSTRAAL, H., and M. N. KAISER. 1959a. Ticks (Ixodoidea) of Arabia. *Fieldiana. Zoology, 39:* 297–322.

HOOGSTRAAL, H., and G. THEILER. 1959. Ticks (Ixodoidea, Ixodidae) parasitizing lower primates in Africa, Zanzibar, and Madagascar. *J. Parasit. 45:* 217–222.

HOPKINS, G. H. E. 1949. The host-associations of the lice of mammals. *Proc. zool. Soc. Lond. 119:* 387–604.

HOPKINS, G. H. E., and T. CLAY. 1952. *A checklist of the genera and species of Mallophaga.* London: British Museum (Nat. Hist.). 362 pp.

HOPKINS, G. H. E., and M. ROTHSCHILD. 1953. An illustrated catalogue of the Rothschild collection of fleas (Siphonaptera) in the British Museum (Nat. Hist.). Part 1. London: British Museum. xv + 361 pp. + 1 map + 45 pls.

HOPKINS, G. H. E., and M. ROTHSCHILD. 1956. An illustrated catalogue of the Rothschild collection of fleas (Siphonaptera) in the British Museum (Nat. Hist.). Part 2. London: British Museum. xi + 445 pp. + 1 map + 32 pls.

HOPLA, C. E. 1955. The multiplication of tularemia organisms in the lone star tick. *Amer. J. Hyg. 61:* 371–380.

HOPLA, C. E. 1955a. Observations on the life history of a rabbit tick (*Otobius lagophilus*). *J. Kans. ent. Soc. 28:* 114–116.

HORSFALL, W. R. 1955. *Mosquitoes: their bionomics and relation to disease.* New York: The Ronald Press Co. viii + 723 pp.

HORTON-SMITH, C. (ed.) 1957. Biological aspects of the transmission of disease. Edinburgh: Oliver & Boyd, Ltd. viii + 184 pp.

HUBBARD, C. A. 1947. *Fleas of western Northern America.* Ames, Iowa: Iowa State College Press. xi + 533 pp.

HUDSON, A., J. A. McKIEL, A. S. WEST, and T. K. R. BOURNS. 1958. Reactions to mosquito bites. *Mosquito News 18:* 249–252.

HURLBUT, H. S. 1956. West Nile virus infection in arthropods. *Amer. J. trop. Med. Hyg. 5:* 76–85.

HUTCHISON, W. F., H. C. RICKS, SR., and D. S. WOOLDRIDGE. 1959. A new record of human infection with *Dipylidium caninum* in the United States. *Amer. J. trop. Med. Hyg. 8:* 603.

HYMAN, L. H. 1940. *The invertebrates through Ctenophora.* New York: McGraw-Hill Book Co., Inc. xii + 726 pp.

HYMAN, L. H. 1951. *The invertebrates: Acanthocephala, Aschelminthes, and Entoprocta, The pseudocoelomate Bilateria.* New York: McGraw-Hill Book Co., Inc. 572 pp.

IMMS, A. D. 1957. *A general textbook of entomology.* 9th ed., revised by O. W. Richards and R. G. Davies. London: Methuen & Co. x + 886 pp.

IYENGAR, M. O. T. 1956. Annotated bibliography of filariasis and elephantiasis. Part II. Studies on mosquitoes of the South Pacific Region. *Tech. Paper S. Pacif. Comm. No. 88.* xi + 114 pp.

JACKSON, E. B., J. X. DANAUSKAS, M. C. COALE, and J. E. SMADEL. 1957. Recovery of *Rickettsia akari* from the Korean vole, *Microtus fortis pelliceus. Amer. J. Hyg. 66:* 301–308.

JACKSON, W. B., and P. P. MAIER. 1955. Dispersion of marked American cockroaches from sewer manholes in Phoenix, Ariz. *Amer. J. trop. Med. Hyg. 4:* 141–146.

JAMES, M. T. 1947. The flies that cause myiasis in man. *U. S. Dept. Agr. misc. Publ. 631:* 175 pp.

JASCHKE, W. 1933. Beiträge zur Kenntnis der symbiontischen Einrichtungen bei Hirudineen und Ixodiden. *Z. Parasitenk. 5:* 515–541.

JEANNEL, R. 1949. Les insectes: classification et phylogénie les insectes fossiles évolution et géonémie. In GRASSÉ, *Traité de Zoologie,* Vol. 9: pp. 1–110. Paris: Masson et Cie.

JEFFERY, G. M. 1960. Infectivity to mosquitoes of *Plasmodium vivax* and *Plasmodium falciparum* under various conditions. *Amer. J. trop. Med. Hyg. 9:* 315–320.

JELLISON, W. L. 1940. The burrowing owl as a host to the argasid tick, *Ornithodorus parkeri. U. S. Publ. Hlth Rept. 55:* 206–208.

JENKINS, D. W. 1950. Bionomics of *Culex tarsalis* in relation to western equine encephalomyelitis. *Amer. J. trop. Med. 30:* 909–916.

JOBLING, B. 1925. A contribution to the biology of *Ornithodorus moubata,* Murray. *Bull. ent. Res. 15:* 271–279.

JOBLING, B. 1928. The structure of the head and mouth parts in *Culicoides pulicaris* L. (Diptera Nematocera). *Bull. ent. Res. 18:* 211–236 + 4 pls.

JOBLING, B. 1933. A revision of the structure of the head, mouth part and salivary glands of *Glossina palpalis* Rob. Desv. *Parasitology 24:* 449–490 + 4 pls.

JOBLING, B. 1949. Host-parasite relationship between the American Streblidae and the bats, with a new key to the American genera and a record of the Streblidae from Trinidad, British West Indies (Diptera). *Parasitology 39:* 315–329.

JOHNSON, C. G. 1941. The ecology of the bed bug, *Cimex lectularius* L., in Britain: A report on research, 1935–40. *J. Hyg. 41:* 345–461.

JOHNSON, C. G., and K. MELLANBY. 1942. The parasitology of human scabies. *Parasitology. 34:* 285–290.

JOHNSON, P. T. 1957. A classification of the Siphonaptera of South America. *Mem. ent. Soc. Wash. No. 5.* 275 pp.

JONES, B. M. 1950. A method for studying the distribution and bionomics of trombiculid mites (Acarina: Trombidiidae). *Parasitology 40:* 1–13.

JONES, R. M. 1930. Some effects of temperature and humidity as factors in the biology of the bed bug (*Cimex lectularius* Linn.). *Ann. ent. Soc. Amer. 23:* 105–119.

JOYCE, C. R., and G. W. EDDY. 1943. Hosts and seasonal notes on the rabbit tick, *Haemaphysalis leporis-palustris. Iowa St. Coll. J. Sci. 17:* 205–212.

KARSTAD, L., S. VADLAMUDI, R. P. HANSON, D. O. TRAINER, JR., and V. H. LEE. 1960. Eastern equine encephalitis studies in Wisconsin. *J. infect. Dis. 106:* 53–59.

KARTMAN, L. 1954. Frequency and intensity of *Dirofilaria immitis* infections in mosquitoes. *Exp. Parasit. 3:* 25–29.

KARTMAN, L., V. I. MILES, and F. M. PRINCE. 1958. Ecological studies of wild rodent plague in the San Francisco Bay area of California. *Amer. J. trop. Med. Hyg. 7:* 112–124.

KARTMAN, L., F. M. PRINCE, and S. F. QUAN. 1956. Studies on *Pasteurella pestis* in fleas. Comparative plague-vector efficiency of *Xenopsylla vexabilis hawaiiensis* and *Xenopsylla cheopis. Bull. Wld Hlth Org. 14:* 681–704.

KARTMAN, L., S. F. QUAN, and V. I. MILES. 1960. Ecological studies of wild rodent plague in the San Francisco Bay area of California. V. The distribution of naturally infected fleas during an epizootic in relation to their infection rates. *Amer. J. trop. Med. Hyg. 9:* 96–103.

KARULIN, B. E. 1960. The geographico-ecological analysis of foci of Q fever. *J Microbiol. Epidemiol. Immunobiol. 31:* 1597–1604.

KASSIANOFF, L. 1937. Étude morphologique et biologique de la famille des cimicidés. *Ann. Parasit. hum. comp. 15:* 97–124, 193–217, 289–319, 385–408.

KATES, K. C., and C. E. RUNKEL. 1948. Observations on oribatid mite vectors of *Moniezia expansa* on pastures with a report of several new vectors from the United States. *Proc. helminth. Soc. Wash. 15:* 20–33.

KEAY, G. 1937. The ecology of the harvest mite (*Trombicula autumnalis*) in the British Isles. *J. Anim. Ecol. 6:* 23–25.

KEILIN, D. 1944. Respiratory systems and respiratory adaptations in larvae and pupae of Diptera. *Parasitology 36:* 1–66 + 2 pls.

KÉLER, S. 1939. Übersicht über die gesamte Literatur der Mallophagen. *Z. angew. Ent. 25:* 487–524.

KÉLER, S. 1957. Über die Deszendenz und die Differenzierung der Mallophagen. *Z. Parasitenk. 18:* 55–160.

KEMPER, H. 1958. Experimentelle Untersuchungen über die Wirkung von Raupenhaaren auf die menschliche Haut. *Proc. 10th int. Congr. Ent. 3:* 719–723.

KERSHAW, W. E. 1955. Symposium on loaiasis. VIII. The epidemiology of infections with *Loa loa. Trans. R. Soc. trop. Med. Hyg. 49:* 143–150.

KERSHAW, W. E. 1958. The population dynamics of infection with *Onchocerca volvulus* in the vector *Simulium damnosum. Proc. 10th int. Congr. Ent. 3:* 499–501.

KERSHAW, W. E., W. CREWE, and R. M. GORDON. 1949. The local reaction of the animal host to the bites of snakes and the stings of venomous creatures. *Trans. R. Soc. trop. Med. Hyg. 43:* 6–7.

KERSHAW, W. E., R. W. J. KEAY, W. L. NICHOLAS, and A. ZAHRA. 1953. Studies on the epidemiology of filariasis in West Africa, with special reference to the British Cameroons and the Niger Delta. IV. The incidence of *Loa loa* and *Acanthocheilonema perstans* in the rain forest, the forest fringe and the mountain grasslands of the British Cameroons with observations on the species of *Chrysops* and *Culicoides* found. *Ann. trop. Med. Parasit. 47:* 406–425.

KESSEL, Q. C. 1925. A synopsis of the Streblidae of the world. *J. N. Y. ent. Soc. 33:* 11–34.

KILPATRICK, J. W., and H. F. SCHOOF. 1956. Fly production in treated and untreated privies. *U. S. Publ. Hlth Rept. 71:* 787–796.

KILPATRICK, J. W., and H. F. SCHOOF. 1959. Interrelationship of water and *Hermetia illucens* breeding to *Musca domestica* production in human excrement. *Amer. J. trop. Med. Hyg. 8:* 597–602.

KING, A. F. A. 1883. Insects and disease. Mosquitoes and malaria. *Pop. Sci. Mon. 23:* 644–658.

KIRK, R. 1956. Studies in leishmaniasis in the Anglo-Egyptian Sudan. XII. Attempts to find a reservoir host. *Trans. R. Soc. trop. Med. Hyg. 50:* 169–177.

KIRK, R., and D. J. LEWIS. 1955. Studies in leishmaniasis in the Anglo-Egyptian Sudan. XI. *Phlebotomus* in relation to leishmaniasis in the Sudan. *Trans. R. Soc. trop. Med. Hyg. 49:* 229–290.

KISSLING, R. E., R. W. CHAMBERLAIN, D. B. NELSON, and D. D. STAMM. 1955. Studies on the North American arthropod-borne encephalitides. VIII. Equine encephalitis studies in Louisiana. *Amer. J. Hyg. 62:* 233–254.

KITAOKA, M., and A. SHISHIDO. 1950. Surviving period of *Rickettsia* in feces from lice infected with epidemic and murine typhus. *Japan. med. J. 3:* 265–272.

KOHLS, G. M. 1956. Colorado tick fever discovered in California. *Calif. Vector Views 2:* 17.

KOKERNOT, R. H., H. E. PATERSON, and B. DEMEILLON. 1958. Studies on the transmission of Wesselsbron virus by *Aedes (Ochlerotatus) caballus* (Theo.). *S. Afr. med. J. 32:* 546–548.

KOKERNOT, R. H., K. C. SMITHBURN, H. E. PATERSON, and B. M. McINTOSH. 1960. Isolation of germiston virus, a hitherto unknown agent, from culicine mosquitoes, and a report of infection in two laboratory workers. *Amer. J. trop. Med. Hyg. 9:* 62–69.

KRULL, W. H. 1939. Observations on the distribution and ecology of the oribatid mites. *J. Wash. Acad. Sci. 29:* 519–528.

KRÜMMEL, H., and A. BRAUNS. 1956. Myiasis des Auges. Medizinische und entomologische Grundlagen. *Z. angew. Zool. 43:* 129–190.

KUDO, R. R. 1954. Protozoology. 4th ed. Springfield, Ill.: Charles C Thomas. xi + 966 pp.

KULAGIN, S. M., G. P. SOMOV, V. A. SILICH, N. I. FEDOROVA, M. I. SHAPIRO, L. V. SUVOROVA, and V. N. BOBROVSKII. 1960. Further observations on tick-borne rickettsiosis in the Maritime Territory. *J. Microbiol. Epidemiol. Immunobiol. 31:* 1652–1660.

KUMM, H. W. 1935. The natural infection of *Hippelates pallipes* Loew with the spirochaetes of yaws. *Trans. R. Soc. trop. Med. Hyg. 29:* 265–272.

KUMM, H. W. 1935a. The digestive mechanism of one of the West Indian 'eye gnats', *Hippelates pallipes* Loew. *Ann. trop. Med. Parasit. 29:* 283–298 + 2 pls.

LA FACE, L. 1926. Ricerche sulla biologia del "*Culex pipiens*". L'alimentazione e l'ibernamento. *Riv. Malariol. 5:* 132–156.

LAING, A. B. G., J. F. B. EDESON, and R. H. WARTON. 1960. Studies on filariasis in Malaya: The vertebrate hosts of *Brugia malayi* and *B. pahangi. Ann. trop. Med. Parasit. 54:* 92–99 + 2 pls.

LAMBORN, W. A. 1930. The remarkable adaptation by which a dipterous pupa (Tabanidae) is preserved from the danger of fissures in drying mud. *Proc. roy. Soc. Ser. B 106:* 83–87.

LAMOTTE, L. C. 1960. Japanese B encephalitis virus in the organs of infected mosquitoes. *Amer. J. Hyg. 72:* 73–87.

LARUE, G. R. 1957. The classification of digenetic Trematoda: a review and a new system. *Exp. Parasit. 6:* 306–344 + 2 pls.

LAVOIPIERRE, M. M. J. 1958. The development of *Loa loa* in *Chrysops silacea*, the escape of the infective forms from the head of the fly, and the effect of the worm on its insect host. *Proc. 10th int. Congr. Ent. 3:* 497–498.

LAVOIPIERRE, M. M. J. 1958a. Studies on the host-parasite relationships of filarial nematodes and their arthropod hosts. I. The sites of development and the migration of *Loa loa* in *Chrysops silacea*, the escape of the infective forms from the head of the fly, and the effect of the worm on its insect host. *Ann. trop. Med. Parasit. 52:* 103–121 + 2 pls.

LAVOIPIERRE, M. M. J. 1958b. Studies on the host-parasite relationships of filarial nematodes and their arthropod hosts. II. The arthropod as a host to the nematode: a brief appraisal of our present knowledge, based on a study of the more important literature from 1878 to 1957. *Ann. trop. Med. Parasit. 52:* 336–345.

LAVOIPIERRE, M. M. J., and R. F. RIEK. 1955. Observations on the feeding habits of argasid ticks and on the effect of their bites on laboratory animals, together with a note on the production of coxal fluid by several of the species studied. *Ann. trop. Med. Parasit. 49:* 96–113.

LAVOIPIERRE, M. M. J., G. DICKERSON, and R. M. GORDON. 1959. Studies on the methods of feeding of bloodsucking arthropods. I. The manner in which triatomine bugs obtain their blood-meal, as observed in the tissues of the living rodent, with some remarks on the effects of the bite on human volunteers. *Ann. trop. Med. Parasit. 53:* 235–250 + 1 pl.

LEES, A. D. 1946. The water balance of *Ixodes ricinus* L. and certain other ticks. *Parasitology 37:* 1–20.

LEES, A. D., and J. W. L. BEAMENT. 1948. An egg-waxing organ in ticks. *Quar. J. micro. Sci. 89:* 291–332 + 1 pl.

LEESON, H. S. 1941. The effect of temperature upon the hatching of the eggs of *Pediculus humanus corporis* De Geer (Anoplura). *Parasitology 33:* 243–249.

LE GAC, P. 1951. Le typhus de savanes chez l'enfant. *Bull. Soc. Path. exot. 44:* 169–173.

LENNETTE, E. H., M. I. OTA, F. J. FUJIMOTO, A. WIENER, and E. D. LOOMIS. 1957. Turlock virus: a presumably new arthropod-borne virus. Isolation and identification. *Amer. J. trop. Med. Hyg. 6:* 1024–1035.

LÉON, J. R. DE. 1957. Simuliid vectors of onchocerciasis in Guatemala. *Bull. Wld Hlth Org. 16:* 523–529.

LEVI, H. W. 1958. The spider genus *Latrodectus* (Araneae, Theridiidae). *Trans. Amer. micr. Soc. 78:* 7–43.

LEVI, M. I., and Y. M. RALL'. 1960. Additional data characterizing the main reservoirs of *Pasteurella pestis*. *J. Microbiol. Epidemiol. Immunobiol. 31:* 1628–1633.

LEVI-CASTILLO, R. 1952. The problem of human and equine encephalomyelitis in Ecuador. *Acta trop.* (Basel). *9:* 77–80.

LEVINE, N. D. 1961. *Protozoan parasites of domestic animals and of man.* Minneapolis: Burgess. iii + 412 pp.

LEWIS, D. J. 1953. The *Stegomyia* mosquitoes of the Anglo-Egyptian Sudan. *Ann. trop. Med. Parasit. 47:* 51–61.

LEWIS, D. J. 1956. The anopheline mosquitoes of the Sudan. *Bull. ent. Res. 47:* 475–494.

LEWIS, D. J., and R. KIRK. 1954. Notes on the Phlebotominae of the Anglo-Egyptian Sudan. *Ann. trop. Med. Parasit. 48:* 33–45.

LEWIS, E. A. 1946. Nairobi sheep disease: the survival of the virus in the tick *Rhipicephalus appendiculatus*. *Parasitology 37:* 55–59.

LEWIS, R. T. 1892. Note on the process of oviposition as observed in a species of cattle tick. *J. R. micro. Soc. 1892:* 449–454 + 1 pl.

LIBIKOVA, H., D. BLASKOVIC, J. VILCEK, J. REHACEK, M. GRESIKOVA, O. MACICKA, E. ERNEK, and V. MAYER. 1960. Incidence of antibodies against tick-borne encephalitis virus in man and domestic animals in a small village in a natural focus of infection. *J. Hyg. Epidemiol., Microbiol., Immunol. 4:* 327–332.

LINK, V. B. 1955. A history of plague in the United States of America. *U. S. Publ. Hlth Monog. 26.* viii + 120 pp.

LIPOVSKY, L. J., G. W. BYERS, and E. N. KARDOS. 1957. Spermatophores: the mode of insemination of chiggers (Acarina: Trombiculidae). *J. Parasit. 43:* 256–262.

LISTON, W. G. 1905. Plague, rats and fleas. *J. Bombay nat. Hist. Soc. 16:* 253–274 + 2 pls.

LUGINBUHL, R. E., S. F. SATRIANO, C. F. HELMBOLDT, A. L. LAMSON, and E. L. JUNGHERR. 1958. Investigation of eastern equine encephalomyelitis. II. Outbreaks in Connecticut pheasants. *Amer. J. Hyg. 67:* 4–9.

LUH, P. L., and W. C. WOO. 1950. A list of Chinese ticks. *In Chinese. Chin. J. ent. 1:* 195–222. (Trans. No. 19. U. S. Nav. Med. Unit 3.)

LUMBRERAS, V. H., W. FLORES, and A. ESCALLÓN. 1959. Allergische Reaktionen auf Stiche von Reduviiden und ihre Bedeutung bei der Chagaskrankheit. *Z. Tropenmed. u. Parasit. 10:* 6–19.

LUMSDEN, W. H. R. 1955. Entomological studies, relating to yellow fever epidemiology, at Gede and Taveta, Kenya. *Bull. ent. Res. 46:* 149–183.

LUOTO, L. 1959. The epidemiology of Q fever in the United States. *Amer. J. publ. Hlth 49:* 334–338.

MACCHIAVELLO, A. 1954. Reservoirs and vectors of plague. *J. trop. med. (Hyg.) 57:* 3–8, 45–48, 65–69, 116–121, 158–176, 191–197, 220–224, 238–243, 275–279, 294–298.

McDANIEL, I. N., and W. R. HORSFALL. 1957. Induced copulation of aedine mosquitoes. *Science 125:* 745.

MACDONALD, G. 1956. Theory of the eradication of malaria. *Bull. Wld Hlth Org. 15:* 369–387.

MACDONALD, G. 1956a. Epidemiological basis of malaria control. *Bull. Wld Hlth Org. 15:* 613–626.

MACDONALD, G. 1957. *The epidemiology and control of malaria.* London: Oxford University Press. liv + 201 pp.

McKEOWN, K. C. 1952. *Australian spiders: their lives and habits.* 2nd ed. Sydney, Aus.: Angus & Robertson Ltd. xiv + 274 pp.

McKIEL, J. A., and J. C. CLUNIE. 1960. Chromatographic fractionation of the non-dialyzable portion of mosquito extract and intracutaneous reactions of mosquito-bite-sensitive subjects to the separated components. *Canad. J. Zool. 38:* 479–488.

McLEAN, D. M. 1955. Multiplication of viruses in mosquitoes following feeding and injection into the body cavity. *Aust. J. exp. Biol. med. Sci. 33:* 53–65.

MacLENNON, K. J. R., and W. W. KIRKBY. 1958. The eradication of *Glossina morsitans submorsitans* Newst. in part of a river flood plain in Northern Nigeria by chemical means. *Bull. ent. Res. 49:* 123–131.

MacLEOD, J. 1948. The distribution and dynamics of ked populations. *Melophagus ovinus* Linn. *Parasitology 39:* 61–68.

McLINTOCK, J., and K. R. DEPNER. 1954. A review of the life-history and habits of the horn fly, *Siphona irritans* (L.) (Diptera: Muscidae). *Canad. Ent. 86:* 20–33.

MAIER, P. P., W. C. BAKER, M. D. BOGUE, J. W. KILPATRICK, and K. D. QUARTERMAN. 1952. Field studies on the resting habits of flies in relation to chemical control. Part I. In urban areas. *Amer. J. trop. Med. Hyg. 1:* 1020–1025.

MALLOCH, J. R. 1917. A preliminary classification of Diptera exclusive of Pupipara based upon larval or pupal characters with keys to imagines in certain families. Part I. *Bull. Ill. lab. nat. Hist. 12* (3): 161–409 + 30 pls.

MANALANG, C. 1931. Origin of the irritating substance in mosquito bite. *Philipp. J. Sci. 46:* 39–43 + 1 pl.

416 BIBLIOGRAPHY

MANDOUL, R., E. HADIDA, and J. SABATIER. 1956. Dermatite érythématopapuleuse provoquée par *Eotetranychus telarius* L. *Bull. Soc. Path. exot. 49:* 303–305 + 1 pl.

MANSON, P. 1880. Additional notes on *Filaria sanguinis hominis* and filaria disease. *Med. Rep. Shanghai 18:* 31–51.

MANSON-BAHR, P. E. C., R. B. HEISCH, and P. C. C. GARNHAM. 1959. Studies in leishmaniasis in East Africa. IV. The Montenegro test in kala-azar in Kenya. *Trans. R. Soc. trop. Med. Hyg. 53:* 380–383.

MARETIC, Z., and M. STANIC. 1954. The health problem of arachnidism. *Bull. Wld Hlth Org. 11:* 107–122.

MARMION, B. P. 1954. Q fever. II. Natural history and epidemiology of Q fever in man. *Trans. R. Soc. trop. Med. Hyg. 48:* 197–203 + disc. 203–207.

MARSHALL, J. F. 1938. *The British mosquitoes.* London: British Museum. xi + 341 pp. + 20 pls.

MARSHALL, T. K. 1957. Wasp and bee stings. *Practitioner 178:* 712–722.

MARTINI, E. 1923. *Lehrbuch der medizinischen Entomologie.* Jena: Gustav Fischer. xvi + 462 pp.

MASON, P. J., and A. J. HADDOW. 1957. An epidemic of virus disease in Southern Province, Tanganyika Territory, in 1952–53. An additional note on Chikungunya virus isolations in serum antibodies. *Trans R. Soc. trop. Med. Hyg. 51:* 238–240.

MATTINGLY, P. F. 1958. Genetical aspects of the *Aedes aegypti* problem. II. Disease relationships, genetics and control. *Ann. trop. Med. Parasit. 52:* 5–17.

MAULL, W. C. 1880. Window screens as a prophylactic of malarial poisoning. *Mich. med. News. 1880:* 266–267.

MEILLON, B. DE. 1957. Bionomics of the vectors of onchocerciasis in the Ethiopian geographical region. *Bull. Wld Hlth Org. 16:* 509–522.

MELLANBY, K. 1942. Natural population of the head-louse (*Pediculus humanus capitis:* Anoplura) on infected children in England. *Parasitology 34:* 180–184.

MEYER, K. F. 1948. The animal kingdom, a reservoir of human disease. *Ann. inter. Med. 29:* 326–346.

MICHENER, C. D. 1946. Observations on the habits and life history of a chigger mite, *Eutrombicula batatas* (Acarina: Trombiculinae). *Ann. ent. Soc. Amer. 39:* 101–118.

MICHENER, C. D., and M. H. MICHENER. 1951. *American social insects: a book about bees, ants, wasps and termites.* New York: D. Van Nostrand Co. xiv + 296 pp.

MIDDLEKAUFF, W. 1950. The horse flies and deer flies of California. (Diptera: Tabanidae). *Bull. Calif. Insect. Sur.* Vol. 1, no. 1.

MILANI, R. 1955. Considerazioni genetiche su alcuni aspetti della biologica della mosca domestica e osservazioni sulla fecondita e sulla fertilita. *Riv. Parassit. 16:* 257–270.

MILLER, R. H. 1947. The toxicity of the venom of tarantula (*Aphonopelma*). Part II. Toxicity of venom upon vertebrates. *J. Ent. Zool. 39:* 57–67.

MILLOT, J. 1949. Ordre des Araneides (Araneae). *In* GRASSÉ, *Traité de zoologie,* Vol. 6: pp. 589–743. Paris: Masson et Cie.

MILLOT, J., and M. VACHON. 1949. Ordre des scorpions. *In* GRASSÉ, *Traité de Zoologie,* Vol. 6: pp. 386–436. Paris: Masson et Cie.

MILNE, A. 1952. Features of the ecology and control of the sheep tick, *Ixodes ricinus* L., in Britain. *Ann. appl. Biol. 39:* 144–146.

MIRZA, M. B. 1938. Behandlung des Medina-Wurms in India. *Zool. Anz. Supp.* (*Verhandl. deutsch. Zool. Ges. 41*) 11: 170–172.

MITRA, R. D. 1959. Notes on sandflies. Sandflies of Punch and Riasi districts of Kashmir. *Z. Tropenmed. u. Parasit. 10:* 56–66.

MITZMAIN, M. B. 1910. General observations on the bionomics of the rodent and human fleas. *U. S. Publ. Hlth Bull. 38.* 34 pp.

MITZMAIN, M. B. 1913. The biology of *Tabanus striatus* Fabr., the horsefly of the Philippines. *Philipp. J. Sci. (B) 8:* 197–221 + 7 pls.

MITZMAIN, M. B. 1913a. The bionomics of *Stomoxys calcitrans* Linnaeus; a preliminary account. *Philipp. J. Sci. (B) 8:* 29–48.

MJÖBERG, E. 1910. Studien über Mallophagen und Anopluren. *Ark. Zool. 6 (13)*: 1–297 + 5 pls.

MOHR, C. O., W. E. GOOD, and J. H. SCHUBERT. 1953. Status of marine typhus infection in domestic rats in the United States, 1952, and relation to infestation by oriental rat fleas. *Amer. J. publ. Hlth 43*: 1514–1522.

MOISER, B. 1946. Leprosy: a new outlook. *E. Afr. med. J. 23*: 295–300.

MONTESTRUC, E. 1955. La régression du paludisme à la Martinique. *Bull. Soc. Path. exot. 48*: 234–242.

MOORE, W. 1918. An interesting reaction to louse bites. *J. Amer. med. Ass. 71*: 1481–1482.

MOORTHY, V. N. 1938. Observations on the life history of *Camallanus sweeti*. *J. Parasit. 24*: 323–337.

MOOSER, H., and F. WEYER. 1954. Künstliche Infektion von Läusen mit *Borrelia duttoni*. *Z. Tropenmed u. Parasit. 5*: 28–45.

MORRIS, K. R. S. 1952. The ecology of epidemic sleeping sickness. II. The effects of an epidemic. *Bull. ent. Res. 43*: 375–396 + 1 pl.

MORRIS, K. R. S. 1960. Trapping as a means of studying the game tsetse, *Glossina pallidipes* Aust. *Bull. ent. Res. 51*: 533–557 + 1 pl.

MUIR, D. A. 1954. Ants, *Myrmica rubra* L. and *M. scabinodis* Nylander, as intermediate hosts of a cestode. *Nature* (London) *173*: 688–689.

MUIRHEAD-THOMSON, R. C. 1954. Factors determining the true reservoir of infection of *Plasmodium falciparum* and *Wuchereria bancrofti* in a West African Village. *Trans. R. Soc. trop. Med. Hyg. 48*: 208–225.

MUIRHEAD-THOMSON, R. C. 1957. The malarial infectivity of an African village population to mosquitoes (*Anopheles gambiae*). A random xenodiagnostic survey. *Amer. J. trop. Med. Hyg. 6*: 971–979.

MUKERJI, D., and P. SEN-SARMA. 1955. Anatomy and affinity of the elephant louse *Haematomyzus elephantis* Piaget (Insecta: Rhynchophthiraptera). *Parasitology 45*: 5–30.

MULES, M. M. 1940. Notes on the life history and artificial breeding of the Australian "stickfast" flea, *Echidnophaga myrmecobii* Rothschild. *Aust. J. exp. Biol. med. Sci. 18*: 385–390.

MULLA, M. S., and R. B. MARCH. 1959. Flight range, dispersal patterns and population density of the eye gnat, *Hippelates collusor*. *Ann. ent. Soc. Amer. 52*: 641–646.

MULLIGAN, H. W. 1955. Recent investigations on trypanosomyiasis in British West Africa. *Trans. R. Soc. trop. Med. Hyg. 49*: 199–223.

MUNSHI, D. M. 1960. Micro-anatomy of the proventriculus of the common rat flea, *Xenopsylla cheopis* (Rothschild). *J. Parasit. 46*: 362–372.

MURNAGHAN, M. F. 1958. Neuro-anatomical site in tick paralysis. *Nature* (London) *181*: 131.

MUSPRATT, J. 1956. The *Stegomyia* mosquitoes of South Africa and some neighbouring territories. Including chapters on the mosquito-borne virus diseases of the Ethiopian zoo-geographical region of Africa. *Mem. ent. Soc. S. Afr. No. 4.* 138 pp.

MYASNIKOV, Y. A., and M. I. TSAREVA. 1959. The epidemiological significance of the hare in ʼularaemia. *J. Microbiol. Epidemiol. Immunobiol. 30*: (12): 108–113.

NASH, T. A. M., and W. A. PAGE. 1953. The ecology of *Glossina palpalis* in northern Nigeria. *Trans. R. ent. Soc. Lond. 104*: 71–169.

NASH, T. A. M., and J. O. STEINER. 1957. The effect of obstructive clearing on *Glossina palpalis*. *Bull. ent. Res. 48*: 323–339.

NEEDHAM, J. G., J. R. TRAVER, and Y. HSU. 1935. *The biology of mayflies*. Ithaca, N. Y.: Comstock Publishing Co. 759 pp. + 40 pls.

NEITZ, W. O. 1956. Classification, transmission and biology of piroplasms of domestic animals, *Ann. N. Y. Acad. Sci. 64*: 56–111.

NEITZ, W. O. 1959. Theilerioses. *Advanc. vet. Sci. 5*: 241–298.

NEIVA, A., and H. LENT. 1941. Sinopse dos Triatomideos. *Rev. Ent. 12*: 61–92.

NEVEU-LEMAIRE, M. 1936. *Traité d'helminthologie médicale et vétérinaire.* Paris: Vigot Frères. xx + 1514 pp.

NICHOLS, E., M. E. RINGE, and G. G. RUSSEL. 1953. The relationship of the habits of the house mouse and the mouse mite (*Allodermanyssus sanguineus*) to the spread of rickettsialpox. *Ann. inter. Med. 39:* 92–102.

NUTTALL, G. H. F. 1900. Upon the part played by mosquitoes in the propagation of malaria. A historical and critical study. *J. trop. Med. 2:* 198–200, 231–233, 245–247, 275–277, 305–307; and *3:* 11–13.

NUTTALL, G. H. F. 1917. The biology of *Pediculus humanus. Parasitology 10:* 80–185 + 2 pls.

OLDROYD, H. 1952. The horse-flies (Diptera, Tabanidae) of the Ethiopian Region. Parts 1 and 2. London: British Museum (Nat. Hist.). ix + 226 pp. + 25 pls.

OLDROYD, H. 1954. The horse flies (Diptera: Tabanidae) of the Ethiopian Region. Vol. 2. London: British Museum (Nat. Hist.). x + 341 pp.

OLDROYD, H. 1955. III. Some comments on the species of *Chrysops* bred and collected at Kumba, British Cameroons. *Trans. R. Soc. trop. Med. Hyg. 49:* 111–114.

OLDROYD, H. 1957. The horse-flies (Diptera: Tabanidae) of the Ethiopian region. Vol. 3. London: British Museum (Nat. Hist.). xii + 489 pp. + 13 pls.

OLSEN, T., and M. E. RUEGER. 1950. Experimental transmission of *Salmonella oranienburg* through roaches. *U. S. Publ. Hlth Rept. 65:* 531–540.

ORTIZ-MARIOTTE, C., and G. VARELA. 1949. Cultivo del *Rhipicephalus sanguineus* en el laboratorio y vacuna hecha conesta garrapata. *Medicina 29:* 323–335.

OTSURU, M., and S. OGAWA. 1959. Observations on the bite of the tabanid larva in paddy fields (Diptera: Tabanidae). *Acta med. biol. 7:* 37–50.

PARMAN, D. C. 1945. Effect of weather on *Cochliomyia americana* and a review of methods and economic applications of the study. *J. econ. Ent. 38:* 66–76.

PATTERSON, R. A. 1960. Physiological action of scorpion venom. *Amer. J. trop. Med. Hyg. 9:* 410–414.

PATTON, W. S. 1920. Some notes on the arthropods of medical and veterinary importance in Mesopotamia, and on their relation to disease. Part I. The gad flies of Mesopotamia. *Indian J. med. Res. 7:* 735–750 + 1 pl.

PATTON, W. S., and F. W. CRAGG. 1913. *A textbook of medical entomology.* London: Christian Literary Society for India. xxxiv + 768 pp.

PAVLOVSKY, E. N. 1927. *Gifttiere und ihre Giftigkeit.* Jena: G. Fischer. xvi + 516 pp.

PAVLOVSKY, E. N. 1946. On the theory of natural foci of diseases transmissable to man. *In Russian. J. gen. Biol. 7:* 3–33. *English summary.*

PAVLOVSKY, E. N. 1955. The actual state of the doctrine of natural nidality of diseases of man. *In* PAVLOVSKY *et al.,* 1955, pp. 17–26. Leningrad: Medgiz.

PAVLOVSKY, E. N., P. A. PETRISHCHEVA, D. N. ZASUKHIN, and N. G. OLSUF'EV. 1955. Natural nidi of human diseases and regional epidemiology. *In Russian, English summary.* Leningrad: Medgiz. 532 pp.

PAVLOVSKY, E. N., and A. N. SKRUNNIK. 1945. On the period during which females of *Ornithodorus papillipes* are able to transmit the tick relapsing fever. *In Russian. Zool. Zh. 24:* 161. (Abs. *Trop. Dis. Bull. 43:* 223.)

PCHELKINA, A. A., Z. M. ZHMAEVA, and R. I. ZUBKOVA. 1956. Q fever in Northern Kazakhstan. *In Russian. Zhurnal Mikrobiologii, Epidemiologii i Immunobiologii 1956 (11):* 32–35. (*Trop. Dis. Bull. 54:* 554.)

PENNAK, R. W. 1953. *Fresh-water invertebrates of the United States.* New York: The Ronald Press Co. ix + 769 pp.

PENNER, L. R., T. FRANCIS, JR., and G. C. BROWN. 1954. Some observations on the ecology of a North American chigger, *Trombicula (Eutrombicula) lipovskyana* Wolfenbarger, 1952, in a Tennessee community. *J. Kans. ent. Soc. 27:* 113–117.

PENNER, L. R., and F. P. POCIUS. 1956. Nostril entry as the mode of infection by the first stage larvae of a rodent *Cuterebra.* Abs. *J. Parasit. 42: (4 part 2):* 42.

PETERSON, G. D., JR. 1956. The introduction of mosquitoes of the genus *Toxorhynchites* into American Samoa. *J. econ. Ent. 49:* 786–789.

PETERSON, H. O., I. H. ROBERTS, W. W. BECKLUND, and H. E. KEMPER. 1953. Anaemia in cattle caused by heavy infestations of the blood-sucking louse, *Haematopinus eurysternus*. *J. Amer. vet. Med. Ass. 122:* 373–376.

PETRISHCHEVA, P. A. 1935. Faune, biologie et écologie des phlébotomes de la Turkomanie. *In Russian. Rec. Trav. 25e Anniv. Sci. Pavlovsky, 1909–34:* 202–259. (Abs. *Rev. Appl. Ent.* [B] *24:* 179.)

PETRUNKEVITCH, A. 1952. Principles of classification as illustrated by studies of Arachnida. *Systematic Zool. 1:* 1–19.

PHILIP, C. B. 1931. Two new species of *Uranotaenia* (Culicidae) from Nigeria with notes on the genus in the Ethiopian region. *Bull. ent. Res. 22:* 183–193.

PHILIP, C. B. 1948. Tsutsugamushi disease (Scrub typhus) in World War II. *J. Parasit. 34:* 169–191.

PHILIP, C. B. 1956. Comments on the classification of the order Rickettsiales. *Canad. J. Microbiol. 2:* 261–269.

PHILIPSON, J. 1956. A study of factors determining the distribution of the larvae of the blackfly, *Simulium ornatum* Mg. *Bull. ent. Res. 47:* 227–238.

PIERCE, W. D. 1921. *Sanitary entomology.* Boston: Richard D. Badger. xxvi + 518 pp.

PIERCY, P. L. 1956. Transmission of anaplasmosis. *Ann. N. Y. Acad. Sci. 64:* 40–48.

PIMENTEL, D., J. E. DEWEY, and H. H. SCHWARDT. 1951. An increase in the duration of the life cycle of DDT-resistant strains of the house fly. *J. econ. Ent. 44:* 477–481.

PIONTKOVSKAIA, S. P., and N. K. MISCHENKO. 1959. Ecology of *Dermacentor nuttalli* Olen, and of some other ectoparasites of rodents in a natural reservoir of tick-borne typhus fever in the Tuva autonomous region. *In Russian. Med. Parasit.* (Moscow) *28:* 164–170. (Abs. *Trop. Dis. Bull. 56:* 934–935.)

PIPKIN, A. C. 1949. Experimental studies on the role of filth flies in the transmission of *Endamoeba histolytica. Amer. J. Hyg. 49:* 255–275.

POISSON, R. 1953. Sporozoaires incertains. Superfamille des Babesioidea *nov. In* GRASSÉ, *Traité de Zoologie.* Vol. 1, Part 2: pp. 935–975. Paris: Masson et Cie.

POISSON, R. 1953a. Protistes parasites, intra- ou extra-cellulaires, d'affinités incertaines. *In* GRASSÉ, *Traité de Zoologie.* Vol. 1, Part 2: pp. 976–1005. Paris: Masson et Cie.

POMERANTZEV, B. I. 1935. On the problem of the origin of the breeding grounds of ticks in the Leningrad Province. *In Russian. Cattle Pests:* pp. 32–111. (Abs. *Rev. Appl. Ent.* [B] *24:* 298.)

PORTMAN, R. W. 1945. Pasture management kills lone star ticks. *Missouri Agr. Exp. Sta. Cir. 297.* 4 pp.

PRICE, R. D. 1954. The survival of *Bacterium tularense in lice and louse feces. Amer. J. trop. Med. Hyg. 3:* 179–186.

PRICE, W. H. 1953. A quantitative analysis of the factors involved in the variations in virulence of rickettsiae. *Science 118:* 49–52.

PRICE, W. H. 1954. The epidemiology of Rocky Mountain spotted fever. II. Studies on the biological survival mechanism of *Rickettsia rickettsii. Amer. J. Hyg. 60:* 292–319.

PRICE, W. H. 1955. Studies on the interepidemic survival of louse-borne epidemic typhus fever. *J. Bact. 69:* 106–107.

PRICE, W. H. 1957. Studies on the immunological overlap among certain arthropod-borne viruses. II. The role of serologic relationships in experimental vaccination procedures. *Proc. nat. Acad. Sci. 43:* 115–121.

PRICE, W. H., H. EMERSON, H. NAGEL, R. BLUMBERG, and S. TALMADGE. 1958. Ecologic studies on the interepidemic survival of louse-borne typhus fever. *Amer. J. Hyg. 67:* 154–178.

PRINGLE, G. 1957. Oriental sore in Iraq: historical and epidemiological problems. *Bull. endem. Dis. 2:* 41–76.

PRORESHNAYA, T. L., L. P. RAPOPORT, V. G. EVDOSHENKO, and E. A. KICHATOV. 1960. A study of natural foci of Q fever in Kirgizia. *J. Microbiol. Epidemiol. Immunobiol. 31:* 1613–1618.

PRUZANSKY, J. J., S. M. FEINBERG, A. KAMINKER, and L. N. MELEYCO. 1959. Studies on the antigenic relationship of insect extracts by reagin neutralization. Evidence for nonspecific inactivation of reagin. *J. Allergy 30:* 352–356.

QUAN, S. F., L. KARTMAN, and A. G. McMANUS. 1954. Studies on *Pasteurella pestis* in fleas: II. Experimental blocking of *Xenopsylla cheopis* with an avirulent strain of *P. pestis. Science 120:* 1101–1102.

QUAN, S. F., L. KARTMAN, F. M. PRINCE, and V. I. MILES. 1960. Ecological studies of wild rodent plague in the San Francisco Bay area of California. IV. The fluctuation and intensity of natural infection with *Pasteurella pestis* in fleas during an epizootic. *Amer. J. trop. Med. Hyg. 9:* 91–95.

QUAN, S. F., V. I. MILES, and L. KARTMAN. 1960. Ecological studies of wild rodent plague in the San Francisco Bay area of California. III. The natural infection rates with *Pasteurella pestis* in five flea species during an epizootic. *Amer. J. trop. Med. Hyg. 9:* 85–90.

RADFORD, C. D. 1950. Systematic checklist of mite genera and type species. *Union Internationale des sciences biologiques.* (Ser. *Ent.*) No. 1. 232 pp.

RADVAN, R., J. HANZAK, S. HEJNY, F. REHN, and B. ROSICKY. 1960. Demonstration of elementary foci of tick-borne infections on the basis of microbiological, parasitological and biochemical investigations. *J. Hyg. Epidemiol. Microbiol. Immunol. 4:* 81–93.

RAGHAVAN, N. G. S. 1957. Epidemiology of filariasis in India. *Bull. Wld Hlth Org. 16:* 553–579.

RASKA, K., L. SYRUCEK, O. SOBESLAVSKY, J. POKORNY, M. PRIVORA, O. HAVLIK, D. LIM, and M. ZASTERA. 1956. The role of rodents in the epizootiology of Q rickettsiosis. *In Czech. Ceskoslov. Epidemiol., Mikrobiol., Immunol. 5:* 246–250. (Abs. *Trop. Dis. Bull. 54:* 280.)

RATCLIFFE, F. N. 1955. Review of myxomatosis in Australia. *J. Aust. Inst. Agric. Sci. 21:* 130–133.

RATCLIFFE, F. N., K. MYERS, B. V. FENNESSY, and J. H. CALABY. 1952. Myxomatosis in Australia. A step towards the biological control of the rabbit. *Nature* (London) *170:* 7–21.

REAGAN, R. L., and A. L. BRUECKNER. 1952. Studies of dengue fever virus in the cave bat (*Myotus lucifugus*). *J. inf. Dis. 91:* 145–146.

REEVES, W. C., W. M. HAMMON, W. H. DOETSCHMAN, H. E. McCLURE, and G. SATHER. 1955. Studies on mites as vectors of western equine and St. Louis encephalitis viruses in California. *Amer. J. trop. Med. Hyg. 4:* 90–105.

REHACEK, J. 1960. Experimental hibernation of the virus of the eastern type of North American equine encephalomyelitis (EEE) in Czechoslovakia species of ticks. *J. Hyg. Epidemiol. Microbiol. Immunol. 4:* 61–65.

REHN, F. 1958. The relationship between *Coxiella burnetii* and some ticks, with special reference to the species *Ixodes ricinus. J. Hyg. Epidemiol. Microbiol. Immunol. 2:* 300–313. (Abs. *Trop. Dis. Bull. 56:* 431.)

REHN, J. W. H. 1951. Classification of the Blattaria as indicated by their wings. *Mem. Amer. ent. Soc. 14.* 134 pp.

REISS-GUTFREUND, R. J. 1956. Un nouveau réservoir de virus pour *Rickettsia prowazeki:* les animaux domestiques et leurs tiques. *Bull. Soc. Path. exot. 49:* 946–1021.

REMPEL, J. G., and A. P. ARNASON. 1947. An account of three successive outbreaks of the black fly, *Simulium arcticum,* a serious livestock pest in Saskatchewan. *Sci. Agric. 27:* 428–445.

RICHARDS, A. G., and F. H. KORDA. 1948. Studies on arthropod cuticle. II. Electron microscope studies of extracted cuticle. *Biol. Bull. 94:* 212–235.

RICHARDS, W. S. 1950. The distribution and biology of the harvest mite in Great Britain (Trombiculidae, Acarina). *Parasitology 40:* 118–126.

RICHARDSON, H. 1905. A monograph on the isopods of North America. *U. S. nat. Mus. Bull. 54.* 727 pp.

RIVERS, T. M. (ed.). 1948. *Viral and rickettsial infections of man.* Philadelphia: J. B. Lippincott Co. xvi + 587 pp.

RIVERS, T. M., and F. L. HORSFALL, JR. (eds.). 1959. *Viral and rickettsial infections of man.* 3rd ed. Philadelphia: J. P. Lippincott Co. xviii + 967 pp.

ROBERTS, F. H. S. 1947. The distribution and seasonal prevalence of anopheline mosquitoes in north Queensland. *Proc. roy. Soc. Qd. 59:* 93–100.

ROCA-GARCIA, M. 1944. The isolation of three neurotropic viruses from forest mosquitoes in Eastern Colombia. *J. infect. Dis. 74:* 160–169.

RODANICHE, E. DE. 1956. Survey of mosquitoes captured in Honduras for yellow fever virus. *Amer. J. trop. Med. Hyg. 5:* 480–482.

RODANICHE, E. DE. 1956a. Isolation of the virus of Ilheus encephalitis from mosquitoes of the genus "Psorophora" captured in Honduras. *Amer. J. trop. Med. Hyg. 5:* 797–810.

RODANICHE, E. DE, and P. GALINDO. 1957. Isolation of yellow fever virus from *Haemagogus mesodentatus, H. equinus* and *Sabethes chloropterus* captured in Guatemala in 1956. *Amer. J. trop. Med. Hyg. 6:* 232–237.

RODANICHE, E. DE, P. GALINDO, and C. M. JOHNSON. 1959. Further studies on the experimental transmission of yellow fever by *Sabethes chloropterus. Amer. J. trop. Med. Hyg. 8:* 190–194.

RODENWALDT, E. (ed.). 1952. *World atlas of epidemic diseases. In German and English.* Hamburg: Falk-Verlag. Part I. 123 pp. + 52 maps. Part II. 170 pp. + 40 maps. Part III (1). 36 pp. + 10 maps.

ROSEN, L. 1954. Human filariasis in the Marquesas islands. *Amer. J. trop. Med. Hyg. 3:* 742–745.

ROSEN, L. 1958. Observations on the epidemiology of dengue in Panama. *Amer. J. Hyg. 68:* 45–59.

ROSS, H. H. 1944. The caddisflies or Trichoptera of Illinois. *Bull. Ill. nat. Hist. Surv. 23:* 1–326.

ROSS, H. H. 1956. *A textbook of entomology.* 2nd ed. New York: John Wiley & Sons, Inc. xi + 519 pp.

ROSS, M. S., and H. FRIEDE. 1955. Alopecia due to tick bite. *Arch. Derm. Syph.* (New York) *71:* 524–525.

ROTH, A. R., and A. W. LINDQUIST. 1948. Ecological notes on the deer fly at Summer Lake, Oregon. *J. econ. Ent. 41:* 473–476.

ROTH, L. M., and E. R. WILLIS. 1957. The medical and veterinary importance of cockroaches. *Smithson. misc. Coll. 134* (10). 147 pp. + 7 pls.

ROTH, L. M., and E. R. WILLIS. 1960. The biotic associations of cockroaches. *Smithson. misc. Coll. 141.* 470 pp.

ROTHSCHILD, M., and T. CLAY. 1952. *Fleas, flukes, and cuckoos. A study of bird parasites.* New York: The Philosophical Library, Inc. xiv + 304 pp.

ROUBAUD, E., and M. HOLSTEIN. 1950. Adaptation spontanée aux pores domestiques d'une larva de muscide ectoparasite de l'homme le ver des cases africains (*Auchmeromyia luteola* Fabr.). *C. R. Acad. Sci.* (Paris) *230:* 256–258.

ROWAN, L. C., and J. L. O'CONNOR. 1957. Relationship between some coastal fauna and arthropod-borne fevers of North Queensland. *Nature* (London) *179:* 786–787.

ROY, D. N., and S. M. GHOSH. 1945. Studies on the population of head-lice, *Pediculus humanus* var. *capitis* De G. *Parasitology 36:* 69–71.

ROZEBOOM, L. E., and W. BURGDORFER. 1959. Development of Colorado tick fever virus in the Rocky Mountain wood tick, *Dermacentor andersoni. Amer. J. Hyg. 69:* 138–145.

ROZEBOOM, L. E., and D. M. McLEAN. 1956. Transmission of the virus of Murray Valley encephalitis by *Culex tarsalis* Coquillett, *Aedes polynesiensis* Marks and *A. pseudoscutellaris* Theobald. *Amer. J. Hyg. 63:* 136–139.

RUSSELL, P. F. 1955. *Man's mastery of malaria.* London: Oxford University Press. xv + 308 pp.

RYCKMAN, R. E. 1951. Recent observations of cannibalism in *Triatoma* (Hemiptera: Reduviidae). *J. Parasit. 37:* 433–434.

RYCKMAN, R. E. 1953. *Cuterebra latifrons* reared from *Neotoma fuscipes macrotis. Pan-Pacif. Ent. 29:* 115–156.

SABIN, A. B. 1955. Recent advances in our knowledge of dengue and sandfly fever. *Amer. J. trop. Med. Hyg. 4:* 198–207.

SACKTOR, B., and M. HUTCHINSON. 1948. Biology of the lone star tick (*Amblyomma americanum*) in the laboratory. *J. econ. Ent. 41:* 296–301.

SARASIN, G. 1959. Zum Organotropismus der Spirochaete *B. duttoni* gegenüber der übertragenden Zecke. *Acta trop.* (Basel) *16:* 218–243.

SASA, M. 1954. Comparative epidemiology of tsutsugamushi disease in Japan. (Studies on tsutsugamushi, Part 76.) *Jap. J. exp. Med. 24:* 335–361.

SASA, M., S. HAYASHI, R. KANO, K. SATO, I. KOMINE, and S. ISHII. 1952 Studies on filariasis due to *Wuchereria malayi* (Brug, 1927) discovered from Hachijo-Koshima Island, Japan. *Jap. J. exp. Med. 22:* 357–390.

SAVORY, T. H. 1935. *The Arachnida*. London: Edward Arnold. xi + 218 pp.

SCHERER, W. F., and R. P. J. SMITH. 1960. In vitro studies on the sites of Japanese encephalitis virus multiplication in the heron, an important natural host in Japan. *Amer. J. trop. Med. Hyg. 9:* 50–55.

SCHÖLZEL, G. 1937. Die Embryologie der Anopluren und Mallophagen. *Z. Parasitenk. 9:* 730–770.

SCHOMBERG, O. 1952. Larval habitat of *Tabanus sulcifrons* in Oklahoma. *J. econ. Ent. 45:* 747.

SCHOOF, H. F., G. A. MAIL, and E. P. SAVAGE. 1954. Fly production sources in urban communities. *J. econ. Ent. 47:* 245–253.

SCHOOF, H. F., and R. E. SIVERLY. 1954. Urban fly dispersion studies with special reference to movement pattern of *Musca domestica*. *Amer. J. trop. Med. Hyg. 3:* 539–547.

SCHRÖDER, C. [ed.]. 1925–1929. *Handbuch der Entomologie*. Jena: G. Fischer. Vol. 1. 1426 pp. Vol. 2. 1410 pp. Vol. 3. 1201 pp.

SCHULZE, P. 1941. Über die Hautsinnesorgane der Zecken, besonders über eine bisher unbekannte Art von Arthropodensinnesorganen, die Krobylophoren. *Z. Morph. Ökol. Tiere 38:* 379–419.

SÉGUY, E. 1926. *Faune de France. Vol. 13. Diptères (Brachycères)*. Paris: Paul Lechevalier et Fils. iii + 308 pp.

SÉGUY, E. 1944. *Faune de France. Vol. 43. Insectes ectoparasites*. Paris: Paul Lechevalier et Fils. 684 pp.

SÉGUY, E. 1950. Le biologie des Diptères. In *Encyclopédie Entomologique*. Paris: Paul Lechevalier et Fils. 609 pp.

SEN, S. K. 1958. Studies on the morphology of the mouth parts of biting Diptera. *Proc. 45th Indian Sci. Cong.* Part 4, p. 44.

SERDYUKOVA, G. V. 1955. On the question of differential characteristics of larvae and nymphs of Ixodidae. In *Russian. Zool. Zh. 34:* 1037–1051. (Trans. *No. 18.* U. S. Nav. Med. Unit 3.)

SERGENT, E. 1949. Étude comparative du venin de scorpions mexicains et de scorpions nord-africains. *Arch. Inst. Pasteur* (Algiers) *27:* 31–34.

SHANNON, R. C. 1929. Entomological investigations in connection with Carrión's disease. *Amer. J. Hyg. 10:* 78–111 + 2 pls.

SHARIF, M. 1949. Effects of constant temperature and humidity on the development of the larvae and the pupae of the three Indian species of *Xenopsylla* (Insecta: Siphonaptera). *Phil. Trans. R. Soc. Lond.* (*B*) *233:* 581–633.

SHARP, N. A. D. 1927. Development of *Microfilaria perstans* in *Culicoides grahami*, a preliminary note. *Trans. R. Soc. trop. Med. Hyg. 21:* 70.

SHARP, N. A. D. 1928. *Filaria perstans*: its development in *Culicoides austeni*. *Trans. R. Soc. trop. Med. Hyg. 21:* 371–396 + 2 pls.

SHOSHINA, M. A. 1953. On the mechanism of transmission of cutaneous leishmaniasis. In *Russian. C. R.* (*Doklady*) *Acad. Sci. USSR 92:* 447–448. (Abs. *Trop. Dis. Bull. 52:* 884).

SHUBLADZE, A. K. 1958. On some viruses related to the etiological agent of the spring-summer tick-borne encephalitis. *Acta virologica* (Engl. ed.) *2:* 225–259.

SIMIĆ, C. 1951. Epidemic of sand fly fever in Serbia in 1946 and in Banat in 1950. *In Serbian. Glas Srpske Akad. Nauka; Odeljenje med. Nauka 204:* 143–152. (Abs. *Trop. Dis. Bull. 51:* 911–912.)

SIMMONS, S. W., and W. E. DOVE. 1941. Breeding places of the stable fly or "dog fly" *Stomoxys calcitrans* (L.) in northwestern Florida. *J. econ. Ent. 34:* 457–462.

SKAIFE, S. H. 1955. *African insect life.* London: Longmans Green and Co. viii + 387 pp. + 70 pls.

SMART, J. 1945. The classification of the Simuliidae (Diptera). *Trans. R. ent. Soc.* (London) *95:* 463–528.

SMART, J. 1956. *A handbook for the identification of insects of medical importance.* London: British Museum. xi + 363 pp. + 13 pls.

SMITH, C. E. G. 1956. The history of dengue in tropical Asia and its probable relationship to the mosquito *Aedes aegypti. J. trop. Med.* (*Hyg.*) *59:* 243–251.

SMITH, C. E. G. 1956a. A virus resembling Russian spring-summer encephalitis virus from an ixodid tick in Malaya. *Nature* (London) *178:* 581–582.

SMITH, D. J. W. 1940. Studies in the epidemiology of Q fever. 3. The transmission of Q fever by the tick *Haemaphysalis humerosa. Aust. J. exp. Biol. med. Sci. 18:* 103–118.

SMITH, R. O. A., K. C. HALDER, and I. AHMED. 1940. Further investigations on the transmission of kala-azar. Part III. The transmission of kala-azar by the bite of the sand fly *P. argentipes. Indian J. med. Res. 28:* 585–591.

SMITH, T., and F. L. KILBORNE. 1893. Investigation into the nature, causation and prevention of Texas or southern cattle fever. *U. S. Dept. Agr. Bur. Anim. Ind. Bull.* 301 pp.

SMITHBURN, K. C. 1948. Neurotropic viruses in central Africa. *Int. Congr. trop. Med. Malar.* (*Proc. 4*) *1:* 576–586.

SNODGRASS, R. E. 1944. The feeding apparatus of biting and sucking insects affecting man and animals. *Smithson. misc. Coll. 104* (7): 1–113.

SNODGRASS, R. E. 1948. The feeding organs of Arachnida, including mites and ticks. *Smithson. misc. Coll. 110* (10). 93 pp.

SNODGRASS, R. E. 1952. *A textbook of arthropod anatomy.* New York: Constable and Co. x + 363 pp.

SNODGRASS, R. E. 1954. Insect metamorphosis. *Smithson. misc. Coll. 122* (9). iii + 124 pp.

SNYDER, J. C., and C. M. WHEELER. 1945. The experimental infection of the human body louse, *Pediculus humanus corporis,* with murine and epidemic louse-borne typhus strains. *J. exp. Med. 82:* 1–20 + 3 pls.

SPARROW, H. 1955. Foyer de fièvre récurrente à poux en Ethiopie. *C. R. Acad. Sci.* (Paris) *241:* 1636–1639.

STAHNKE, H. L. 1953. The L-C treatment of venomous bites or stings. *Amer. J. trop. Med. Hyg. 2:* 142–143.

STEUBEN, E. B. 1954. Larval development of *Dirofilaria immitis* (Leidy) in fleas. *J. Parasit. 40:* 580–589.

STEWART, M. A. 1934. The role of *Lucilia sericata* Meig. larvae in osteomyelitis wounds. *Ann. trop. Med. Parasit. 28:* 445–460.

STEWART, M. A. 1937. Phasmid injury to the human eye. *Canad. Ent. 69:* 84–86.

STEYN, J. J. 1958. The South African vector of Rift Valley fever. *Proc. 10th int. Congr. Ent. 3:* 629–632.

STOENNER, H. G. 1959. The occurrence of *Coxiella burnetii, Brucella* and other pathogens among fauna of the Great Salt Lake desert in Utah. *Amer. J. trop. Med. Hyg. 8:* 590–595.

STOENNER, H. G., R. HOLDENRIED, D. LACKMAN, and J. S. ORSBORN, JR. 1959. The occurrence of *Coxiella burnetii, Brucella,* and other pathogens among fauna of the Great Salt Lake Desert in Utah. *Amer. J. trop. Med. Hyg. 8:* 590–596.

STOJANOVICH, C. J., JR. 1945. The head and mouth parts of the sucking lice (Insecta: Anoplura). *Microent. 10:* 1–46.

STONE, A., K. L. KNIGHT, and H. STARCKE. 1959. *A synoptic catalog of the mosquitoes of the world.* (Diptera, Culicidae.) Washington: Entomological Society of America. 358 pp.

STRODE, G. K. (ed.). 1951. *Yellow fever.* New York: McGraw-Hill Book Co., Inc., xv + 710 pp.

STUNKARD, H. W. 1939. The role of oribatid mites as transmitting agents and intermediate hosts of ovine cestodes. *Trans. 7th int. Kongr. Ent. 3:* 1669–1673 + 2 pls.

SUDIA, W. D., D. D. STAMM, R. W. CHAMBERLAIN, and R. E. KISSLING. 1956. Transmission of eastern equine encephalitis to horses by *Aedes sollicitans* mosquitoes. *Amer. J. trop. Med. Hyg. 5:* 902–908.

SWEATMAN, G. K. 1957. Life history, non-specificity, and revision of the genus. *Chorioptes,* a parasitic mite of herbivores. *Canad. J. Zool. 35:* 641–649 + 1 pl.

SYRUCEK, L., and K. RASKA. 1956. Q fever in domestic and wild ducks. *Bull. Wild Hlth Org. 15:* 329–337.

TAGIL'TSEV, A. A. 1960. Certain comparative ecological data on gamasid ticks occurring in the nests of birds and small mammals in an enzootic focus of tick-borne encephalitis. *J. Microbiol. Epidemiol. Immunobiol. 31:* 860–869.

TAHORI, A. S., V. V. STERK, and N. GOLDBLUM. 1955. Studies on the dynamics of experimental transmission of West Nile virus by *Culex molestus. Amer. J. trop. Med. Hyg. 4:* 1015–1027.

TASHIRO, H., and H. H. SCHWARDT. 1953. Some natural enemies of horse flies in New York. *J. econ. Ent. 46:* 680–681.

TAYLOR, R. M., M. A. HASEEB, and T. H. WORK. 1955. A regional reconnaisance on yellow fever in the Sudan with special reference to primate hosts. *Bull. Wld Hlth Org. 12:* 711–725.

TAYLOR, R. M., T. H. WORK, H. S. HURLBUT, and F. RIZK. 1956. A study of the ecology of West Nile virus in Egypt. *Amer. J. trop. Med. Hyg. 5:* 579–620.

TERRY, R. J. 1956. The relations between the bed medium of sewage filters and the flies breeding in them. *J. anim. Ecol. 25:* 6–14.

THEOBALD, F. V. 1901. *A monograph of the Culicidae or mosquitoes.* London: British Museum (Nat. Hist.). Vol. I. xviii + 424 pp.

THEOBALD, F. V. 1901a. *A monograph of the Culicidae or mosquitoes.* London: British Museum (Nat. Hist.). viii + 391 pp.

THEOBALD, F. V. 1910. Second report on the collection of Culicidae in the Indian Museum, Calcutta, with descriptions of new genera and species. *Rec. Indian Mus. 4:* 1–33 + 3 pls.

THEODOR, O. 1935. A study of the reaction to *Phlebotomus* bites with some remarks on "harara." *Trans. R. Soc. trop. Med. Hyg. 29:* 273–284.

THÉODORIDÈS, J. 1950. Considérations sur les *Paederus* vésicants (Coleoptera: Staphylinidae) et essais de vésication avec des espèces de France. *Bull. Soc. Path. exot. 43:* 100–113 + 2 pls.

THORP, R. W., and W. D. WOODSON. 1945. *Black widow, America's most poisonous spider.* Chapel Hill, N. C.: University of North Carolina Press. xi + 222 pp.

TIKHOMIROVA, M. M., M. V. ZAGORSKAYA, and B. V. IL'IN. 1935. Rodents and their fleas in the steppe, transitional and sandy tracts of the districts of Novokanzanka and Slomikhino and their role in the epidemiology of plague. *In Russian. Rev. Microbiol. 14:* 231–254. (Abs. *Rev. Appl. Ent. [B]* 24: 67).

TIMMS, G. L., R. B. HEISCH, and A. E. C. HARVEY. 1959. Further evidence that *Rhipicephalus simus* Koch is a vector of tick typhus in Kenya. *East. Afr. med. J. 36:* 114–115.

TRAUB, R., M. HERTIG, W. H. LAWRENCE, and T. T. HARRIS. 1954. Potential vectors and reservoirs of hemorrhagic fever in Korea. *Amer. J. Hyg. 59:* 291–305.

TRAUB, R., P. T. JOHNSON, M. L. MIESSE, and R. E. ELBEL. 1954. Isolation of *Rickettsia tsutsugamushi* from rodents from Thailand. *Amer. J. trop. Med. 3:* 356–359.

TRAVER, J. R. 1951. Unusual scalp dermatitis in humans caused by the mite *Dermatophagoides. Proc. ent. Soc. Wash. 53:* 1–25.

TREMBLEY, H. L. 1952. The distribution of certain liquids in the esophageal diverticula and stomach of mosquitoes. *Amer. J. trop. Med. Hyg.* 1: 693–710.

TRUBY, A. E. 1943. *Memoir of Walter Reed. The yellow fever episode.* New York: Paul B. Hoeber, Inc. xviii + 239 pp.

TURK, F. A. 1953. A synonymic catalogue of British Acari: Part I. *Ann. Mag. nat. Hist.*, Ser. 12, 6: 1–26, 81–99.

TURKHUD, D. A. 1920. Dracontiasis in animals. *Indian J. med. Res.* 7: 727–734.

UNSWORTH, K. 1946. Studies on the clinical and parasitological aspects of canine demodectic mange. *J. comp. Path.* 56: 114–127.

URIBE, C. 1926. On the biology and life history of *Rhodnius prolixus* Stahl. *J. Parasit.* 12: 129–136.

USINGER, R. L. 1944. The Triatominae of North and Central America and the West Indies and their public health significance. *U.S. Publ. Hlth Bull.* 288. iv + 83 pp. + 12 pls.

VACHON, M. 1953. The biology of scorpions. *Endeavour* 12: 80–89.

VAN CLEAVE, H. J. 1953. *Acanthocephala of North American mammals.* Urbana: University of Illinois Press. 179 pp.

VANDERPLANK, F. L. 1948. Experiments in cross-breeding tsetse-flies (*Glossina* species). *Ann. trop. Med. Parasit.* 42: 131–152.

VAN SOMEREN, V. D., and J. McMAHON. 1950. Phoretic association between *Afronurus* and *Simulium* species and the discovery of the early stages of *Simulium neavei* on fresh-water crabs. *Nature* (London) 166: 350–351.

VARMA, M. G. R. 1956. Comparative studies on the transmission of two strains of *Spirochaeta duttoni* by *Ornithodoros moubata* and of *S. turicatae* by *O. turicata. Ann. trop. Med. Hyg.* 50: 1–17.

VARMA, M. G. R. 1956a. Infections of *Ornithodoros* ticks with relapsing fever spirochaetes and the mechanisms of their transmission. *Ann. trop. Med. Hyg.* 50: 18–31.

VARMA, M. G. R. 1960. Preliminary studies on the infection of culicine mosquitoes with the Tamilnad strain of West Nile virus. *Indian J. med. Res.* 48: 537–548.

VELLARD, J. 1936. Le venin des Araignées. *Monog. Inst. Pasteur.* 311 pp.

VERETA, L. A., and L. M. SUSKINA. 1960. Some results of study of the infection of *Ixodes* ticks with encephalitis virus in Southern districts of the Khabarovsk Region. *Problems of Virology* 5: 319–324.

VERHOEFF, K. W. 1928. Gliederfüssler: Arthropoda, Klasse Diplopoda. In H. G. BRONN, *Klassen und Ordnungen des Tier-Reichs.* Leipsig: Akademie-Verlag 5 (II. Abt. pt. 1). 1071 pp. + 11 pls. 5 (II Abt. pt. 2). 2084 pp. + 11 pls.

VEST, E. D., and N. J. MARCHETTE. 1958. Transmission of *Pasteurella tularensis* among infective carcasses. *Science* 128: 363–364.

VITZTHUM, H. G. 1929. Systematische Betrachtungen zur Frage der Trombidiose. *Z. Parasitenk.* 2: 223–247.

WAGNER, W. H. 1956. Modellinfektionen in der experimentellen chemotherapie der Filariosen. *Z. Tropenmed. u. Parasit.* 7: 163–177.

WALLIS, R. C. 1959. *Culiseta melanura* (Coquillett) and eastern equine encephalitis in Connecticut. *Mosquito News* 19: 157–158.

WALTON, G. A. 1955. Relapsing fever in the Digo district of Kenya Colony. *E. Afr. med. J.* 32: 377–393.

WALTON, G. A. 1959. A biological variant of *Ornithodoros moubata* Murray (Ixodoidea: Argasidae) from South Africa. *Proc. R. ent. Soc.* (London) (A) 34: 63–72.

WARDLE, R. A., and J. A. McLEOD. 1952. *The zoology of tapeworms.* Minneapolis: University of Minnesota Press. xxiv + 780 pp.

WATERSTON, J. 1926. On the crop contents of certain Mallophaga. *Proc. zool. Soc. Lond. Part 4*: 1017–1020.

WATT, J., and D. R. LINDSAY. 1948. Diarrheal disease control studies. I. Effect of fly control in a high morbidity area. *U. S. Publ. Hlth Rept.* 63: 1319–1334.

WEBER, H. 1939. Beiträge zur Kenntnis der Überordnung Psocoidea: 5. Zur Eiablage und Entwicklung der Elefantenlaus *Haematomyzus elephantis* Piaget. *Biol. Zbl.* 59: 98–109.

WEHR, E. E. 1935. A revised classification of the nematode superfamily Filarioidea. *Proc. helminth. Soc. Wash.* 2: 84–88.

WEINBREN, M. P., and M. C. WILLIAMS. 1958. Zika virus: Further isolation in the Zika area, and some studies on the strains isolated. *Trans. R. Soc. trop. Med. Hyg.* 52: 263–268.

WEINMAN, D., and H. PINKERTON. 1937. Carrión's disease. IV. Natural sources of *Bartonella* in the endemic zone. *Proc. Soc. exp. Biol. Med.* 37: 596–598.

WEITZ, B., and P. A. BUXTON. 1953. The rate of digestion of blood meals of various haematophagous arthropods as determined by the precipitin test. *Bull. ent. Res.* 44: 445–450.

WEITZ, B., and J. P. GLASGOW. 1956. The natural hosts of some species of *Glossina* in East Africa. *Trans. R. Soc. trop. Med. Hyg.* 50: 593–612.

WELLS, R. W., and E. F. KNIPLING. 1938. A report of some recent studies on species of *Gasterophilus* occurring in horses in the United States. *Iowa St. Col. J. Sci.* 12: 181–203.

WELSH, H. H., E. H. LENNETTE, F. R. ABINANTI, J. F. WINN, and W. KAPLAN. 1959. Q-fever studies. XXI. The recovery of *Coxiella burnetii* from the soil and surface water of premises harboring infected sheep. *Amer. J. Hyg.* 70: 14–20.

WEST, L. S. 1951. *The house fly.* Ithaca, N. Y.: Comstock Publishing Co. xvi + 584 pp.

WEYER, F. 1952. The behavior of *Rickettsia akari* in the body louse after artificial infection. *Amer. J. trop. Med.* 1: 809–820.

WEYER, F. 1953. Künstliche Infektion der Kleiderlaus mit *Rickettsia tsutsugamushi.* *Z. Hyg. Infekt.* 137: 419–428.

WEYER, F. 1954. Unterschiede im Verhalten mehrerer Stämme von *Rickettsia conori* in der Kleiderlaus. *Z. Tropenmed. u. Parasit.* 5: 477–482.

WEYER, F. 1958. Übertragung mehrerer Stämme von *Rickettsia tsutsugamushi* auf Kleiderläuse *Z. Tropenmed. u. Parasit.* 9: 42–53.

WEYER, F. 1959. Ätiologie und Epidemiologie der Rickettsiosen des Menschen. *Ergebn. Hyg. Bakt.* 32: 73–160.

WHARTON, G. W. (aided by H. S. FULLER). 1952. A manual of the chiggers. The biology, classification, distribution and importance of the larvae of the family Trombiculidae (Acarina). *Mem. ent. Soc. Wash.* 4. 185 pp.

WHEELER, W. M. 1930. *Demons of the dust.* New York: W. W. Norton & Co. xviii + 378 pp.

WHITTINGTON, H. E., and A. F. ROOK. 1923. Observations on the life history and bionomics of *Phlebotomus papatasii.* *Brit. med. J.* 1923 (2): 1144–1151.

WIESINGER, D. 1956. Die Bedeutung der Umweltfaktoren für den Saugakt von *Triatoma infestans.* *Acta trop.* (Basel) 13: 97–141.

WIGGLESWORTH, V. B. 1931. Digestion in *Chrysops silacea* Aust. (Diptera, Tabanidae). *Parasitology* 23: 73–76.

WIJERS, D. J. B. 1958. Factors that may influence the infection rate of *Glossina palpalis* with *Trypanosoma gambiense.* I. The age of the fly at the time of the infected feed. *Ann. trop. Med. Parasit.* 52: 385–390.

WILCOCKS, C. 1956. Summary of recent abstracts. V. Leishmaniasis. *Trop. Dis. Bull.* 53: 705–708.

WILCOCKS, C. 1957. Summary of recent abstracts. V. Leishmaniasis. *Trop. Dis. Bull.* 54: 637–641.

WILCOCKS, C. 1959. Summary of recent abstracts. III. Malaria. *Trop. Dis. Bull.* 56: 261–268.

WILCOCKS, C. 1959a. Summary of recent abstracts. VIII. Typhus group of fevers. *Trop. Dis. Bull.* 56: 1001–1006.

WILLIAMS, R. W. 1946. A contribution to our knowledge of the common North American chigger, *Eutrombicula alfreddugesi* (Oudeman), with a description of rapid collecting method. *Amer. J. trop. Med.* 26: 243–250.

Wilson, F. H. 1933. A louse feeding on the blood of its host. *Science 77:* 490.

Wiseman, R. D., W. G. Woodin, H. C. Miller, and M. A. Myers. 1959. Insect allergy as a possible cause of inhalant sensitivity. *J. Allergy 30:* 191–197.

Wolf, L. S., and D. G. Peterson. 1960. Diurnal behavior and biting habits of black flies (Diptera: Simuliidae) in the forests of Quebec. *Canad. J. Zool. 38:* 489–498.

Wolman, B., and M. Wolman. 1945. Studies in the biological properties of *Spirochaeta recurrentis* in the Ethiopian high plateau. *Ann. trop. Med. Parasit. 39:* 82–93.

Womersley, H. 1952. The scrub-typhus and scrub itch mites of the Asiatic-Pacific Region. *Rec. South Aust. Museum. 10:* 1–673.

Womersley, H. 1954. Species of the subfamily Phytoseiinae (Acarina: Laelaptidae) from Australia. *Aust. J. Zool. 2:* 169–191.

Wood, S. F. 1951. Importance of feeding and defecation times of insect vectors in transmission of Chagas' disease. *J. econ. Ent. 44:* 52–54.

Young, T. C., M. Richmond, and G. R. Brendish. 1926. Sandflies and sandfly fever in the Peshawar District. *Indian J. med. Res. 13:* 961–1021 + 5 pls.

Yunker, C. E. 1955. A proposed classification of the Acaridiae (Acarina: Sarcopti-formes). *Proc. helminth. Soc. Wash. 22:* 98–105.

Zhmaeva, Z. M., A. A. Pchelkina, N. K. Mishchenko, and B. E. Karulin. 1955. The epidemiological importance of ectoparasites of birds in a natural focus of Q fever in the south of Central Asia. *In Russian. Dokl. Akad. Nauk SSSR 101:* 387–389. (Abs. *Trop. Dis. Bull. 53:* 430.)

Zimmer, C. 1926–1927. Crustacea (=Krebse). *Handb. Zool. Berl. 3:* 276–1074.

Zumpt, F. 1958. Remarks on the systematic position of myiasis-producing flies (Diptera) of the African elephant, *Loxodonta africana* (Blumenbach). *Proc. R. ent. Soc.* (London) (*B*) *27:* 8–14.

Zumpt, F., and H. E. Paterson. 1953. Studies on the family Gasterophilidae, with keys to the adults and maggots. *J. ent. Soc. S. Afr. 16:* 59–72.

Index

Numerals in **boldface** indicate principal discussion.

and bite, 185
and *Pasteurella tularensis,* 297
distinctipennis and *Loa loa,* 364
silacea, 143
and *Loa loa,* 364
Cibarium, 67, 69, 91, 95, 160
Cimex, 93
lectularius (*see* Bed bug)
rotundatus (*see* Bed bug)
Cimicidae, 92, **93–96**
Circulatory stasis, 181
Citellus
and *Bartonella,* 310
and *Brucella,* 308
and *Pasteurella pestis,* 299, 302, 304
and *Rickettsia,* 268
and *Virus,* 220
beecheyi and *Virus WEE,* 220
pygmaeus and *Pasteurella pestis,* 302
tridecemlineatus and *Bartonella,* 310
undulatus and *Rickettsia conori,* 268
Cittotaenia, 355
Claw, 51, 89
Clearchus, 336
Cleridae, 75
Clethrionomys and *Virus DM,* 241
Clostridium perfringens, 293
Clubionidae, 28, 78
Clypeus, 68, 160
Cnethocampa, cause of dermatitis, 175
Coagulant, 195, 198
Cobboldia, 165
Cobweb, 25
Coccidia, 205, 312, **335**
Cochliomyia, 162
Cockroach, 73, 76
abatement, 379
American, 73, 74
and Acanthocephala, 375
and bacteria, 292, 293, 306, 309, 310
and cestodes, 357
and nematodes, 361
and protozoa, 313
and *Virus,* 249
brown-banded, 73
cause of asthma, 176
cause of dermatitis, 178
cause of dermatosis, 179
cause of edema, 175, 179
cause of fear, 176
cause of hives, 179
cause of nausea, 179
glands, 179
Oriental, 73
secretions, 179
Coelom, 12
Coenosiinae, 145

Coleoptera, 71, **74–76**
and Acanthocephala, 75, 375
and cestodes, 355, 358
and nematodes, 361
and trematodes, 353
cause of allergy, 176, 177
cause of asthma, 175
cause of conjunctivitis, 178, 179
cause of cough, 177
cause of dermatitis, 177
cause of dermatosis, 177, 178
cause of eruption, 177
cause of erythema, 177
invasion by, 199, 201
irritant, 179
secretions, 177
Collembola and chiggers, 43
Colobus and *Virus YF,* 233, 235
Combretum, 156
caused by beetles, 179
caused by mantids, 179
caused by millipedes, 178
caused by spider, 195
Conspiculum, 361
Convulsion, 195, 198
Copaifera, 156
Copepoda, 17
and cestodes, 355, 356, 358
and nematodes, 361
and trematodes, 353
Copepodid stage, 17
Coracidium, 358
Cordylobia, 161, 162, 201, 202
anthropophaga, 162
Corynebacterium pseudotuberculosis, 293
Cosminomma, 55
Cough, 177
Coxa, 36, 37
Coxiella burnetii, **252–259**
Coxiellosis, 252, 279
Coyote, 100
Crab, 18
and protozoa, 312
and trematodes, 354, 385
black flies on, 135
horse-shoe, 19
Cramp, 201
Crataerina, 170
Crayfish, 18, 19, 354
Crepidostomum, 353
Crithidia, 314, 331
Crocidura and *Borrelia,* 283
Crop, 324
Crow
and *Aegyptianella,* 349
and *Babesiidae,* 349
and *Brucella,* 308